THE WORLD BOOK ENCYCLOPEDIA OF
PEOPLE AND PLACES

4
K-N

WORLD
BOOK

a Scott Fetzer company
Chicago
www.worldbookonline.com

For information about other World Book publications, visit our website at http://www.worldbookonline.com or call 1-800-WORLDBK (1-800-967-5325).

For information about sales to schools and libraries, call 1-800-975-3250 (United States); 1-800-837-5365 (Canada).

Library of Congress Cataloging-in-Publication Data

The World Book encyclopedia of people and places.
  v. cm.
  Summary: "A 7-volume illustrated, alphabetically arranged set that presents profiles of individual nations and other political/geographical units, including an overview of history, geography, economy, people, culture, and government of each. Includes a history of the settlement of each world region based on archaeological findings; a cumulative index; and Web resources"--Provided by publisher.
  Includes index.
  ISBN 978-0-7166-3758-5
  1. Encyclopedias and dictionaries. 2. Geography--Encyclopedias. I. World Book, Inc. Title: Encyclopedia of people and places.
  AE5.W563 2011
  030--dc22
                                          2010011919
This edition ISBN: 978-0-7166-3760-8

Printed in Hong Kong by Toppan Printing Co. (H.K.) LTD
3rd printing, revised, August 2012

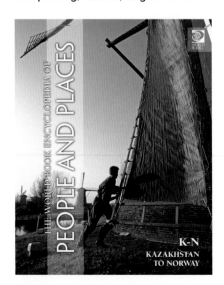

Cover image:
Miller pushing windmill blade, the Netherlands

© Frans Lemmens/SuperStock

CONTENTS

POLITICAL WORLD MAP

The world has 196 independent countries and about 50 dependencies. An independent country controls its own affairs. Dependencies are controlled in some way by independent countries. In most cases, an independent country is responsible for the dependency's foreign relations and defense, and some of the dependency's local affairs. However, many dependencies have complete control of their local affairs.

By 2010, the world's population was nearly 7 billion. Almost all of the world's people live in independent countries. Only about 13 million people live in dependencies.

Some regions of the world, including Antarctica and certain desert areas, have no permanent population. The most densely populated regions of the world are in Europe and in southern and eastern Asia. The world's largest country in terms of population is China, which has more than 1.3 billion people. The independent country with the smallest population is Vatican City, with only about 830 people. Vatican City, covering only 1/6 square mile (0.4 square kilometer), is also the smallest in terms of size. The world's largest nation in terms of area is Russia, which covers 6,601,669 square miles (17,098,242 square kilometers).

Every nation depends on other nations in some way. The interdependence of the entire world and its peoples is called *globalism*. Nations trade with one another to earn money and to obtain manufactured goods or the natural resources that they lack. Nations with similar interests and political beliefs may pledge to support one another in case of war. Developed countries provide developing nations with financial aid and technical assistance. Such aid strengthens trade as well as defense ties.

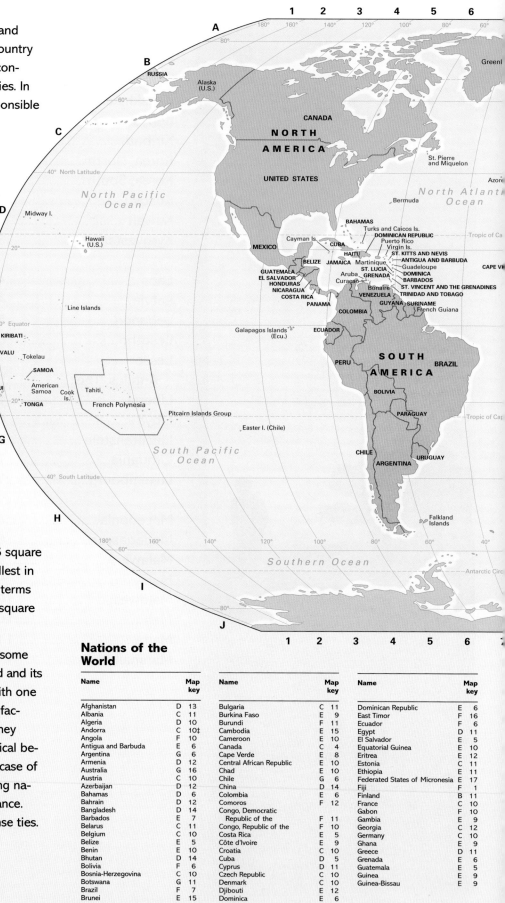

Nations of the World

Name	Map key		Name	Map key		Name	Map key	
Afghanistan	D	13	Bulgaria	C	11	Dominican Republic	E	6
Albania	C	11	Burkina Faso	E	9	East Timor	F	16
Algeria	D	10	Burundi	F	11	Ecuador	F	6
Andorra	C	10‡	Cambodia	E	15	Egypt	D	11
Angola	F	10	Cameroon	E	10	El Salvador	E	5
Antigua and Barbuda	E	6	Canada	C	4	Equatorial Guinea	E	10
Argentina	G	6	Cape Verde	E	8	Eritrea	E	12
Armenia	D	12	Central African Republic	E	10	Estonia	C	11
Australia	G	16	Chad	E	10	Ethiopia	E	11
Austria	C	10	Chile	G	6	Federated States of Micronesia	E	17
Azerbaijan	D	12	China	D	14	Fiji	F	1
Bahamas	D	6	Colombia	E	6	Finland	B	11
Bahrain	D	12	Comoros	F	12	France	C	10
Bangladesh	D	14	Congo, Democratic			Gabon	F	10
Barbados	E	7	Republic of the	F	11	Gambia	E	9
Belarus	C	11	Congo, Republic of the	F	10	Georgia	C	12
Belgium	C	10	Costa Rica	E	5	Germany	C	10
Belize	E	5	Côte d'Ivoire	E	9	Ghana	E	9
Benin	E	10	Croatia	C	10	Greece	D	11
Bhutan	D	14	Cuba	D	5	Grenada	E	6
Bolivia	F	6	Cyprus	D	11	Guatemala	E	5
Bosnia-Herzegovina	C	10	Czech Republic	C	10	Guinea	E	9
Botswana	G	11	Denmark	C	10	Guinea-Bissau	E	9
Brazil	F	7	Djibouti	E	12			
Brunei	E	15	Dominica	E	6			

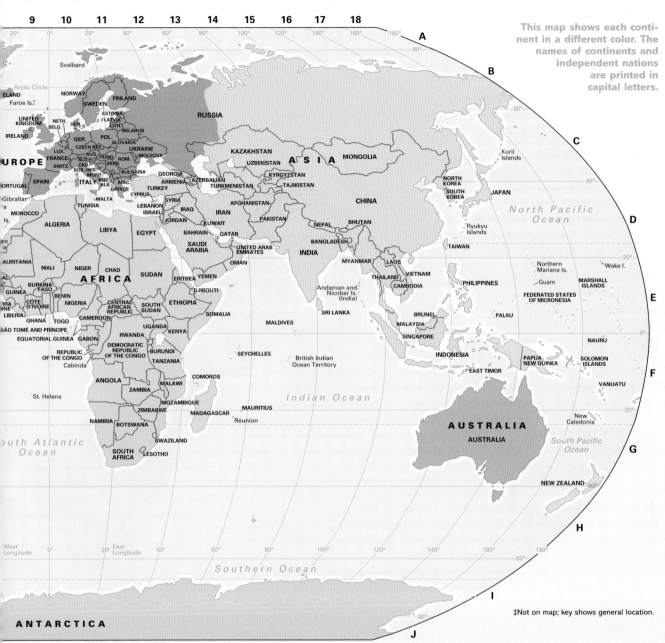

This map shows each continent in a different color. The names of continents and independent nations are printed in capital letters.

‡Not on map; key shows general location.

Name	Map key		Name	Map key		Name	Map key		Name	Map key		Name	Map key	
Guyana	E	7	Lebanon	D	11	Namibia	G	10	St. Vincent and the Grenadines	E	6	Taiwan	D	16
Haiti	E	6	Lesotho	G	11	Nauru	F	18	Samoa	F	1	Tajikistan	D	14
Honduras	E	5	Liberia	E	9	Nepal	D	14	San Marino	C	10‡	Tanzania	F	11
Hungary	C	10	Libya	D	10	Netherlands	C	10	São Tomé and Principe	E	10	Thailand	E	15
Iceland	B	9	Liechtenstein	C	10‡	New Zealand	G	18	Saudi Arabia	D	12	Togo	E	9
India	D	13	Lithuania	C	11	Nicaragua	E	5	Senegal	E	9	Tonga	F	1
Indonesia	F	16	Luxembourg	C	10	Niger	E	10	Serbia	C	10	Trinidad and Tobago	E	6
Iran	D	12	Macedonia	C	11	Nigeria	E	10	Seychelles	F	12	Tunisia	D	10
Iraq	D	12	Madagascar	F	12	Norway	B	10	Sierra Leone	E	9	Turkey	D	11
Ireland	C	9	Malawi	F	11	Oman	E	12	Singapore	E	15	Turkmenistan	D	13
Israel	D	11	Malaysia	E	15	Pakistan	D	13	Slovakia	C	11	Tuvalu	F	1
Italy	C	10	Maldives	E	13	Palau	E	16	Slovenia	C	11	Uganda	E	11
Jamaica	E	6	Mali	D	9	Panama	E	5	Solomon Islands	F	18	Ukraine	C	11
Japan	D	16	Malta	D	10	Papua New Guinea	F	17	Somalia	E	12	United Arab Emirates	D	12
Jordan	D	11	Marshall Islands	E	18	Paraguay	G	7	South Africa	G	11	United Kingdom	C	9
Kazakhstan	C	13	Mauritania	D	9	Peru	F	6	Spain	C	9	United States	C	4
Kenya	E	11	Mauritius	G	12	Philippines	E	16	Sri Lanka	E	14	Uruguay	G	7
Kiribati	F	1	Mexico	D	4	Poland	C	10	Sudan	E	11	Uzbekistan	D	14
Korea, North	C	16	Moldova	C	11	Portugal	D	9	Sudan, South	E	11	Vanuatu	F	18
Korea, South	D	16	Monaco	C	10‡	Qatar	D	12	Suriname	E	7	Vatican City	C	10‡
Kosovo	C	11	Mongolia	C	15	Romania	C	11	Swaziland	G	11	Venezuela	E	6
Kuwait	D	12	Montenegro	C	10	Russia	C	13	Sweden	B	10	Vietnam	E	15
Kyrgyzstan	C	13	Morocco	D	9	Rwanda	F	11	Switzerland	C	10	Yemen	E	12
Laos	E	15	Mozambique	F	11	St. Kitts and Nevis	E	6	Syria	D	11	Zambia	F	11
Latvia	C	11	Myanmar	D	14	St. Lucia	E	6				Zimbabwe	G	11

PHYSICAL WORLD MAP

The surface area of the world totals about 196,900,000 square miles (510,000,000 square kilometers). Water covers about 139,700,000 square miles (362,000,000 square kilometers), or 71 percent of the world's surface. Only 29 percent of the world's surface consists of land, which covers about 57,200,000 square miles (148,000,000 square kilometers).

Oceans, lakes, and rivers make up most of the water that covers the surface of the world. The water surface consists chiefly of three large oceans—the Pacific, the Atlantic, and the Indian. The Pacific Ocean is the largest, covering about a third of the world's surface. The world's largest lake is the Caspian Sea, a body of salt water that lies between Asia and Europe east of the Caucasus Mountains. The world's largest body of fresh water is the Great Lakes in North America. The longest river in the world is the Nile in Africa.

The land area of the world consists of seven continents and many thousands of islands. Asia is the largest continent, followed by Africa, North America, South America, Antarctica, Europe, and Australia. Geographers sometimes refer to Europe and Asia as one continent called Eurasia.

The world's land surface includes mountains, plateaus, hills, valleys, and plains. Relatively few people live in mountainous areas or on high plateaus since they are generally too cold, rugged, or dry for comfortable living or for crop farming. The majority of the world's people live on plains or in hilly regions. Most plains and hilly regions have excellent soil and an abundant water supply. They are good regions for farming, manufacturing, and trade. Many areas unsuitable for farming have other valuable resources. Mountainous regions, for example, have plentiful minerals, and some desert areas, especially in the Middle East, have large deposits of petroleum.

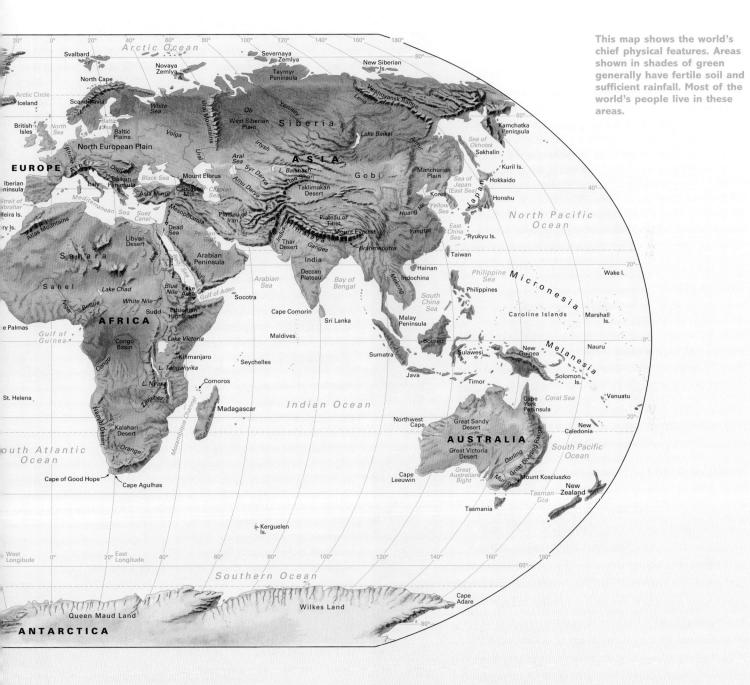

This map shows the world's chief physical features. Areas shown in shades of green generally have fertile soil and sufficient rainfall. Most of the world's people live in these areas.

KAZAKHSTAN

Kazakhstan is an independent country bordered by China in the east; Turkmenistan, Uzbekistan, and Kyrgyzstan in the south; Russia and the Caspian Sea in the west; and Siberia (part of Russia) in the north.

History

Turkish tribes originally settled the region that is now Kazakhstan. In the 1200's, they were conquered by the Mongols, who established *khanates*—realms ruled by Mongol chieftains—that dominated the area until the Russian conquest began in 1730.

The Russians set up forts throughout the land and established the capital of Verny, now called Almaty. In 1920, the Kazakh Republic was formed as an *autonomous* (self-governing) republic. As an autonomous republic of Russia, it joined the Soviet Union in 1922. In 1936, Kazakhstan became a separate union republic known as the Kazakh Soviet Socialist Republic.

In 1990, Kazakhstan declared that its laws took precedence over those of the Soviet Union. However, unlike most of the other Soviet republics, Kazakhstan did not immediately declare its independence. An upheaval in the Soviet Union was sparked by a failed coup in August 1991 against Soviet President Mikhail Gorbachev's government. Kazakhstan declared its independence on December 16.

On Dec. 8, 1991, Belarus, Russia, and Ukraine announced that they were establishing a loose confederation of former Soviet republics called the Commonwealth of Independent States (CIS). Gorbachev and Russian President Boris Yeltsin agreed to dissolve the Soviet Union by the end of the year and replace it with the CIS. The presidents of 11 former Soviet republics met in the Kazakh capital of Almaty and signed a declaration containing the terms of the union. The agreement became known as the Almaty Declaration, and Kazakhstan became the second largest country in the new commonwealth. In 1997, Kazakhstan moved its capital from Almaty to Akmola, now called Astana.

In December 1991, Nursultan Nazarbayev

FACTS

Official name:	Qazaqstan Respublikasy (Republic of Kazakhstan)
Capital:	Astana
Terrain:	Extends from the Volga to the Altai Mountains and from the plains in western Siberia to oases and desert in Central Asia
Area:	1,052,090 mi² (2,724,900 km²)
Climate:	Continental; cold winters and hot summers, arid and semiarid
Main rivers:	Syr Darya, Irtysh, Ural
Highest elevation:	Mount Tengri, 20,991 ft (6,398 m)
Lowest elevation:	Karagiye Depression, 433 ft (132 m) below sea level
Form of government:	Republic
Head of state:	President
Head of government:	Prime minister
Administrative areas:	14 oblystar (provinces), 3 qala (cities)
Legislature:	Parliament consisting of the Senate with 47 members serving six-year terms and the Mazhilis with 107 members serving five-year terms
Court system:	Supreme Court, Constitutional Council
Armed forces:	49,000 troops
National holiday:	Independence Day - December 16 (1991)
Estimated 2010 population:	15,889,000
Population density:	15 persons per mi² (6 per km²)
Population distribution:	58% urban, 42% rural
Life expectancy in years:	Male, 62; female, 73
Doctors per 1,000 people:	3.9
Birth rate per 1,000:	20
Death rate per 1,000:	10
Infant mortality:	28 deaths per 1,000 live births
Age structure:	0-14: 24%; 15-64: 68%; 65 and over: 8%
Internet users per 100 people:	12
Internet code:	.kz
Languages spoken:	Kazakh, Russian
Religions:	Sunni Muslim 47%, Russian Orthodox 44%, Protestant 2%, other 7%
Currency:	Kazakhstani tenge
Gross domestic product (GDP) in 2008:	$132.23 billion U.S.
Real annual growth rate (2008):	3.0%
GDP per capita (2008):	$8,605 U.S.
Goods exported:	Mostly: crude oil Also: chemicals, copper, food, iron and steel
Goods imported:	Crude oil and petroleum products, electrical equipment, iron and steel, machinery, motor vehicles
Trading partners:	China, Germany, Italy, Russia, Switzerland

became the first democratically elected president in Kazakh history. Kazakhstan replaced its Communist government with one based on democratic principles. But in 1995, Nazarbayev disbanded the parliament. Voters in a referendum extended his term to 2000 and later approved a new constitution. Nazarbayev was reelected in 1999, 2005, and 2011. The 2011 election was widely criticized as undemocratic.

Land and people

Before the Bolshevik Revolution of 1917, the Kazakhs were a nomadic people who roamed the land grazing their livestock. Because they had no written language, the Kazakhs had no books, newspapers, or schools.

The Soviet Virgin Lands project of the 1950's and 1960's changed Kazakhstan. The nation's vast steppes were transformed into cropland. As a result, thousands of people from all over the Soviet Union—particularly Russia—migrated to Kazakhstan to work in the fields. Although the Virgin Lands project was largely a failure, many immigrants settled in Kazakhstan. Today, Kazakhs make up about 65 percent of the population, and Russians, about 25 percent. Other groups include Belarusians, Germans, Tatars, Ukrainians, Uyghurs, and Uzbeks.

Kazakhstan has an economy based on industry and agriculture. Rich deposits of oil, gas, and such minerals as coal, copper, gold, iron ore, uranium, and zinc have contributed to the nation's industrial development and play a major role in the economy. Barley, cotton, rice, and wheat are important crops, and farmers raise sheep and cattle throughout the country.

The Soviet government located its first nuclear test site at Semipalatinsk in Kazakhstan. Soviet scientists launched Sputnik 1, the first artificial Earth satellite, from Baikonur, in central Kazakhstan. Since then, Russia has launched all its crewed missions, including those to the International Space Station, from the site.

Kazakhstan is a vast wilderness of broad, sandy deserts and low, grassy plateaus.

Ak Orda is the official workplace of the president of Kazakhstan in the capital of Astana. Ak Orda means "the white horde" in the Kazakh language. The building was completed in 2004. The president is the head of state. The prime minister is the head of the government.

The country of Kenya, on the east coast of Africa, attracts thousands of tourists each year. Kenya's beautiful landscape and spectacular variety of wildlife draw visitors from around the world.

Land and wildlife

Kenya's coast is lined with beautiful sandy beaches and lagoons. Mangrove swamps, cashew trees, coconut palms, and patches of tropical rain forest thrive in the hot, humid climate.

Inland, Kenya consists of dry, grassy plains with no cities or towns. Nomads roam this region in search of pasture and water for their animals.

In southwestern Kenya, the highland region has lofty mountains, fertile valleys, and grassy plateaus. There, Mount Kenya rises more than 17,000 feet (5,000 meters) high, and the Great Rift Valley, formed by cracks in Earth's surface, cuts across the highland.

Kenya's highland and plains regions are home to a fascinating variety of animals. Antelope, buffalo, cheetahs, elephants, giraffes, leopards, lions, rhinoceroses, and zebras roam the open country. Ostriches and storks add grace to the landscape, and crocodiles and hippopotamuses are found where water is plentiful.

History

Kenya has a rich and varied human history. Scientists believe that the remains of human beings found in Kenya may be 2 million years old. About 3,000 years ago, people from other parts of Africa began moving into what is now Kenya. Arabs began visiting the coast about 2,000 years ago and eventually established settlements there.

In the early 1500's, the Portuguese came to the Kenyan coast and took control of the area from the Arabs. In the 1600's, the Arabs defeated the Portuguese and regained control. However, these events had little impact on the people living in the interior plains or the highland area.

In the 1800's, the British became interested in the region, and in 1887 British businessmen leased part of the coast from the sultan of Zanzibar. The British government took over the coastal area in 1895 and soon extended its control to all of Kenya, which became known as British East Africa.

KENYA

The United Kingdom completed a railroad between the port city of Mombasa and Lake Victoria in 1901 and encouraged Britons and other Europeans to settle in the area. Soon, Europeans owned large Kenyan farms and hired Africans to work for them. The Africans had no say in their government.

During the 1940's, the Kikuyu people of central Kenya and other Africans began opposing British rule. Many Kikuyu were living in poverty under the British. The Kikuyu and other Kenyans formed a political party called the Kenya African Union (KAU) in 1944, and a Kikuyu named Jomo Kenyatta became the party's leader in 1947.

During this time, a secret movement—sometimes called *Mau Mau*—developed among Kikuyu KAU members. The Mau Mau sought greater unity among Kenyan Africans and demanded new British policies and programs to improve Africans' lives.

In 1952, when Mau Mau members began committing terrorist acts to further their cause, the British jailed thousands of them. Fighting then broke out. Kenyatta, convicted of leading the Mau Mau, was jailed in 1953, but the fighting continued for three more years. By 1956, about 13,500 Africans, 95 Europeans, and 29 Asians had been killed.

During the late 1950's, Kenya's Africans began demanding self-rule. The British agreed to the demand, and in February 1961, elections were held for a new parliament. Kenyatta's political party, called the Kenya African National Union (KANU), won the elections, but the party refused to take office until their leader was released from jail. The United Kingdom refused to release Kenyatta until August of that year. In the meantime, a rival party, the Kenya African Democratic Union (KADU), formed a government.

Full independence was finally gained on Dec. 12, 1963, and Kenyatta became prime minister. When Kenya became a republic in 1964, Kenyatta's title was changed to president, and he remained in that office until his death in 1978.

In 1964, KADU members dissolved their party and joined KANU. From 1982 to 1991, KANU was the only political party allowed in Kenya. In 1991, the Constitution was amended to allow for a multiparty system.

KENYA TODAY

Although Kenya has made much economic progress since it became independent, the country faces major problems. Less than 10 percent of the land is suitable for farming, and the population is growing at a rapid rate. Today, finding ways to feed its growing population is Kenya's chief challenge.

Since independence, Kenya has greatly increased its industry and tourist trade. Some of the money and machinery needed for the new industries has come from foreign investors. Some Kenyans object to foreign investment because they are afraid it gives too much influence over their country to outsiders. They also object to tourism because it relies on money from outsiders. These Kenyans compare their country's current situation to its colonial past, when Kenya's economic and cultural life was dominated by non-Africans. However, other Kenyans support the growth in industry and tourism as a way to improve the nation's economy—and therefore, the people's lives.

Many Kenyan parents value education as the key to a better life for their children. Because of their demands, Kenya's government has greatly increased the number of schools throughout the country. Also, in many places without government schools, people have set up their own self-help, or *harambee,* schools. *Harambee* means *pulling together* in Swahili.

Kenya today is a republic headed by a president. The president selects about 40 members of the National Assembly (Kenya's legislature) to serve as Cabinet ministers and chooses a vice president. Kenya's original Constitution, adopted in 1963, established the 224-member National Assembly. It also granted the people such rights as freedom of speech and religion and allowed Kenyan citizens 18 years old or older to vote in presidential and legislative elections.

In a referendum in 2010, voters approved a new Constitution. Among other changes, the document limits the president's powers; establishes a second chamber of the legislature, the Senate; and creates a

FACTS

Official name:	Jamhuriya Kenya (Republic of Kenya)
Capital:	Nairobi
Terrain:	Low plains rise to central highlands bisected by Great Rift Valley; fertile plateau in west
Area:	224,081 mi² (580,367 km²)
Climate:	Varies from tropical along coast to arid in interior
Main rivers:	Athi/Galana, Tana
Highest elevation:	Mount Kenya, 17,058 ft (5,199 m)
Lowest elevation:	Indian Ocean, sea level
Form of government:	Republic
Head of state:	President
Head of government:	President
Administrative areas:	7 provinces, 1 area
Legislature:	Bunge (National Assembly) with 224 members serving five-year terms
Court system:	Court of Appeal, High Court
Armed forces:	24,100 troops
National holiday:	Independence Day - December 12 (1963)
Estimated 2010 population:	40,602,000
Population density:	181 persons per mi² (70 per km²)
Population distribution:	79% rural, 21% urban
Life expectancy in years:	Male, 55; female, 56
Doctors per 1,000 people:	0.1
Birth rate per 1,000:	39
Death rate per 1,000:	12
Infant mortality:	77 deaths per 1,000 live births
Age structure:	0-14: 42%; 15-64: 55%; 65 and over: 3%
Internet users per 100 people:	9
Internet code:	.ke
Languages spoken:	English (official), Swahili (official), numerous indigenous languages
Religions:	Protestant 45%, Roman Catholic 33%, Muslim 10%, indigenous beliefs 10%, other 2%
Currency:	Kenyan shilling
Gross domestic product (GDP) in 2008:	$32.05 billion U.S.
Real annual growth rate (2008):	2.2%
GDP per capita (2008):	$862 U.S.
Goods exported:	Cement, clothing, coffee, cut flowers, fish, tea, petroleum products, vegetables
Goods imported:	Aircraft, food, iron and steel, machinery, motor vehicles, petroleum products, plastics
Trading partners:	China, India, Japan, Netherlands, South Africa, Uganda, United Arab Emirates, United Kingdom, United States

The graceful Jamaa Mosque is one of many important buildings in the central district of Nairobi, Kenya's capital and largest city. Although Nairobi is a major commercial center, the city has a national park within its borders where lions and other wild animals roam the open land.

Kenya, a country on the east coast of Africa, extends deep into the interior of the continent. The equator runs through the center of Kenya.

land commission to decide ownership disputes. Such disputes between members of Kenya's various ethnic groups have led to frequent outbreaks of violence over the years.

In Kenya's first multiparty elections, held in 1992, Daniel arap Moi was elected president. Moi stepped down in 2002, as required by Kenya's 1963 Constitution. Mwai Kibaki became the next president. In 2007, Kibaki was announced as the winner of a presidential election over Raila Odinga. However, Odinga accused Kibaki of election fraud, and riots broke out. In 2008, a power-sharing agreement created the post of prime minister to head Kenya's National Assembly. Kibaki remained president, and Odinga was sworn in as prime minister. The power-sharing agreement ended the violence and protests, but political infighting continued. The power-sharing government was to remain in office until the new Constitution fully took effect and new presidential elections could be held.

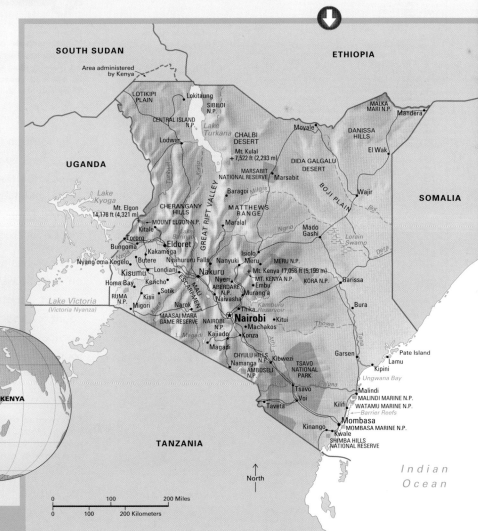

PEOPLE AND ECONOMY

Kenya's population is more than 40 million, and the number is growing at a rate of about 2 percent a year. Small numbers of Asian Indians, Europeans, and Arabs live in Kenya, but about 99 percent of Kenya's people are *indigenous* (native) Africans.

The Africans belong to about 40 different ethnic groups. The largest group, the Kikuyu, make up about 20 percent of the entire population. Four other ethnic groups—the Kalenjin, Kamba, Luhya, and Luo—each make up from 10 to 15 percent of the population. The Maasai, a well-known ethnic group, are nomads who tend herds of cattle on the vast plains of Kenya.

Kenya's ethnic groups speak different languages and may follow different ways of life. These differences—as well as differences in economic and social development—have sometimes led to tension between the groups. The Kenyan government has tried to overcome these ethnic divisions and create a sense of national unity.

Maasai people perform a traditional dance. These tall, slender nomads are famous for their traditional dress, including beaded jewelry and vivid red fabrics. The Maasai move from place to place in search of grazing land and water for their animals. They rely on their animals for milk and other food.

In addition to their local languages, most Kenyans also speak Swahili (which Africans call Kiswahili). Swahili helps unite the people. It is Kenya's national language and is widely used between people of different ethnic groups. English, the other official language, is spoken by most educated Kenyans.

Kenya has a developing economy that relies heavily on agriculture, but manufacturing is becoming more important. Together, manufacturing and construction account for about a sixth of Kenya's economic production. Service industries such as government, real estate, tourism, and wholesale and retail trade account for most of the rest.

A herdsman tends his cattle in southwestern Kenya. Most of Kenya's rural people raise crops and livestock for a living. Many must also work at other jobs to support their families.

Rural life

Most of Kenya's people live in rural areas, mainly in farm settlements made up of small houses with thatched or tin roofs, mud or cement walls, and dirt floors. They raise crops and livestock for a living.

Corn (called *maize* in Kenya), the basic food crop, is often ground into meal to make porridge and used to make stew.

Many Kenyan farmers struggle to produce enough food for themselves, but some have extra crops or beef and milk to sell. Many farmers work at part-time jobs for added income. Some work as blacksmiths, carpenters, shoemakers, or tailors. Others work part-time on large farm estates—especially coffee and tea plantations—that are owned by wealthy landowners.

Coffee and tea are Kenya's chief *cash crops*—that is, crops raised for export. Kenya is one of the world's largest producers and exporters of tea. Kenyan farmers also grow bananas, beans, cashews, cotton, pineapples, potatoes, sugar cane, sweet potatoes, wheat, *pyrethrum* (used to make insecticide), and *sisal* (fiber used to make rope). These crops account for much of Kenya's economic production.

Kenya's most important livestock products are beef and dairy products. Other important livestock include sheep and poultry.

A nomads' camp, made up of a few simple huts, shelters livestock herders in the desertlike region near Lake Turkana, at Kenya's northern border.

Urban life and tourism

Every year, many rural Kenyans move to the cities to find work in manufacturing or service industries. Urban factory workers help manufacture such products as cement, ceramics, beer and soft drinks, cigarettes, soap, furniture, leather goods, machinery, motor vehicle parts, paper, processed food, and textiles. Other urban Kenyans work in stores and offices.

Most city people live in modern houses made of stone or cement. Some are simple working-class homes; others are large, expensive houses or apartments for the well-to-do.

Many Kenyans work in the tourism industry, which is a leading source of foreign income in Kenya. Every year, more than a million tourists visit Kenya to enjoy the tropical coast and, more often, to view and photograph Kenya's magnificent wild animals. Many of the tourists come from Asia, Germany, the United Kingdom, and the United States.

Workers on a tea plantation in the highland region harvest one of Kenya's main cash crops. Kenya is one of the world's largest producers and exporters of tea.

KIRIBATI

The small island country of Kiribati (pronounced *KIHR ih bahs*) in the southwest Pacific Ocean is made up of the 16 Gilbert Islands, Banaba (formerly called Ocean Island), the 8 Phoenix Islands, and 8 of the Line Islands. Although it has a total land area of only 313 square miles (811 square kilometers), its islands are scattered over about 2 million square miles (5 million square kilometers) of the Pacific.

Almost all of Kiribati's islands are coral reefs, and many are *atolls,* ring-shaped reefs that enclose a lagoon. Kiribati has a tropical climate, with temperatures of about 80° F (27° C) the year around. The annual rainfall is about 100 inches (254 centimeters) in the northern islands, and about 40 inches (100 centimeters) in the other islands.

People and history

Kiribati has about 105,000 people. The islanders call themselves *I-Kiribati.* Most are Micronesians, and more than 95 percent live in the Gilbert Islands. Tarawa, one of the Gilberts, is the country's capital. It is an atoll composed of many coral islets.

Most I-Kiribati live in rural villages, with dwellings clustered around a church and a meeting house. Many of the village houses are made of wood and leaves from palm trees, although cement block houses with iron roofs are becoming more common. The language of the islanders is Gilbertese, but most people also speak some English, which is used in official communications. The people of Kiribati grow most of their own food, which includes bananas, breadfruit, papaya, pandanus fruit, sweet potatoes, and *babai* (giant taro). The islanders also raise pigs and chickens and catch fish for food. They wear light cotton clothing.

Most of the I-Kiribati are descended from Samoans who invaded the islands around 1400 and from people who had settled there earlier. In the 1500's, Spanish explorers became the first Europeans to sight the islands.

FACTS

Official name:	Republic of Kiribati
Capital:	Tarawa
Terrain:	Mostly low-lying coral atolls surrounded by extensive reefs
Area:	313 mi² (811 km²)
Climate:	Tropical; marine, hot and humid, moderated by trade winds
Main rivers:	N/A
Highest elevation:	Unnamed location on Banaba, 266 ft (81 m)
Lowest elevation:	Pacific Ocean, sea level
Form of government:	Republic
Head of state:	President
Head of government:	President
Administrative areas:	6 districts and 21 island councils
Legislature:	Maneaba Ni Maungatabu (House of Assembly) with 46 members serving four-year terms
Court system:	Court of Appeal, High Court, Magistrates' courts
Armed forces:	Australia and New Zealand provide Kiribati's defense
National holiday:	Independence Day - July 12 (1979)
Estimated 2010 population:	105,000
Population density:	335 persons per mi² (129 per km²)
Population distribution:	56% rural, 44% urban
Life expectancy in years:	Male, 60; female, 65
Doctors per 1,000 people:	0.2
Birth rate per 1,000:	29
Death rate per 1,000:	8
Infant mortality:	48 deaths per 1,000 live births
Age structure:	0-14: 37%; 15-64: 59%; 65 and over: 4%
Internet users per 100 people:	2
Internet code:	.ki
Languages spoken:	English (official), Gilbertese
Religions:	Roman Catholic 55%, Kiribati Protestant 36%, Mormon 3%, Baha'i 2%, Seventh-day Adventists 2%, other 2%.
Currency:	Australian dollar
Gross domestic product (GDP) in 2008:	$131 million U.S.
Real annual growth rate (2008):	3.7%
GDP per capita (2008):	$1,236 U.S.
Goods exported:	Copra, fish, seaweed
Goods imported:	Food, fuel, machinery, manufactured goods, transportation equipment
Trading partners:	Australia, Fiji, Japan, New Zealand, United States

During the 1890's, the United Kingdom took control of the Gilbert Islands and other neighboring islands. The United Kingdom gained control of Ocean Island in 1901. It made all these islands a colony in 1916. Some of the Line Islands and the Phoenix Islands were added to the colony later.

During World War II (1939-1945), Japanese troops occupied several of the islands. The United States Marines invaded Tarawa in 1943 and defeated the Japanese in one of the bloodiest battles of the war. Thirty-three islands in the former colony gained independence as Kiribati on July 12, 1979.

Government and economy

Kiribati is a republic headed by a president. The people elect the president from among candidates nominated by the House of Assembly. The House, the nation's lawmaking body, consists of 46 members whom the people elect to four-year terms. Most of Kiribati's inhabited islands have a local governing council. The government receives economic aid from Australia, the United Kingdom, and New Zealand.

Kiribati exports *copra* (dried coconut meat), fish, and seaweed. The commercial and shipping center of the country is Betio, in southwest Tarawa. Bairiki, east of Betio, is the government center. Bonriki, in the southeast, has an international airport.

In 2006, Kiribati's government created the Phoenix Islands Protected Area, one of the largest marine reserves in the world.

Houses with roofs of coconut tree leaves stand on Tabuaeran Island, one of the eight Line Islands that are part of Kiribati.

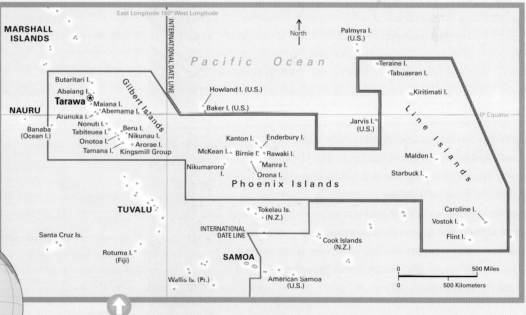

The republic of Kiribati consists of 33 islands spread across about 2 million square miles (5 million square kilometers) of the Pacific Ocean. The islands straddle the equator, the International Date Line, and the cultural boundary between Micronesia and Polynesia.

KOREA, NORTH

North Korea—officially known as the Democratic People's Republic of Korea—is one of two countries on the Korean Peninsula, which extends south from northeastern China. North Korea covers the northern half of the peninsula, and South Korea occupies the southern half. North Korea has a Communist government.

Various Korean and foreign governments ruled the Korean Peninsula from ancient times to the 1900's. Korea was a colony of Japan from 1910 until World War II ended in 1945. After Japan's defeat in the war, Korea became divided. Communists gained control of the North in 1945. The separate governments of North and South Korea were formed in 1948, and Kim Il-sung became the leader of North Korea.

Kim Il-sung's government was a dictatorship. He ruled North Korea until his death in 1994. Kim's son and designated heir, Kim Jong-il, succeeded his father as head of state. In the early 2000's, Kim Jong-il's rule was marked by a series of international disputes over North Korea's nuclear program. Kim Jong-il died in 2011 and was succeeded by his son Kim Jong-un.

Foreign relations

From 1948 to 1971, North Korea was one of the most isolated countries in the world. During this time, the country's foreign relations were conducted almost exclusively with other Communist nations, particularly China and the Soviet Union. During the 1970's, however, military and economic assistance from both countries decreased.

When the Soviet Union and China began increasing their contacts with South Korea in the 1980's, Kim Il-sung, fearing total isolation, tried to improve the nation's relations with other countries. In 1991, both Koreas agreed to accept each other's existence. They also agreed not to use force against each other and not to use or possess nuclear weapons. That same year, North Korea and South Korea joined the United Nations as separate states.

FACTS

Official name:	Choson-minjujuui-inmin-konghwaguk (Democratic People's Republic of Korea)
Capital:	Pyongyang
Terrain:	Mostly hills and mountains separated by deep, narrow valleys; coastal plains wide in west, discontinuous in east
Area:	46,540 mi² (120,538 km²)
Climate:	Temperate, with rainfall concentrated in summer
Main rivers:	Yalu, Taedong, Tumen
Highest elevation:	Paektu-san (Paektu Mountain), 9,003 ft (2,744 m)
Lowest elevation:	Sea of Japan, sea level
Form of government:	Communist
Head of state:	Chairman of National Defense Commission
Head of government:	Premier
Administrative areas:	9 do (provinces)
Legislature:	Ch'oego Inmin Hoeui (Supreme People's Assembly) with 687 members serving five-year terms
Court system:	Central Court
Armed forces:	1,106,000 troops
National holiday:	Founding of the Democratic People's Republic of Korea - September 9 (1948)
Estimated 2010 population:	24,033,000
Population density:	516 persons per mi² (199 per km²)
Population distribution:	62% urban, 38% rural
Life expectancy in years:	Male, 65; female, 70
Doctors per 1,000 people:	3.3
Birth rate per 1,000:	15
Death rate per 1,000:	10
Infant mortality:	42 deaths per 1,000 live births
Age structure:	0-14: 23%; 15-64: 68%; 65 and over: 9%
Internet users per 100 people:	N/A
Internet code:	.kp
Language spoken:	Korean
Religions:	Buddhism, Confucianism, Christian, Chondogyo (Religion of the Heavenly Way)
Currency:	North Korean won
Gross domestic product (GDP) in 2008:	$26.20 billion U.S.
Real annual growth rate (2008):	-2.3%
GDP per capita (2008):	$1,136 U.S.
Goods exported:	Clothing, electronics, fish products, machinery, metals and metals products, textiles
Goods imported:	Coal, crude petroleum, food, machinery, textiles
Trading partners:	China, Japan, South Korea, Thailand

In 2002, North Korea held talks with Japan, the United States, and other countries in efforts to establish more friendly relations. However, these efforts were thwarted when North Korea revealed that it had a secret program to develop nuclear weapons. In late 2002 and early 2003, North Korea expelled international atomic energy inspectors from the country. In 2006, a nuclear test caused the United Nations to impose economic sanctions on North Korea.

Disagreements over North Korea's nuclear program continued through the first decade of the 2000's.

Relations with South Korea

Hostilities between North Korea and South Korea have existed since 1945. In 1950, North Korean troops invaded South Korea, starting the Korean War. The war ended in 1953, but neither side won a complete victory. During the 1960's and 1970's, North Korea's frequent attacks in the demilitarized zone (DMZ) between the two countries created worldwide tension. Each country has claimed to be the only legitimate government on the Korean Peninsula.

In December 1991, North and South Korea signed a treaty promising to end aggression and permit travel, trade, and humanitarian exchanges between the two countries. In 2000, the leaders of North and South Korea met to discuss relations. As a result of this meeting, the two countries have made some additional moves toward improving relations. For example, some North Korean and South Korean relatives have been allowed to visit one another, and road and rail links have been reestablished.

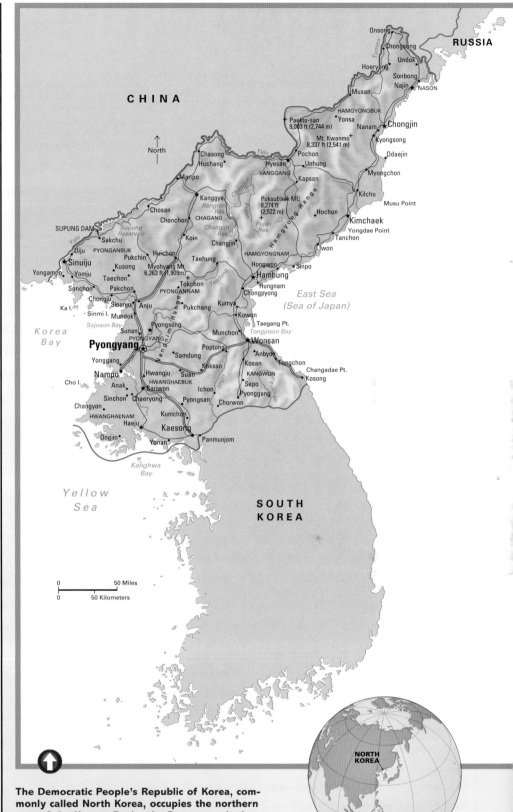

The Democratic People's Republic of Korea, commonly called North Korea, occupies the northern part of the Korean Peninsula. Pyongyang is the capital and largest city of North Korea.

LAND AND PEOPLE

Mountains cover about 80 percent of North Korea. Plains stretch along the western and northeastern coasts of the country. Most of North Korea's 24 million people live on the coastal plains or in river valleys.

Rolling hills divide western North Korea into a series of broad, level plains. The plains have most of the country's farmland, as well as its major industrial areas, including Pyongyang. About half of North Korea's people live in the region.

Forested mountains cover almost all of central North Korea. These mountains are an important source of valuable minerals and forest products. North Korea's highest mountain, Paektu-san (Paektu Mountain), rises 9,003 feet (2,744 meters) on the border with China. North Korea's longest river, the Yalu, flows westward from this mountain for 490 miles (789 kilometers) to the Yellow Sea. Almost a fourth of North Korea's people live in the central mountain region.

The strip of land along North Korea's east coast consists of narrow plains separated by low hills. The plains provide much farmland, and fishing also is important in this region. The region also has some industrial areas. More than a fourth of North Korea's people live in the eastern lowland region.

Climate

North Korea's climate is affected by monsoons throughout the year. A summer monsoon brings hot, humid weather, with temperatures in July and August averaging about 85° F (30° C) in Pyongyang. Mountains protect the eastern plains from the cold, dry winter monsoon, producing mild winter seasons, but winters on the northern border are very cold, with temperatures in January averaging –5° F (–20° C). Annual precipitation in North Korea generally ranges from 30 to 60 inches (76 to 150 centimeters), but most of the country's rain falls in the summer months between June and August.

North Korean children are required to attend school for 11 years, including a year of preschool. The state pays all educational expenses. Students must work for the state during part of the summer.

Visitors enjoy the view from a bridge in scenic Myohyang Mountains in North Korea's Northern Mountains region. Forested mountains and hills cover most of the country.

Life under Communism

After the Korean War, North Korea's Communist government made many changes in the traditional Korean way of life. The government's emphasis on industrialization encouraged many North Koreans to leave rural farm areas for jobs in the cities, thus weakening strong family ties. In addition, the Communists actively discouraged religion because they felt it conflicted with the teachings of Communism.

The Communist government sought to make an idol of President Kim Il-sung, to replace the North Korean people's traditional Confucian values and family loyalties. The North Korean media constantly acclaimed Kim's genius as a leader, and the people were required to spend at least two hours a day studying his writings. The government hoped to inspire the people's unquestioned devotion to the regime's policies.

The North Korean Constitution says that political power belongs to the people. However, the country's Communist Party, called the Korean Workers' Party, holds the real political power, and the North Korean people have little freedom. The government controls cultural and social life, including most forms of recreation and entertainment. Art forms that conflict with Communist principles are prohibited.

Industry accounts for the largest part of North Korea's economy. Most of the country's workers live in cities and towns. They live in large, state-built and state-owned apartment buildings. About 30 percent of North Koreans work in agriculture, mostly on state-controlled collective farms or cooperatives. About 30 percent of North Korea's people work in manufacturing and mining, and about 40 percent are employed in service activities.

Pyongyang is North Korea's most modern city, with skyscrapers, broad boulevards, cultural centers, and sports stadiums. However, it has few restaurants or places of entertainment. Few North Koreans own automobiles.

Construction workers at a dam site take a break. All industry in North Korea is owned by the government, and workers are compensated according to the quality and quantity of work done.

Workers prepare for the rice harvest on a North Korean collective farm. The workers receive a share of the products and some cash payment in exchange for their labor.

The Republic of Korea—usually called South Korea—covers the southern half of the Korean Peninsula in eastern Asia. The Communist-ruled Democratic People's Republic of Korea—usually called North Korea—lies to the north. The Korean Peninsula is bounded by the Yellow Sea on the west, the Korea Strait on the south, and the East Sea (also called the Sea of Japan) on the east. The northern part of the peninsula is bordered mostly by China and a small area of Russia.

More than 48 million people live in South Korea. Seoul, South Korea's capital and largest city, is also the country's cultural, economic, and educational center. About 20 percent of South Korea's people live in Seoul.

Mountains extend through most of central and eastern South Korea. The graceful Buddhist shrine at Hajodae perches along the rocky eastern coastline of the Taebaek Mountains, which plunge eastward into the East Sea. Plains cover much of the rest of the country, and numerous islands lie off the southern and western coasts of the peninsula.

North Korea and South Korea have pursued very different political courses since the peninsula became divided in the mid-1940's. Nevertheless, they share a long history.

Early history

People have lived in the southwestern part of the Korean Peninsula for at least 30,000 years. Scholars believe the ancestors of today's Korean people may have migrated into the peninsula about 5,000 years ago. According to tradition, the earliest Korean state, called Choson, developed in the northern part of the peninsula in 2333 B.C. In 108 B.C., China conquered parts of this territory and strongly influenced Korean arts, sciences, and government.

During the last century B.C., the Three Kingdoms emerged—Koguryo in the northeastern part of the peninsula, Paekche in the southwest, and Silla in the southeast. Buddhism became the chief religion in the kingdoms during the A.D. 300's and 400's. Silla gained control of most of the peninsula in the 660's. Art and learning flourished in Silla, and Confucianism was introduced from China. Provincial warlords broke up the kingdom in the 800's. By 935, a

KOREA, SOUTH

general named Wang Kon had conquered Silla and the surrounding states and named the area Koryo. The word *Korea* came from the word *Koryo*.

In 1388, a general named Yi Songgye took control of Koryo, and in 1392 he became king and renamed the country Choson. In the 1630's, Manchu armies from the north defeated the Koreans. Though members of the Yi family continued as kings, the Manchus demanded payments from Korea until the late 1800's.

Between the 1600's and 1800's, Korea was called the *Hermit Kingdom* because its rulers closed the country to all foreigners except the Chinese and Japanese. In 1876, Japan forced the kingdom to open some ports to trade. Japan took complete control in 1910 and ruled Korea until Japan's defeat in World War II (1939-1945).

The Korean War

When World War II ended, Soviet troops occupied the northern half of the Korean Peninsula, and American troops occupied the southern half. In 1948, two separate Korean states were formed—the Democratic People's Republic of Korea in the north and the Republic of Korea in the south. By mid-1949, both the Soviet Union and the United States had withdrawn their troops from the peninsula.

In June 1950, troops from Communist-ruled North Korea invaded South Korea, and the Korean War began. The United Nations (UN) demanded that the Communists withdraw, and when the Communists refused to comply, the UN called on its member nations to give military aid to South Korea. Sixteen countries sent troops and 41 countries sent military supplies, but the United States sent about 90 percent of the troops and supplies. China fought on the side of North Korea, and the Soviet Union gave the Communists military equipment.

The Korean War ended on July 27, 1953. An armistice agreement established a buffer zone called the *demilitarized zone* (DMZ) between North and South Korea, but a permanent peace treaty has never been signed.

SOUTH KOREA TODAY

The Korean War destroyed many of South Korea's factories and farm crops, so the nation was faced with grave economic problems when the fighting stopped. President Syngman Rhee's efforts to develop his country's economy were based largely on aid from the United States, and he failed to develop an economic plan for South Korea. In the early 1950's, members of the National Assembly, the country's legislature, became increasingly critical of Rhee.

Rhee's use of undemocratic methods to control the government eventually aroused opposition among the South Korean people, especially students. In 1960, widespread student-led demonstrations forced Rhee to resign.

The new government was weak, however, and in 1961 it was overthrown by a group of military officers led by General Park Chung Hee. In 1963, Park was elected president. South Korea's economy developed rapidly under Park, but he used his power to hold down opposition and deny the people's civil rights. Freedom of speech and freedom of the press were limited, and many of Park's political opponents were jailed. In 1972, he put a new constitution in force that gave him almost unlimited powers. It provided that the president would be chosen by members of the Electoral College—rather than elected directly by the people—and allowed an unlimited number of terms.

In 1979, Park was assassinated. The government delayed a promised constitutional revision that would allow for direct presidential elections. Many South Koreans took part in demonstrations that were brutally put down by the government, and in 1980 martial law was declared. In August of that year, Lieutenant General Chun Doo Hwan was elected president by the Electoral College.

During the 1980's, students demonstrated against Chun, demanding a new, more democratic constitution that allowed direct election of the president. Mounting public sympathy for the protesters finally forced Chun to

FACTS

Official name:	Taehan-min'guk (Republic of Korea)
Capital:	Seoul
Terrain:	Mostly hills and mountains; wide coastal plains in west and south
Area:	38,486 mi^2 (99,678 km^2)
Climate:	Temperate, with rainfall heavier in summer than winter
Main rivers:	Naktong, Han
Highest elevation:	Halla-san (Halla Mountain) 6,398 ft (1,950 m)
Lowest elevation:	Sea of Japan, sea level
Form of government:	Republic
Head of state:	President
Head of government:	Prime minister
Administrative areas:	9 do (provinces), 7 gwangyoksi (special cities)
Legislature:	Kukhoe A (National Assembly) with 299 members serving four-year terms
Court system:	Supreme Court
Armed forces:	687,000 troops
National holiday:	Liberation Day - August 15 (1945)
Estimated 2010 population:	48,653,000
Population density:	1,264 persons per mi^2 (488 per km^2)
Population distribution:	82% urban, 18% rural
Life expectancy in years:	Male, 76; female, 82
Doctors per 1,000 people:	1.6
Birth rate per 1,000:	10
Death rate per 1,000:	5
Infant mortality:	4 deaths per 1,000 live births
Age structure:	0-14: 18%; 15-64: 72%; 65 and over: 10%
Internet users per 100 people:	78
Internet code:	.kr
Language spoken:	Korean
Religions:	Buddhist 23%, Protestant 18%, Roman Catholic 11%, other 48%
Currency:	South Korean won
Gross domestic product (GDP) in 2008:	$929.12 billion U.S.
Real annual growth rate (2008):	2.5%
GDP per capita (2008):	$19,009 U.S.
Goods exported:	Chemicals, electronics, iron and steel, motor vehicles, petroleum products, plastics, ships
Goods imported:	Chemicals, crude oil, electronics and electronic equipment, iron and steel, machinery, transportation equipment
Trading partners:	China, Japan, Saudi Arabia, Singapore, United Arab Emirates, United States

meet their demands. Roh Tae Woo became the first directly elected president in 1987.

Since 1945, the relationship between North Korea and South Korea has been one of mutual suspicion, and American troops have guarded the neutral demilitarized zone since 1953. However, in 1991, North and South Korea signed a treaty ending aggression and permitting some travel, trade, and humanitarian exchanges between the two countries. That same year, each country joined the United Nations as a separate state.

In 1997, Kim Dae-jung, a strong advocate of democracy, was elected president. He was the first politician from an opposition party—a party that does not have a majority of seats in parliament—to become president. In 2000, Kim Dae-jung went to Pyongyang, North Korea, and met face-to-face with North Korean leader Kim Jong-il. It was the first meeting between leaders of the two nations since the peninsula was divided. The two countries later made additional moves toward improving relations. Some North Korean and South Korean relatives were allowed to visit one another. In addition, some road and railroad links were reestablished between the north and south.

Tensions remained, however. In 2002, North Korea admitted that it was pursuing a nuclear weapons program. In 2010, a South Korean warship patrolling a border between the two countries was sunk, and an international investigation determined that North Korea had fired a torpedo at the vessel.

In 2002, Roh Moo-hyun was elected president of South Korea. He was impeached in 2004 for violations of election law and incompetence, but the Constitutional Court overturned the impeachment. Corruption allegations continued, however, and in 2007, voters elected Lee Myung-bak as president. Roh committed suicide in 2009.

The Republic of Korea, or South Korea, has been divided from North Korea since 1945. This division continues to be a source of bitter sorrow for many Koreans.

The skyscrapers of Seoul glitter in the twilight in a view from Namsan Hill in the center of the city.

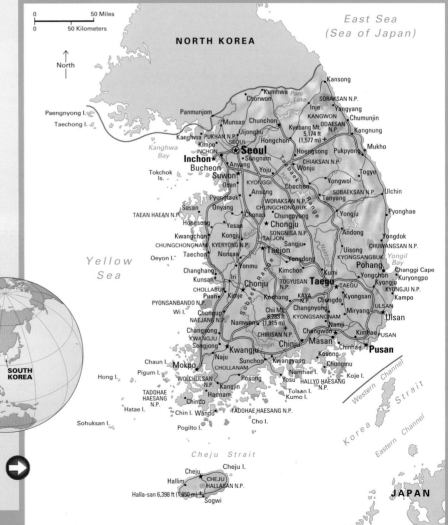

LAND AND PEOPLE

South Korea has three main land regions—the Central Mountains, the Southern Plains, and the Western Plains. The Central Mountains region extends throughout most of central and eastern South Korea. Lush forests cover the mountains in this region, even extending along much of the seacoast. Hillsides, river valleys, and some land along the eastern coast are used for farming, while coastal waters yield plentiful supplies of fish. More than 25 percent of South Korea's people live in the Central Mountains region.

The Southern Plains, which cover the country's entire southern coast, consist of a series of plains separated by low hills. Pusan, one of the country's major industrial centers, is located in the Southern Plains, and South Korea's longest river, the Naktong, flows through the region from mountains in the north to the Korea Strait. The Southern Plains are an important agricultural and industrial region.

The Western Plains, which extend along almost the entire western coast of South Korea, are covered by

Outdoor dining is a popular activity in Seoul. The favorite dishes include kimchi, a highly spiced mixture of Chinese cabbage, onions, white radishes, and other vegetables.

A fishing village on South Korea's southern coast, above, overlooks rocky islands off the mainland. Many South Koreans make their living by fishing, and seafood forms an important part of the people's diet.

rolling hills and plains. The region has much of the country's best farmland, as well as the important industrial area around Seoul. The Han River flows through the region from mountains in the east to the Yellow Sea.

About 3,000 islands lie off the southern and western coasts of the Korean Peninsula. However, only about 200 of these islands are inhabited. The largest island, Cheju, lies about 50 miles (80 kilometers) south of the peninsula and covers about 700 square miles (1,800 square kilometers). South Korea's highest mountain, Halla-san (Halla Mountain) towers 6,398 feet (1,950 meters) on this island. Cheju has its own provincial government, while other islands are governed by provinces on the mainland.

South Korea's climate is affected the year around by monsoon winds. During the summer, a monsoon blows in from the south and southeast, bringing hot, humid

Sorak-san (Snow Peak Mountain) National Park, located on South Korea's eastern coast in the Central Mountains region, has some of the country's most striking scenery.

Bicycles crowd busy Yoido Plaza in Seoul. Many people live in high-rise apartment buildings on Yoido Island in the Han River, an area of the city just southwest of the downtown district.

weather and temperatures averaging between 70° F (21° C) and 80° F (27° C). In the winter, a cold, dry monsoon blowing in from the north and northwest brings cold weather. The average January temperature in Seoul is about 23° F (-5° C). Mountains protect the east coast from the winter monsoon, so temperatures in the east stay warmer. January temperatures in southeastern Korea average about 35° F (2° C).

Most of South Korea receives from 30 to 50 inches (76 to 130 centimeters) of *precipitation* (rain, melted snow, and other forms of moisture) per year, with heavy rainfall from June through August accounting for about half of that total. Strong tropical storms called *typhoons* pose a threat to the Korean Peninsula during July and August.

Way of life

The population of the Korean Peninsula consists almost entirely of Koreans. A small minority of people are of Chinese descent.

Before the 1900's, most Koreans lived in small villages and worked on farms. Often, several generations lived together. The oldest male was head of the family, and all people were expected to obey their elders.

This way of life changed quickly after Japan seized control of the Korean Peninsula in 1910. The Japanese brought industry to Korean cities and took much farmland away from the farmers. They forced many young Koreans to work in the cities. Life changed even more after Korea's division into two countries in the 1940's. Economic growth, industrialization, and ties to Western nations brought change to South Korean lifestyles.

Today, about 80 percent of South Koreans live in cities. Job opportunities, colleges and universities, better health care, and a greater variety of entertainment have drawn people to the urban areas. The population is highly educated, and South Korea has more than 250 college-level schools.

The cities have many high-rise apartment buildings and modern houses, but meeting the rapidly rising need for housing has been a problem. Many South Koreans, including those in rural areas, live in houses made of bricks or concrete blocks, with roofs of cement tiles and slate.

Whether in the city or the country, most Korean houses have *ondol*—floors of thick stone slabs covered by oiled papers or mats. In traditional Korean houses, channels under the floors carried hot air from the kitchen or from an indoor fireplace to heat the rooms. In many homes today, pipes carry heated water under the floors to provide heat. In the cities, many ondol are heated by electric coils.

ECONOMY

South Korea has one of the largest economies in Asia. The boom began in the 1960's, when President Park Chung Hee focused South Korea's economy on manufacturing and export trade, rather than on agriculture.

In the early 1960's, economic growth in South Korea came mainly from light industries, such as textiles. By the 1970's and 1980's, the nation's heavy industries—including the production of such items as automobiles and electric appliances—were developing rapidly. More recently, service industries, which provide services rather than produce goods, have become major contributors to South Korea's economic growth.

In the late 1990's, much of Asia experienced severe economic problems. As a result, the value of South Korea's currency fell, and its stock market plunged. Businesses went bankrupt, and South Korea faced widespread unemployment. By 2000, however, the economy had largely recovered, and it grew in the first decade of the 2000's.

Service industries

Service industries employ about two-thirds of South Korea's workers. Finance, insurance, real estate, and business services are the country's leading service industries. Other important areas include wholesale and retail trade, hotels, restaurants, education, government services, and transportation and communications. South Korea's booming tourist industry also has contributed to the growth of the country's industries.

Industry

Industrial activities—including manufacturing, construction, and mining—employ about one-fourth of the nation's workers. Almost all of South Korea's industry is privately owned.

South Korea ranks as a major producer of chemicals, fertilizers, iron and steel, machinery, and ships. In the 1970's and 1980's, the country

Robots assemble vehicles in an automobile factory in South Korea. Manufacturing accounts for about 75 percent of the country's industrial production.

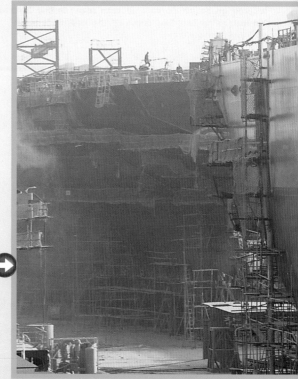

A massive shipyard is at Ulsan on South Korea's east coast. International trade is a major part of the economy. South Korea's main trading partners are China, Japan, Saudi Arabia, Singapore, the United Arab Emirates, and the United States.

Planting rice by hand in flooded paddy fields is a slow and difficult job. Today, many South Korean farms use modern agricultural methods, and machines do much of the work.

expanded production of automobiles, computer equipment and parts, electric appliances, telecommunications equipment, and televisions sets. Other manufactured products include cement, clothing, processed foods, rubber tires, and textiles.

South Korea's change from an agricultural to an industrial society also spurred a boom in construction that still continues. South Korea has few mineral reserves, but it does mine some *anthracite* (hard coal), cadmium, gold, graphite, iron ore, lead, limestone, silver, and zinc. The country's manufacturers rely heavily on imports for raw minerals.

Agriculture and fishing

The plains near the southern and western coasts are South Korea's main agricultural regions. However, South Korea's agricultural production has decreased over the years, and the country has been importing more food.

Rice is by far South Korea's chief crop. South Korean farms also produce apples, barley, cabbage, grapes, onions, pears, potatoes, strawberries, sweet potatoes, and tomatoes. Some farmers raise cattle, chickens, and hogs. Oranges and tangerines are grown on the island of Cheju, off Korea's southern coast.

Many farmers supplement their income by fishing. The modernization of its fishing industry has made South Korea one of the world's leading fishing countries. The catch includes anchovies, mackerel, squid, and tuna.

CULTURE AND ART

Koreans have an ancient and distinctive culture. Philosophy, scholarship, and religion have played important roles in the culture's development.

Taoism, Buddhism, and Confucianism have been important to Korean culture and art. All three were introduced into Korea from China. The Taoist emphasis on living in harmony with nature is reflected on the South Korean flag, which shows a Taoist symbol called *yin* and *yang* that represents the balance in the universe between opposites—such as male and female, and life and death.

Buddhism became the chief religion of the Three Kingdoms—Koguryo, Silla, and Paekche—during the 300's and 400's. Temples and monasteries constructed during this time became centers of learning and of the arts. Much of Korean art reflects the influence of Buddhist teaching, and Buddha's birthday is a national holiday in South Korea.

Honoring their royal ancestors, descendants of Korea's Yi dynasty, which ruled from 1392 until 1910, solemnly take part in a Confucian ceremony at Chongmyo Shrine.

Confucianism became an important part of Korean thought and culture after the Silla absorbed the other two kingdoms in the 660's. Confucianism stresses the duties that people have toward one another, particularly within the family.

Confucianism remains important in South Korea today. For example, most South Korean families continue to honor their ancestors in special ceremonies, according to the teachings of Confucius.

Roman Catholic missionaries brought Christianity to Korea during the 1830's. Christianity influenced modern Korea through its emphasis on learning and social reform.

Today, about 23 percent of South Koreans are Buddhists, about 18 percent are Protestants, and about 11 percent are Roman Catholics.

Drummers pound out a rhythm on the changgo at a traditional Korean farmers' dance. At these spirited affairs, some dancers play the changgo, while others play smaller drums, gongs, trumpets, or oboes. One performer twirls a long white streamer attached to his hat and leaps in and out of its circles.

Music and dance

Traditional Korean court music developed largely under Chinese influence. Although Korea's last royal dynasty ended in 1910 when the Japanese took control of the country, the court music and its ancient instruments were preserved in South Korea. Today, court orchestras perform the music throughout the nation and keep this ancient heritage alive.

Folk music is another important element of traditional Korean music. Traditional Korean folk musicians used a variety of special instruments, including an hourglass drum called a *changgo* and a 12-stringed zither called a *kayagum*.

Folk music and folk dance were used primarily to express religious beliefs. Farmers' dances, for example, were performed in the spring to ask for good crops, and in the fall to give thanks for the harvest. Folk songs expressing Buddhist or Confucian beliefs celebrated the virtues of honoring parents and chastity.

Masked dance dramas, on the other hand, were intended to entertain audiences. Accompanied by music and song, these dramas used wit to make fun of the upper class and life in general.

Poetry, painting, and ceramics

In the 1440's, Koreans invented their own alphabet. Until then, Koreans had used Chinese characters for writing. Sejong, the Korean king, wanted to develop a simpler form of writing to introduce Buddhist scripture and ideas to the common people. King Sejong's alphabet, which had 40 letters, was first published in 1446. Today, the Korean alphabet, known as *han'gul,* uses 24 letters.

Korean poetry, traditionally the most admired form of writing, often has a religious theme. Nature has also served as an inspiration in both Korean literature and painting.

Art in Korea was closely associated with Confucian scholarship, which emphasized poetry, *calligraphy* (the art of beautiful handwriting), and painting. Korean art generally included landscapes, animals, and the "four gentlemen"—bamboo, chrysanthemum, orchid, and plum blossoms.

Many historians believe that Korean art reached its greatest heights in ceramics. The blue-green pottery known as *celadon* is particularly admired for its graceful lines and depth of color.

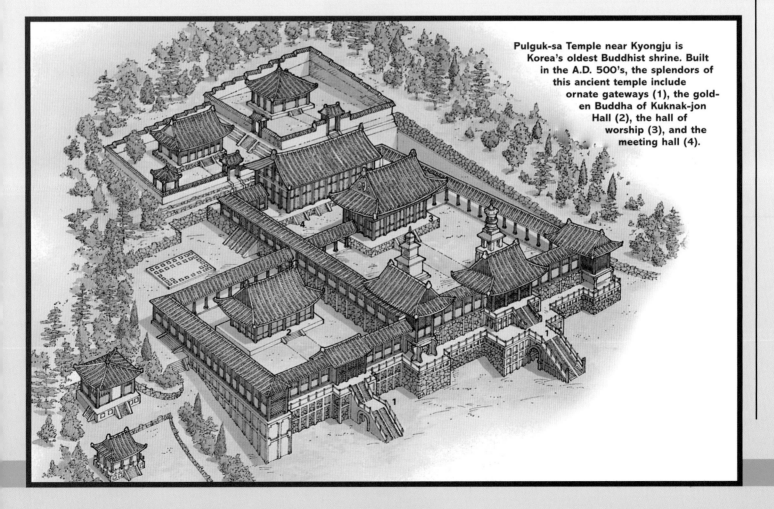

Pulguk-sa Temple near Kyongju is Korea's oldest Buddhist shrine. Built in the A.D. 500's, the splendors of this ancient temple include ornate gateways (1), the golden Buddha of Kuknak-jon Hall (2), the hall of worship (3), and the meeting hall (4).

KOSOVO

Kosovo is a small, mountainous country in south-eastern Europe. It is bordered by Albania to the southwest, Montenegro to the northwest, Serbia to the north, and Macedonia to the southeast.

About 90 percent of Kosovars are Albanians, and about 8 percent are Serbs. Other ethnic groups include Bosniaks (also called Bosnian Muslims), Croats, Egyptians, Montenegrins, Roma, and Turks. Albanian and Serbian are the official languages. The main religious groups are Islam, Eastern Orthodoxy, and Roman Catholicism.

During most of the 1900's, Kosovo was part of Serbia. Kosovo was torn by ethnic conflict during the late 1990's and early 2000's, and the desire for independence grew among the Albanian majority. Kosovo declared its independence from Serbia in 2008. Serbia, which considered Kosovo a historic part of its country, refused to recognize the declaration.

Kosovo's economic growth was slow during most of the 1900's, and the conflict during the 1990's also damaged it. Between 1999 and 2008, Kosovo was governed by international authorities sent by the United Nations (UN), and it experienced some growth in trade and construction.

Farming and mining are the major industries in Kosovo. The main crops include corn, melons, peppers, sunflowers, tomatoes, and wheat. Mines produce coal, lead, magnesium, nickel, and zinc. Priština, Kosovo's capital, is also the largest city.

History

The Illyrians were the earliest known inhabitants of what is now Kosovo. Slavs arrived in the A.D. 500's. Historical records first mention Albanians in Kosovo in 1043.

Between 1180 and 1216, Serbian rulers gradually brought the region under their control. But in 1389, the Ottoman Empire, which was based in what is now Turkey, defeated the Serbs at the Battle of Kosovo Polje. The Ottomans completed their conquest of the Serbs in the mid-1400's.

FACTS

Official name:	Republika e Kosoves (Republic of Kosovo)
Capital:	Priština
Terrain:	Mostly mountainous territory; flatlands and valleys near rivers
Area:	4,212 mi^2 (10,908 km^2)
Climate:	Summers are hot and dry; winters are relatively cold, with heavy snowfall; rainfall is heaviest between October and December
Main rivers:	Beli Drim, Ibar, Lepenac
Highest elevation:	Mount Daravica, 8,714 ft (2,656 m)
Lowest elevation:	974 ft (297 m) above sea level on Beli Drim River at western border with Albania
Form of government:	Republic
Head of state:	President
Head of government:	Prime minister
Administrative areas:	30 komuna (municipalities)
Legislature:	Kosovo Assembly with 120 members serving four-year terms
Court system:	Supreme Court
Armed forces:	N/A
National holiday:	Independence Day - February 17 (2008)
Estimated 2010 population:	2,262,000
Population density:	537 persons per mi^2 (207 per km^2)
Population distribution:	N/A
Life expectancy in years:	Male, 67; female, 71
Doctors per 1,000 people:	N/A
Birth rate per 1,000:	21
Death rate per 1,000:	7
Infant mortality:	33 deaths per 1,000 live births
Age structure:	0-14: 31%; 15-64: 63%; 65 and over: 6%
Internet users per 100 people:	N/A
Internet code:	N/A
Languages spoken:	Albanian (official), Serbian (official), Bosnian, Turkish, Roma
Religions:	Muslim, Serbian Orthodox, Roman Catholic
Currency:	Euro
Gross domestic product (GDP) in 2008:	N/A
Real annual growth rate (2008):	N/A
GDP per capita (2008):	N/A
Goods exported:	Food and beverages, iron and steel, leather products, machinery
Goods imported:	Agricultural products, chemicals, machinery, petroleum products
Trading partners:	Germany, Macedonia, Serbia, Turkey

Kosovo is a country in southeastern Europe. It is bordered by Albania to the southwest, Montenegro to the northwest, Serbia to the north, and Macedonia to the southeast.

Serbia regained its independence in 1878, but Kosovo remained part of the Ottoman Empire until 1912, when the Serbian Army seized it during the First Balkan War (1912-1913). In 1918, Kosovo became part of the Kingdom of the Serbs, Croats, and Slovenes, later renamed Yugoslavia.

After World War II (1939-1945), Yugoslavia became a Communist country organized into six republics—Bosnia-Herzegovina, Croatia, Macedonia, Montenegro, Serbia, and Slovenia. Kosovo was an *autonomous* (self-governing) region, and later an autonomous province, within Serbia.

Road to independence

During the 1980's, resentment against Serbia's dominance in Yugoslavia grew among some of the country's other ethnic groups. Four of the Yugoslav republics withdrew from the country in the early 1990's. In 1992, Serbia and Montenegro formed a new Yugoslavia, with Kosovo still a part of Serbia.

Meanwhile, in 1989 and 1990, the Serbian government had stripped Kosovo of its autonomy and dissolved Kosovo's government. It ended the use of the Albanian language in Kosovo's schools and denied various rights to the Albanian Kosovars.

In 1997, the Kosovo Liberation Army (KLA), which demanded independence for Kosovo, attacked Serbian police stations and vehicles. In late 1998, Serbian forces launched a campaign against Kosovo's Albanians, driving many from their homes.

During 1999, the North Atlantic Treaty Organization (NATO) tried to arrange a peace. Representatives of the Albanian Kosovars agreed to NATO's peace plan, but Serbia did not. NATO began air strikes against military targets in Serbia to force the government to accept the peace plan, but Serbian forces continued to attack Kosovo. Hundreds of thousands of people fled. In June 1999, Serbian leaders agreed to withdraw their troops from Kosovo. NATO stopped its bombing. The UN then sent officials to serve as a temporary regional government in Kosovo. Many refugees returned home, but tension and outbreaks of violence continued.

In 2006, Montenegro and Serbia became separate countries. In 2007, Serbia rejected a UN plan to give Kosovo more autonomy. Serbia then offered to grant Kosovo more control over its affairs, but Kosovo's Albanians rejected the offer.

Kosovo declared independence on Feb. 17, 2008, but Serbia refused to accept the declaration. Other countries were divided. However, by 2012, more than 80 countries had recognizied Kosovo's independence, including the United States and most member nations of the European Union.

Kosovska Mitrovica is an important city in northern Kosovo. The city is divided between ethnic Albanians and ethnic Serbs.

KUWAIT

Kuwait is a tiny Arab nation at the northern end of the Persian Gulf. A poor desert land until 1946, Kuwait became one of the richest and most progressive countries of the world after it began exporting petroleum from its vast deposits.

Kuwait's rulers used its oil profits to turn a desert wilderness into a prosperous welfare state. Kuwait is now one of the world's wealthiest nations in terms of national income per person. It has free education, free health and social services, and no income tax. The city of Kuwait is the nation's capital.

Most Kuwaiti people are Arabs and Muslims. Kuwait's population has increased rapidly since the 1930's. Immigration has accounted for most of the increase. Most of the other residents of Kuwait are Arabs from foreign lands, Asian Indians, Iranians, or Pakistanis. Palestinian Arabs are by far the largest group of non-Kuwaiti residents in the country.

Kuwait is a hot, dry land. An average of 2 to 6 inches (5 to 15 centimeters) of rain falls each year from October to March. Some grass may grow then, but otherwise Kuwait has little vegetation except desert scrub. The country has no rivers or lakes, and before 1950 drinking water was brought by ships from Iraq. Today, fresh water is produced in Kuwait by distilling seawater and mixing it with well water. Also, a large underground source of fresh water was discovered in 1960.

The region that is now Kuwait had few settlements until the 1700's. Around that time, members of an Arab tribal group found fresh water on the southern shore of Kuwait Bay and settled in what is now the port city of Kuwait. The group elected the head of the Al-Sabah family to rule them as Sabah I. Descendants of this family, headed by a powerful leader called an *emir,* ruled Kuwait until August 1990, when Iraqi forces invaded and occupied the country.

FACTS

Official name:	Dowlat al Kuwait (State of Kuwait)
Capital:	Kuwait
Terrain:	Flat to slightly undulating desert plain
Area:	6,880 mi² (17,818 km²)
Climate:	Dry desert; intensely hot summers, short, cool winters
Main rivers:	N/A
Highest elevation:	Unnamed location, 928 ft (283 m)
Lowest elevation:	Persian Gulf, sea level
Form of government:	Nominal constitutional monarchy
Head of state:	Emir
Head of government:	Prime minister
Administrative areas:	6 muhafazat (governorates)
Legislature:	Majlis al-Umma (National Assembly) with 50 members serving four-year terms
Court system:	High Court of Appeal
Armed forces:	15,500 troops
National holiday:	National Day - February 25 (1950)
Estimated 2010 population:	2,919,000
Population density:	424 persons per mi² (164 per km²)
Population distribution:	98% urban, 2% rural
Life expectancy in years:	Male, 77; female, 79
Doctors per 1,000 people:	1.8
Birth rate per 1,000:	21
Death rate per 1,000:	2
Infant mortality:	9 deaths per 1,000 live births
Age structure:	0-14: 24%; 15-64: 74%; 65 and over: 2%
Internet users per 100 people:	32
Internet code:	.kw
Languages spoken:	Arabic (official), English
Religions:	Muslim (mainly Sunni) 85%, other (Christian, Hindu, Parsi) 15%
Currency:	Kuwaiti dinar
Gross domestic product (GDP) in 2008:	$158.09 billion U.S.
Real annual growth rate (2008):	8.5%
GDP per capita (2008):	$54,608 U.S.
Goods exported:	Mostly: crude oil and petroleum products Also: chemicals, fertilizers, plastics
Goods imported:	Food, iron and steel, machinery, motor vehicles
Trading partners:	Germany, Japan, Singapore, South Korea, Taiwan, United States

Iraq's president, Saddam Hussein, justified the action by claiming that Kuwait was legally a part of Iraq.

The United Nations (UN) condemned the invasion of Kuwait and refused to recognize Hussein's declaration that his country had annexed Kuwait as an Iraqi province. On Jan. 17, 1991, after months of pressuring Iraq to leave Kuwait, a coalition of international forces led by the United States began conducting bombing attacks on Iraqi military and industrial targets.

In late February, the coalition forces launched a massive ground attack into Kuwait and southern Iraq and quickly defeated the Iraqi troops. On Feb. 26, Hussein ordered his troops to withdraw from Kuwait, thus freeing the country from Iraq's grip. However, the Persian Gulf War of 1991 caused immense human suffering and property damage in Kuwait. Hundreds of thousands of people were killed or wounded or became refugees.

In October 1992, Kuwait elected a new 50-member parliament. In addition, the constitution was reinstated.

In March 2003, Kuwait served as a staging ground for another coalition of forces, led again by the United States, that invaded Iraq to topple the government of Saddam Hussein. Iraq fired a number of missiles into Kuwait during the war. Hussein's government fell in April.

In January 2006, Kuwait's emir, Sheik Jabir, died. His successor, the crown prince, was too ill to rule. The parliament approved Sheik Sabah al-Ahmad al-Jabir al-Sabah, who had been prime minister since 2003, as emir.

Kuwait is a small desert land at the tip of the Persian Gulf that sits atop huge oil reserves. Iraq and Saudi Arabia border Kuwait. Iran lies to the northeast. The area was the center of major conflict in the early 1990's.

Liberation Tower is one of the tallest structures in Kuwait and one of the city's most famous landmarks. Originally it was to be named Independence Tower. It was renamed Liberation Tower after Kuwait's liberation from Iraq in 1991.

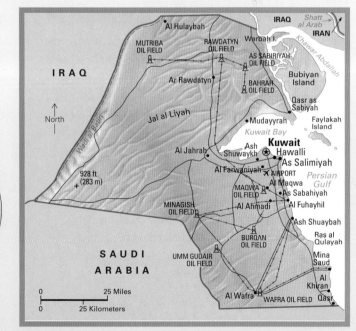

ECONOMY

Kuwait draws most of its income from a single source—oil. Natural gas, produced in conjunction with oil, is the second most important product. The government also receives large amounts of money from earnings on investments in the United States and other countries.

Although the oil industry produces vast wealth for Kuwait, it does not employ many people. Most of the work is done by machines, and the majority of the jobs available are held by noncitizens. Many Kuwaitis depend on welfare for a living.

Kuwait is trying to provide more jobs by developing new industries. Large petroleum refineries operate south of the city of Kuwait. Kuwait also produces small amounts of cement, fertilizer, and petrochemicals.

Kuwait's dry environment severely limits agriculture. The small number of farms in the country produce cucumbers, dates, potatoes, and tomatoes. People also raise camels, cattle, chickens, goats, and sheep. The government has worked to increase production by developing irrigation systems and *hydroponic farming*. The hydroponic projects attempt to grow crops in trays of sand fed with water and plant foods, rather than in fertile soil.

Formation and discovery of oil

Millions of years ago, much of what is now the Middle East lay under a sea, according to most geologists. Countless tiny life forms in that sea sank to the sea floor when they died. There, they became trapped in *sediments* (particles of mud and sand). These sediments piled up, sank deeper and deeper under further layers of mud, and began to change chemically under the pressure and the heat. Gradually, they decayed into *hydrocarbons*—the basic ingredients of oil and natural gas.

Over time, the mixture of oil and gas seeped upward through pores, or natural passageways, in the rock. Meanwhile, the sea above drew back until much of the oil and gas eventually lay under desert land. There, the deposits lay undisturbed until the 1930's.

In 1934, Kuwait's ruler allowed the Kuwait Oil Company, a joint American-British group, to explore for oil.

A Kuwaiti stands on oil pipelines bombed and burned by Iraqi forces during the Persian Gulf War of 1991. The war severely damaged the Kuwaiti oil industry.

Drilling began in 1936 and showed that vast quantities of petroleum lay under the desert of Kuwait. When World War II ended in 1945, Kuwait became a major petroleum exporter and an extremely wealthy country. In 1975, the government *nationalized,* or took control of, the Kuwait Oil Company and now owns almost all of the industry in the country.

The politics of oil

As a member of the Organization of the Petroleum Exporting Countries (OPEC), Kuwait has sometimes used its valuable oil to influence world affairs. For about two months in 1967, in response to the Six-Day War, Kuwait cut off oil shipments to the United States and other Western countries that supported Israel. In 1973, it joined other Arab nations in stopping shipments to the United States and the Netherlands because of another Arab-Israeli war.

Kuwait's valuable oil made the country a focal point of international attention during the late 1980's and early 1990's. In 1987, Kuwait's support of Iraq in its eight-year conflict with Iran triggered attacks by Iran on Kuwaiti oil tankers in the Persian Gulf.

In 1990, Iraqi president, Saddam Hussein, ordered his troops to invade Kuwait, in part to acquire its oil wealth. Iraq had suffered serious economic damage during the Iran-Iraq War. By seiz-

Pipelines carry Kuwait's petroleum across the desert to the Persian Gulf. The natural gas that accompanies the petroleum is often recovered for export, but here it is being burned off.

ing Kuwait, Hussein also sought to eliminate the huge debt Iraq owed Kuwait.

The Persian Gulf War of 1991, which was fought to liberate Kuwait from Iraq, created tremendous problems for Kuwait's oil industry. Iraqi troops badly damaged almost half of Kuwait's 1,300 oil wells. In most cases, they set them on fire, which produced a thick black smoke—and severe air pollution—throughout the region.

After the war, Kuwait began the huge task of repairing its oil storage, refining, and transportation facilities. By early 1992, Kuwait had restored only half of its oil refining capacity.

After the war, Kuwait was exempt from OPEC production quotas so it could rebuild its economy. By early 1993, Kuwait was able to produce 2 million barrels of oil a day.

Today, crude oil and refined petroleum are, by far, Kuwait's leading export products. The country imports food, iron and steel, machinery, and motor vehicles. Its leading trade partners include Germany, Japan, Singapore, South Korea, Taiwan, and the United States.

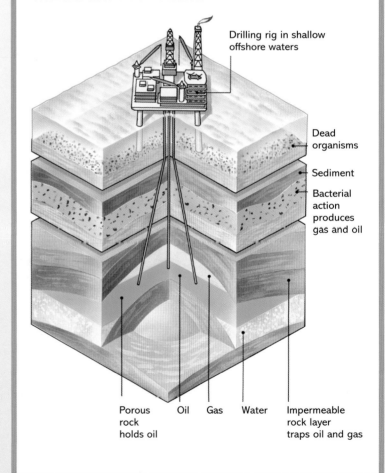

The formation of oil in the Persian Gulf region began with the decay of tiny marine plants and animals many millions of years ago. Pressure applied by layers of sediments aided the oil formation.

Drilling rig in shallow offshore waters

Dead organisms

Sediment

Bacterial action produces gas and oil

Porous rock holds oil

Oil

Gas

Water

Impermeable rock layer traps oil and gas

KYRGYZSTAN

Kyrgyzstan *(kihr guh STAHN* or *KIHR guh* STAHN) is a mountainous country bordered by China in the southeast, Tajikistan in the south, Uzbekistan in the southwest, and Kazakhstan in the north and northwest.

The Alay and Tian Shan mountains cover much of Kyrgyzstan. Nestled in the Tian Shan is Issyk-Kul Lake, one of the world's largest and deepest mountain lakes.

Nomads from northern Asia were the first people to live in what is now Kyrgyzstan. They raised livestock. Turkic tribes began to move into the area in about the A.D. 700's. Mongols conquered the region in the 1200's and established *khanates* ruled by chieftains. Muslim missionaries brought Islam to the area in the 1600's. China ruled the area from 1758 until the 1830's.

In 1876, the Russian Empire took control. It encouraged immigration by Russian, Ukrainian, and Slavic peasants. The Kyrgyz staged a large, unsuccessful rebellion in 1916.

Kyrgyzstan was made an *autonomous* (self-governing) region within the Russian Republic of the Soviet Union in 1924, and it became a separate Soviet republic in 1936. It remained under the strict control of the Soviet central government until the early 1990's. In the midst of political upheaval in the Soviet Union in 1991, Kyrgyzstan declared its independence. Voters elected Askar Akayev president.

In early 2005, protesters, claiming that parliamentary elections had been rigged, forced Akayev from office. Opposition leader Kurmanbek Bakiev was named interim president. Bakiev was elected as president later in 2005 and reelected in 2009.

In April 2010, large opposition protests forced Bakiyev to flee the country. An interim government held a referendum in June during which voters approved a new constitution. The Constitution limited the power of the president and increased the power of the parliament and the prime minister. In 2011, voters elected former Prime Minister Almazbek Atambaev as president.

FACTS

Official name:	Kyrgyz Respublikasy (Kyrgyz Republic)
Capital:	Bishkek
Terrain:	Peaks of Tian Shan and associated valleys and basins encompass entire nation
Area:	77,182 mi^2 (199,900 km^2)
Climate:	Dry continental to polar in high Tian Shan, subtropical in southwest (Fergana Valley), temperate in northern foothill zone
Main river:	Naryn
Highest elevation:	Peak Pobedy, 24,406 ft (7,439 m)
Lowest elevation:	Naryn river at the western border, 1,640 ft (500 m)
Form of government:	Parliamentary republic
Head of state:	President
Head of government:	Prime minister
Administrative areas:	7 oblasts, 1 municipality
Legislature:	A unicameral parliament with 120 members
Court system:	Supreme Court, Higher Court of Arbitration
Armed forces:	10,900 troops
National holiday:	Independence Day - August 31 (1991)
Estimated 2010 population:	5,494,000
Population density:	71 persons per mi^2 (27 per km^2)
Population distribution:	64% rural, 36% urban
Life expectancy in years:	Male, 64; female, 72
Doctors per 1,000 people:	2.4
Birth rate per 1,000:	23
Death rate per 1,000:	7
Infant mortality:	34 deaths per 1,000 live births
Age structure:	0-14: 30%; 15-64: 64%; 65 and over: 6%
Internet users per 100 people:	14
Internet code:	.kg
Languages spoken:	Kyrgyz (official), Uzbek , Russian (official), Dungun
Religions:	Muslim (predominant), Russian Orthodox
Currency:	Kyrgyz som
Gross domestic product (GDP) in 2008:	$5.05 billion U.S.
Real annual growth rate (2008):	6.0%
GDP per capita (2008):	$946 U.S.
Goods exported:	Clothing, cotton, gold, machinery, textiles
Goods imported:	Chemicals, food and beverages, machinery, petroleum products
Trading partners:	China, Kazakhstan, Russia, Uzbekistan

Slightly more than half of the people in Kyrgyzstan belong to the Kyrgyz nationality group. They speak a Turkic language. Most Kyrgyz live by herding and farming. Tribal organizations and large family groups called *clans* are important in Kyrgyz society. Tribal leaders hold most government offices in the country.

After the Kyrgyz, the next largest ethnic groups are Russians and Uzbeks. Other groups include the Dungans (ethnic Chinese) and Ukrainians. Most Kyrgyz, Uzbeks, and Dungans are Muslims. The other groups are mostly Christian. Ethnic tensions between the Kyrgyz and the Uzbeks over territorial claims and other issues led to violence in the 1990's and again in 2010.

For centuries, many Kyrgyz were nomads who raised sheep in the mountain meadows in the summer and brought them down to the foothills in winter. During the 1930's, the Soviet government forced many of the Kyrgyz to live and work on collective farms. Today, agriculture accounts for about one-third of the value of Kyrgyzstan's economic production. Raising livestock, especially cattle and sheep, is the chief agricultural activity. People also raise goats. and graze yaks in the high mountains. Less than 10 percent of Kyrgyzstan's land is suitable for raising crops. Farmers rely on irrigation to provide water for most crop growth. Chief agricultural products include apples, corn, cotton, potatoes, tobacco, tomatoes, and wheat.

Manufacturing accounts for about one-tenth of the value of the country's economic production. The chief manufactured products include construction materials, food products, machinery, and textiles. Bishkek is the main industrial center. Gold is the main mining product. Mines also produce antimony, coal, mercury, petroleum, and other minerals.

Although modern development has forever changed the lives of the Kyrgyz, some old traditions have endured. For example, the folklore of the Kyrgyz lives on in *Manas,* the longest oral chronicle of its kind in the world today. The tale describes the many adventures of the hero Manas the Strong, including how he defended his people against the threat of conquerors.

The rugged peaks and rivers of the Tian Shan, which cover much of Kyrgyzstan, are home to abundant fish and wildlife. Only about 15 percent of Kyrgyzstan is less than 3,000 feet (915 meters) above sea level. Most of the people live in these lowland plains and mountain valleys.

Kyrgyzstan is a land of towering, snow-capped peaks, alpine meadows, and deep valleys.

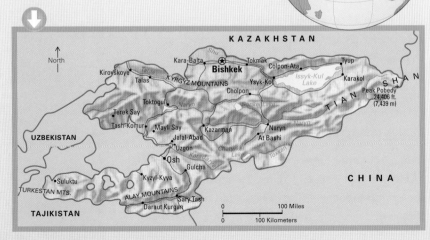

Laos, a tropical land of mountains and thick forests, is the only landlocked country on the Southeast Asian peninsula. It is bordered by China to the north, Vietnam to the east, Cambodia to the south, and Thailand and Myanmar to the west. The capital of Laos is Vientiane.

Laos lies in the Mekong Basin, between the Mekong River and the Annamite Range. The Mekong River, the chief means of transportation in Laos, also waters the country's fertile lowland.

The people of Laos belong to more than 50 ethnic groups and speak many languages. The Lao, who have given their name to the country and to its official language, make up the majority of the population. Many of the ethnic groups in Laos have lived in the region for more than 1,000 years.

Land of a million elephants

Ancestors of the Lao and Tai ethnic groups probably moved into Laos from southwest China in the A.D. 700's to 900's. They established a number of small states on the Mekong River, notably Muong Swa (now Louangphrabang). In 1353, the ruler of Muong Swa united most of what is now Laos to form the kingdom of Lan Xang (Land of a Million Elephants).

The kingdom remained unified for almost 350 years. About 1700, however, quarreling among powerful groups in Lan Xang destroyed the kingdom's unity, and it was divided into three principalities—Louangphrabang, Vientiane, and Champasak. By the early 1800's, all three had come under the control of Siam (now Thailand).

French Indochina and independence

By the late 1800's, the French had gained considerable power and influence throughout *Indochina*—that is, the eastern half of the Southeast Asian peninsula, which includes Laos, Cambodia, and Vietnam. Between the 1880's and 1907, France incorporated nearly all of Laos into its Indochina empire, though one section remained under Siamese control.

In 1940, after France surrendered to Germany in World War II (1939-1945), the Japanese moved their forces into Indochina. They persuaded the rulers of Vietnam, Cambodia, and Laos to declare their coun-

LAOS

tries independent under pro-Japanese governments. The government of Laos was headed by three princes—Phetsarat, Souvanna Phouma, and Souphanouvong. France reasserted its control in 1946.

In 1949, when the French declared Laos an independent kingdom, the three princes split into rival factions. Souphanouvong moved to northeastern Laos and established the Communist-inspired Pathet Lao movement with North Vietnamese Communist leader Ho Chi Minh.

Civil war

In 1960, Captain Kong Le, a Laotian army officer, overthrew Laos's pro-Western government, and civil war broke out. A coalition government was set up in 1962 with Souvanna Phouma as prime minister, but Souphanouvong withdrew from the government in 1963. Fighting again broke out. By 1970, Souvanna Phouma's government troops controlled only western Laos, while Souphanouvong and the Pathet Lao held eastern Laos.

During the Vietnam War (1957-1975), North Vietnam used the Ho Chi Minh Trail in Laos and Cambodia to move troops and supplies into South Vietnam. United States planes bombed the trail and other areas in Laos. In 1971, South Vietnamese troops attacked Communist supply routes in Laos, but Communist forces drove them out.

The Laotian government and the Pathet Lao agreed to a cease-fire in 1973 and formed a coalition government, but by 1975 the government was dominated by Communists. South Vietnam and Cambodia fell to the Communists in April 1975. Later that year, the Pathet Lao seized control of Laos, so that country too became a Communist state.

The new Communist government seized ownership of farms and factories and persecuted Buddhists. But, beginning in the 1980's, opposition to these policies among the Laotian peasants led the government to adopt more moderate policies.

LAOS TODAY

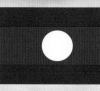

In 1975, Souphanouvong was installed as the president of the Lao People's Democratic Republic, but this was largely an honorary post. Real power lay with the country's Communist organization, the Lao People's Revolutionary Party (LPRP). The secretary-general of the LPRP became prime minister of Laos.

Socialism

Soon after coming to power, the LPRP attempted to restructure Laos according to socialist principles. The country's few industries were taken over by the government, and many small family-run farms were consolidated into state-run collective farms.

The government's task was hindered by the Laotian economy, which was largely undeveloped. Agriculture had traditionally been the country's chief economic activity, but old-fashioned equipment and methods held down agricultural output. In addition, many farmers preferred to destroy or abandon their farms rather than submit to *collectivization,* a government program in which the state owns the land and controls the workers.

Many Laotian people also resisted other repressive government policies, including seizures of private property and the suppression of religion. Thousands of people fled the country, most of them to Thailand.

Reforms

By 1980, the Laotian leaders had launched a number of economic reforms. The government halted the creation of new collective farms, and some private enterprise was allowed in business. In addition, farmers were paid more for agricultural goods. In 1981, rice production reached record levels. The Lao People's Democratic Republic made progress toward self-sufficiency in food production during the 1980's.

In 1989, LPRP leaders took steps to improve Laos's economic and diplomatic relations with the rest of the world. They sought foreign trade and investment. In March 1989, the first national elections were held in Laos since the Communists came to power.

FACTS

Official name:	Sathalanalat Paxathipatai Paxaxon Lao (Lao People's Democratic Republic)
Capital:	Vientiane
Terrain:	Mostly rugged mountains; some plains and plateaus
Area:	91,429 mi² (236,800 km²)
Climate:	Tropical monsoon; rainy season (May to November), dry season (December to April)
Main river:	Mekong
Highest elevation:	Phou Bia, 9,245 ft (2,818 m)
Lowest elevation:	Mekong River, 230 ft (70 m)
Form of government:	Communist state
Head of state:	President
Head of government:	Prime minister
Administrative areas:	16 khoueng (provinces), 1 nakhon luang (capital city)
Legislature:	National Assembly with 132 members serving five-year terms
Court system:	Supreme People's Court
Armed forces:	29,100 troops
National holiday:	Republic Day - December 2 (1975)
Estimated 2010 population:	6,167,000
Population density:	67 persons per mi² (26 per km²)
Population distribution:	73% rural, 27% urban
Life expectancy in years:	Male, 57; female, 61
Doctors per 1,000 people:	0.4
Birth rate per 1,000:	34
Death rate per 1,000:	10
Infant mortality:	70 deaths per 1,000 live births
Age structure:	0-14: 41%; 15-64: 55%; 65 and over: 4%
Internet users per 100 people:	1.6
Internet code:	.la
Languages spoken:	Lao (official), French, English, various ethnic languages
Religions:	Buddhist 67%, Christian 1.5%, other (animist, Baha'i, Muslim) 31.5%
Currency:	Kip
Gross domestic product (GDP) in 2008:	$5.29 billion U.S.
Real annual growth rate (2008):	7.5%
GDP per capita (2008):	$832 U.S.
Goods exported:	Clothing, coffee, copper, electricity, gold, wood and wood products
Goods imported:	Consumer goods, machinery, motor vehicles, petroleum products
Trading partners:	China, Thailand, Vietnam

A woman sells rice on a village street in Laos. Most Laotians live in rural areas and are poor. But as the population expands, more Laotians are moving to cities along the Mekong River.

Laos has a National Assembly elected by the people. The Assembly elects the nation's president. All candidates, however, must by approved by the LPRP, which is the only political party. The leaders of the party's Political Bureau and Central Committee are the most powerful officials in the country. In 1997, Laos joined the Association of Southeast Asian Nations (ASEAN), a regional organization that promotes economic, cultural, and social cooperation among its members.

At times during the early 2000's, small uprisings occurred against the regime. However, the clashes diminished by 2010. In 2011, the government enacted a law to enlarge the National Assembly to 132 seats. Other decrees were issued to help the government meet its goal of joining the World Trade Organization, an international group that works to reduce trade barriers between member nations.

Laos occupies a strategic position on the Southeast Asian peninsula. In 1954, it was established as a neutral country—a "buffer" between Communist North Vietnam and non-Communist Thailand. Laos lost this status, however, after Communists within the country began to challenge the government.

LAND AND ECONOMY

Densely forested mountains and rugged plateaus cover much of Laos. The country's northern mountains encircle the Plain of Jars, a wide plateau of rolling hills and wooded areas. Just south of the Plain of Jars, the country's highest peak, Phou Bia (Mount Bia), soars to a height of 9,245 feet (2,818 meters).

Southern Laos, narrower and less mountainous than the northern part of the country, is bordered on the east by the Annamite Range, which separates Laos from Vietnam and slopes gently westward to the Mekong Basin. The Khammouan Plateau lies in the central region, and the Bolovens Plateau lies in the extreme south.

The most productive farmland in Laos lies along the Mekong River and its tributaries, and most of the country's rice is grown in this fertile region. The river and its tributaries are also the chief means of transportation in Laos.

A square in Louangphrabang, once the royal capital of Laos, is shaded by lush vegetation. The city lies in the fertile flood plain along the Mekong River, northwest of the high plateau known as the Plain of Jars.

Overflowing with passengers and luggage, a bus prepares to pull out of Vientiane. Transportation in Laos is poor, with most roads open only during the dry season.

Laos has a tropical climate marked by humidity, high temperatures, and seasonally heavy rainfall. From May to October, southwest monsoons bring up to 10 inches (25 centimeters) of rain a month—twice that on the Bolovens Plateau. Temperatures can reach 104° F (40° C) at the end of the dry season in March and April but can fall below freezing in the mountains during winter.

The warm, wet climate of Laos makes the country an ideal place for agriculture. But only a small amount of Laos's total land area is cultivated annually. In addition, old-fashioned equipment and methods keep farm production low. The land is rich in mineral resources, but these have been only partially developed. The country has little industry.

All these factors combine to make Laos one of the poorest countries in the world.

About three-fourths of the Laotian people live in rural areas, and agriculture is the country's chief economic activity. Most farmers own small farms, on which they grow rice, the country's main crop. The fertile river valleys are the most productive agricultural areas. Some farmers raise cattle, goats, horses, poultry, and water buffaloes. Coffee is the main export crop. In the mountains along the Myanmar and Thailand borders, some farmers grow opium for export. The Laotian government, however, has taken steps to stamp out this illegal crop.

Small amounts of tin, gypsum, rock salt, and coal are mined. Like the country's industrial development,

Paddy rice is grown all over Asia in much the same way. In the first stage, farmers plant rice seeds, which have been saved from the previous season's crop, in a small seedbed (1).

While the seeds are sprouting, farmers plow the main paddy field (2).

The young rice plants are transplanted into the field after it has been flooded (3).

Farmers weed the field while the rice grows, and ducks are often brought in to eat insects that damage the plants (4).

When the rice ripens, the water is drained off by a simple irrigation system (5). A deep golden color indicates that the rice is ready for harvesting (6).

After the harvest, the rice is tied in bundles and dried in the sun before being taken to the threshing area, where the grain is separated from the rest of the plant (7).

mining is hampered by a lack of electrical power and inadequate transportation. Most roads are impassable during the rainy season, and Laos has no railroads. In many areas, airplanes are the only means of moving supplies.

The country is rich in rattan, teak, and other valuable woods. However, much of the country's forestland is being cleared for farming.

Laos depends on foreign aid to develop its economy. Some of these funds have been used for forestry, irrigation, road and bridge construction, and hydroelectric power projects.

Most of Laos's trade is with neighboring countries, especially Thailand. Laos sells most of the hydroelectric power that it produces to Thailand.

PEOPLE

Most of the people of Laos live in the fertile lowlands that stretch along the Mekong River. However, the nation is sparsely populated, with an average of only about 67 people per square mile (26 per square kilometer).

The people of Laos are officially divided into three broad categories: (1) the Lao Lum, the *Lao of the lowlands,* (2) the Lao Thoeng, the *Lao of the mountain slopes,* and (3) the Lao Sung, the *Lao of the mountain tops.*

People of the lowlands

The Lao Lum include the ethnic Lao, as well as the Lu, Phuan, and various upland Tai tribes. The Lao Lum speak Tai languages, including Lao, which is the official language of Laos. Most Lao Lum are rice farmers who live in villages of 40 to 50 households along the Mekong River. The villagers live in bamboo houses with thatched roofs. The houses are built on stilts to protect them from flooding during the rainy season.

Most Lao Lum are Buddhists, and village life centers around the *pagoda* (temple), where a Buddhist monk conducts religious ceremonies. The pagoda may also be used as a schoolhouse, or as a meeting place where the village headman leads a discussion on local affairs. The social life of the villagers centers around Buddhist festivals and holidays.

About a fourth of the Laotians live in urban areas and work in trade or industry. Many Westernized Lao and most of the foreigners in Laos live in the capital city of Vientiane. The capital has a population of 420,000 and ranks as Laos's largest city, as well as an important trading center.

The mountain peoples

The Lao Thoeng—the Lao of the mountain slopes—speak Mon-Khmer languages. They grow rice by using slash-and-burn cultivation, in which

Buddhist monks relax in a rural monastery. When the Pathet Lao came to power, they discouraged religious practice. However, objections from Laotians caused many restrictions against religion to be lifted.

trees are chopped and burned to make way for farmland. Chief groups of the Lao Thoeng include the Khmu and Lamet in northern Laos and the Alak, Laven, and Oy in the south. Most Lao Thoeng are *animists* who worship a variety of nature spirits and carry out animal sacrifices.

The Lao Sung—the Lao of the mountaintops—live in northern Laos. They speak Tibeto-Burman or Hmong-Mien languages. Most follow animistic religions. The main ethnic groups of the Lao Sung include the Hmong and the Yao (also known as the Iu Mien).

The Hmong people, who live on the higher mountain slopes, have no unit of social organization larger than the village, which is led by a headman. The Hmong clear small forest areas to raise live-stock and grow crops. One of their main crops is opium—an illegal but highly profitable product that is exported all over Southeast Asia.

Hmong are fiercely independent people who have little in common—either socially or politically—with the other people of Laos, or even with Hmong in other villages. During the civil war years of the 1960's and 1970's, some Hmong people supported the Communist-led Pathet Lao, while others waged a guerrilla campaign against the Communists. The Hmong who resisted Communism suffered severe persecution after the Pathet Lao came to power in 1975. Those who supported the U.S. presence were particularly oppressed. From 1975 to 1996, about 130,000 Hmong were resettled in the United States. By 2001, according to the United Nations High Commissioner for Refugees, the Hmong who remained in Laos were no longer experiencing systemic discrimination.

Laotian women prepare food offerings for the monks at a Buddhist pagoda. Lao Buddhists believe that they will earn merit in a future life by maintaining the pagoda and feeding the monks.

Lao villagers wade across the shallow Ou River in central Laos near Louang-phrabang. The river waters the villagers' crops and provides a bountiful catch of fish.

Religion and education

Most Laotians follow the Theravada school of Buddhism. In Laos, as in other Southeast Asian countries, many Buddhists combine their religious practices with a belief in spirits.

Although the Pathet Lao discouraged the practice of religion when they first came to power, the government today is more tolerant of religion. In an effort to align Communist principles and Buddhist beliefs, the Communists portrayed Buddha as a "revolutionary" who, by leaving his home, questioned the value of wealth and possessions.

Under the Pathet Lao, education is state-controlled, but money for educational facilities is still limited. About two-thirds of the Laotian people 15 years of age or older can read and write. Most Laotians attend elementary school, which lasts five years. Some attend a further six years of secondary school. In some areas, however, villages lack schools, and the monks in the village pagoda provide the only education for the local children.

LATVIA

Latvia is a country on the Baltic Sea in northeastern Europe. A large plain covers most of Latvia, and the landscape consists chiefly of low hills and valleys. Many small lakes and swamps dot the countryside, and forests cover about 40 percent of the land. Riga is the country's capital and largest city.

History

About 2,000 years ago, the original inhabitants of Latvia were forced out by invaders who became the ancestors of present-day Latvians. The area later came under attack from the Vikings in the 800's and the Russians in the 900's. The Teutonic Knights took control in the 1200's and ruled Latvia as part of a larger state called Livonia.

By 1562, most of Latvia fell under Polish and Lithuanian control, while the rest was a German-ruled duchy. Sweden conquered northern Latvia in 1621. Between 1710 and 1800, the Russians gained control of the country. In 1918, Latvia declared its independence. It adopted a new constitution in 1922 and established a democratic government.

Latvian democracy, however, did not survive the worldwide depression of the 1930's. In 1936, the nation's president seized power and reduced the role of parliament and the rights of the country's political parties. In 1940, the Soviet Union forced Latvia to sign a treaty under which the Soviets built military bases in the country. In June 1940, Soviet troops occupied Latvia, and Latvian Communists took over the government.

Through the years, the Latvians expressed their opposition to Soviet rule. A strong nationalist movement took shape during the late 1980's, when Latvian reformers established the People's Front, a large non-Communist organization. On May 4, 1990, Latvia's parliament declared the restoration of Latvian independence and called for a gradual separation from the Soviet Union. The Soviet central government declared the action illegal.

In August 1991, conservative Communist leaders in the Soviet Union attempted to overthrow the

FACTS

Official name:	Latvijas Republika (Republic of Latvia)
Capital:	Riga
Terrain:	Low plain
Area:	24,938 mi² (64,589 km²)
Climate:	Maritime; wet, moderate winters
Main rivers:	Gauja, Lielupe, Venta, Daugava
Highest elevation:	Gaizina (mountain), 1,020 ft (311 m)
Lowest elevation:	Baltic Sea, sea level
Form of government:	Parliamentary democracy
Head of state:	President
Head of government:	Prime minister
Administrative areas:	33 administrative regions
Legislature:	Saeima (Parliament) with 100 members serving four-year terms
Court system:	Supreme Court
Armed forces:	5,200 troops
National holiday:	Independence Day - November 18 (1918)
Estimated 2010 population:	2,242,000
Population density:	90 persons per mi² (35 per km²)
Population distribution:	68% urban, 32% rural
Life expectancy in years:	Male, 66; female, 77
Doctors per 1,000 people:	3.1
Birth rate per 1,000:	10
Death rate per 1,000:	14
Infant mortality:	8 deaths per 1,000 live births
Age structure:	0-14: 14%; 15-64: 69%; 65 and over: 17%
Internet users per 100 people:	55
Internet code:	.lv
Languages spoken:	Latvian (official), Russian, Lithuanian
Religions:	Lutheran, Roman Catholic, Russian Orthodox
Currency:	Lat
Gross domestic product (GDP) in 2008:	$33.91 billion U.S.
Real annual growth rate (2008):	-5.0%
GDP per capita (2008):	$14,959 U.S.
Goods exported:	Food, machinery, metals, textiles, wood and wood products
Goods imported:	Chemicals, electrical equipment, machinery, motor vehicles, petroleum products
Trading partners:	Estonia, Germany, Lithuania, Russia, Sweden

Latvia lies in northern Europe on the eastern shore of the Baltic Sea. Along with Estonia and Lithuania, it is one of the three Baltic States.

Soviet central government, but the coup failed. During the political upheaval that followed, Latvia declared its independence, and the Soviet government recognized Latvia's independence.

After independence, Latvians sought to reduce Russian influence in the country. They also reduced government control of the economy. Most farms and businesses became privately owned. In 2004, Latvia joined the North Atlantic Treaty Organization (NATO), a defense alliance, and the European Union (EU), which promotes economic and political cooperation.

People

About 60 percent of the people who live in Latvia are Latvians, a distinct nationality group which has its own culture and language. The Latvian language is one of the oldest in Europe. It is related to Sanskrit, a language of ancient India. Russians make up about 30 percent of Latvia's population.

Service industries—especially education, government, transportation, communication, and trade—employ about half the country's workers. About a sixth of the people work in manufacturing, and about a tenth work in agriculture, many on cattle and dairy farms.

A graceful suspension bridge spans the Daugava in Riga, the capital and largest city of Latvia. Riga is a major shipping center and accounts for more than half of Latvia's industrial output.

Located between the Mediterranean world to the west and Asia to the east, Lebanon is a Middle Eastern land that has developed in its own unique way. The sea has helped make Lebanon an important trading region for thousands of years, and the area has been exposed to people of many cultures. Some left their mark on Lebanon, while others invaded and even ruled the country. However, the rugged mountains that lie within the country have helped protect the people of the region and have enabled Lebanon to survive with an identity of its own.

Lebanon today has an Arab culture influenced heavily by Western and Christian ideas. Beirut, on the coast, is Lebanon's capital and largest city. About half of the country's people live in the Beirut area.

Ancient seafarers and Roman rule

Lebanon's history of sailing and trading can be traced back nearly 5,000 years. By about 2000 B.C., the Phoenicians moved into the region and established powerful city-states along the coast. The Phoenicians were skillful sailors who traded with ancient Egypt and other regions and founded colonies along the shores of the Mediterranean Sea. According to some ancient historical accounts, Phoenicians sailed around Africa some 2,000 years before the Portuguese did.

Beginning about 1800 B.C., other foreign powers began to conquer and control the city-states of Lebanon. Egyptians, Hittites, Assyrians, Babylonians, and Persians all included the region as part of their ancient empires. Alexander the Great of Macedonia conquered Lebanon during 333 and 332 B.C.

Lebanon became part of the vast Roman Empire in 64 B.C. Roman ruins, such as the temples at Baalbek in the Bekaa Valley, still stand in the countryside. The Romans eventually adopted Christianity, and so did many Lebanese.

Christians and Muslims

In the A.D. 600's, Arab Muslims invaded the region. As they did in other nations in North Africa and the Middle East, the Arabs converted many people to the religion of Islam. However, Islam replaced Christianity only along Lebanon's coast. Most of the Lebanese who lived in the mountains remained Christians.

50

LEBANON

Christian crusaders from Europe invaded Lebanon about 1100, hoping to win back control of the Holy Land south of Lebanon from the Muslims. The crusaders established friendly relations with the Christians in the mountains. The Lebanese Christians became open to European influences and were more willing to be approached by Westerners. But the Mamluks, the Muslim rulers of Egypt, drove the crusaders out of Lebanon about 200 years later.

The powerful Ottoman Empire, based in what is now Turkey, conquered Lebanon in 1516 and ruled the region for more than 400 years. During part of this time, local rulers in Mount Lebanon—the largely Christian region in the central mountainous part of the country—was able to retain limited self-rule.

When the Ottoman Empire was defeated in World War I (1914-1918), the United Kingdom and France occupied Lebanon. France was given control of the region's political affairs in 1922. The French united the Christians in Mount Lebanon and the Muslims along the coast under one government. Lebanon became a fully independent nation in 1943.

A new nation

In the new nation, Christian and Muslim leaders agreed to share power. Lebanon kept its strong ties with Western nations and enjoyed increasing prosperity as a center of trade and finance. Lebanon also became an important financial center. Many banks—including branches of foreign banks—operated within the country.

The differences between Christians and Muslims eventually led to trouble, however. In 1958, some Lebanese, mostly Muslims, rebelled against the government and its close alliance with the West. War flared up in the 1970's, and various factions fought off and on through the 1980's.

A peace plan led most of Lebanon's private military groups, called *militias,* to disarm and disband in 1991. Although some violence continued, national reconstruction began.

LEBANON TODAY

The fighting that occurred in Lebanon until the early 1990's affected every aspect of Lebanese life. Thousands of people were killed, sections of cities were destroyed, and the economy was severely damaged.

According to its Constitution, Lebanon is a republic. The people elect members of the National Assembly to make the country's laws, and the Assembly members elect a president. The president then appoints a prime minister, who chooses a Council of Ministers to help run the government.

Traditionally, the president and the prime minister have worked as a team. To maintain a power balance between the country's Muslims and Christians, the government has been made up of members of both groups according to predetermined quotas. Different Christian and Muslim religious subgroups are assigned fixed numbers of seats. A Maronite Christian serves as president, a Sunni Muslim as prime minister, and a Shiite Muslim as speaker of the Assembly.

During the 1970's, this careful balance was disrupted when the Muslim population grew larger than the Christian population, and Muslims began demanding more power. Another disruption involved the presence of the Palestine Liberation Organization (PLO) in the country. The PLO demanded an independent state in the Middle East for the Palestinian people. Many Palestinians had fled from Israel during the Arab-Israeli wars of the mid-1900's and lived in refugee camps in Lebanon. The PLO established bases in southern Lebanon from which they could launch attacks on Israel to the south. The Lebanese Muslims supported the PLO, while the Christians opposed them.

In 1975, a civil war broke out between the Christians and a Muslim-PLO alliance. Soon, conflict also developed between competing factions within the Christian and Muslim communities. In

FACTS

Official name:	Al Jumhuriyah al Lubnaniyah (Lebanese Republic)
Capital:	Beirut
Terrain:	Narrow coastal plain; Bekaa Valley separates Lebanon and Anti-Lebanon Mountains
Area:	4,015 mi² (10,400 km²)
Climate:	Mediterranean; mild to cool, wet winters with hot, dry summers; Lebanon mountains experience heavy winter snows
Main rivers:	Litani, Nahr Ibrahim, Orontes
Highest elevation:	Qurnat as Sawda, 10,115 ft (3,083 m)
Lowest elevation:	Mediterranean Sea, sea level
Form of government:	Republic
Head of state:	President
Head of government:	Prime minister
Administrative areas:	6 provinces
Legislature:	Majlis Alnuwab, in Arabic, or Assemblee Nationale, in French (both meaning National Assembly), with 128 members serving four-year terms
Court system:	Courts of Cassation, Constitutional Council, Supreme Council
Armed forces:	56,000 troops
National holiday:	Independence Day - November 22 (1943)
Estimated 2010 population:	4,236,000
Population density:	1,055 persons per mi² (407 per km²)
Population distribution:	87% urban, 13% rural
Life expectancy in years:	Male, 70; female, 75
Doctors per 1,000 people:	2.4
Birth rate per 1,000:	18
Death rate per 1,000:	6
Infant mortality:	22 deaths per 1,000 live births
Age structure:	0-14: 27%; 15-64: 66%; 65 and over: 7%
Internet users per 100 people:	38
Internet code:	.lb
Languages spoken:	Arabic (official), English, French, Armenian
Religions:	Muslim 59.7%, Christian 39%, other 1.3%
Currency:	Lebanese pound
Gross domestic product (GDP) in 2008:	$28.54 billion U.S.
Real annual growth rate (2008):	7.0%
GDP per capita (2008):	$7,329 U.S.
Goods exported:	Base metals, chemicals, electric power machinery, food, jewelry, paper, tobacco
Goods imported:	Machinery, motor vehicles, petroleum products, pharmaceuticals, plastics
Trading partners:	China, France, Germany, Italy, Syria, United States

1976, Syria sent troops to Lebanon to try to stop the conflict. Fighting between Syrian troops and Christian Lebanese forces soon began.

In 1982, an Israeli force invaded, drove the PLO out of southern Lebanon, and attacked PLO forces in western Beirut. In 1985, Israel withdrew most of its troops, leaving some in a security zone it created along its border with Lebanon.

Lebanon's internal factions worked out a peace plan in 1990 that ended most of the violence. Most of the private militias disbanded in 1991. The government also ordered the PLO and some other Palestinians to leave their bases in southern Lebanon. When the PLO refused, the Lebanese army defeated and disarmed them, ending most of the fighting in Lebanon.

In the years that followed, Syrian forces remained in parts of the country, and Syria strongly influenced Lebanese political affairs. In addition, the Israelis continued to occupy their security zone in southern Lebanon. Many opponents of the Israeli occupation joined a movement known as Hezbollah, which often clashed with the Israelis and the Israeli-backed South Lebanon Army.

In 2000, Israeli troops finally left southern Lebanon. Many Lebanese citizens and foreign nations then pressed Syria to withdraw its troops, which it did in 2005.

In July 2006, Hezbollah guerillas entered Israel, killed several Israeli soldiers, and kidnapped others. Israel retaliated with air strikes. A United Nations Security Council resolution ended the war a month later, though conflict between Hezbollah and Israel at the border has continued.

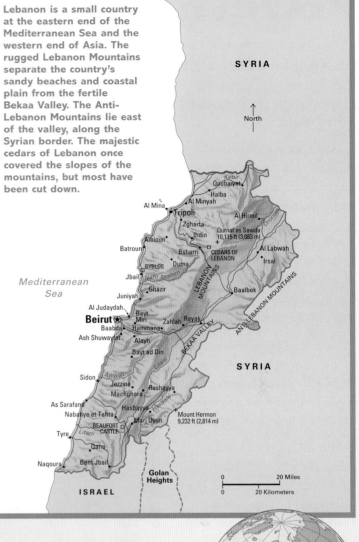

Lebanon is a small country at the eastern end of the Mediterranean Sea and the western end of Asia. The rugged Lebanon Mountains separate the country's sandy beaches and coastal plain from the fertile Bekaa Valley. The Anti-Lebanon Mountains lie east of the valley, along the Syrian border. The majestic cedars of Lebanon once covered the slopes of the mountains, but most have been cut down.

Beirut is the capital of Lebanon and largest city. It is also the country's chief commercial and cultural center. The city lies on the eastern shore of the Mediterranean Sea.

PEOPLE

Lebanon is home to more than 4 million people. About 90 percent of the Lebanese people are Arabs.

This Arab population includes about 400,000 Palestinian Arabs, refugees from the Arab-Israeli wars that have troubled the Middle East since 1948. These refugees had lived on land that is now part of Israel. Other ethnic minorities in Lebanon include Armenians, Assyrians, and Kurds.

Almost all Lebanese speak Arabic, the official language. Many also speak French or English. Armenian Lebanese speak the Armenian language.

About 60 percent of the Lebanese are Muslims; almost all the rest are Christians. Most Lebanese Muslims belong to one of two major branches of Islam—the Sunni or the Shiah. The Druses are a regional religious group that practice a religion related to Islam. Other small Muslim groups include the Ismailis and the Alawis.

The majority of Lebanese Christians are members of the Maronite Church, an Eastern Catholic Church. Other Lebanese Christian groups include Greek Orthodox, Armenian Apostolics, and Jacobites.

Urban and rural family life

About 87 percent of Lebanon's people live in urban areas. Most upper-class and middle-class Lebanese live in cities, and most are either Christians or Sunni Muslims.

Residents of Beirut serve themselves at a restaurant in the city. About a fourth of Lebanon's population lives in the Beirut area.

Traditional clothing, like this woman's hat and scarf, is rare today in Lebanon, but some rural people still dress as their ancestors did. Most Lebanese wear Western-style clothes.

Most poor Lebanese live in rural areas or in run-down city slums, and most are Shiah Muslims or Palestinian Arabs. Many of the Palestinian refugees live in crowded camps.

The family is important in all areas of Lebanese life. Family loyalty is highly valued, and well-to-do family members are expected to share their wealth with less fortunate relatives. Many wealthy city people help support family members in rural villages.

In business, employers prefer to hire relatives, and many businesses are family run. The wealth and status of a family can also affect the kind of education a child receives. Most parents send their children to both elementary and secondary school. More than half go to private schools, for which they must pay tuition, and the rest attend free public schools. Unfortunately, overall school attendance has been disrupted by the fighting and unrest that has plagued the country.

Way of life

The Lebanese combine Western ways with their traditional or Arabic way of living. Many Lebanese houses have thick limestone walls and roofs made of orange tiles or earth. But in the cities, this type of house is rapidly being replaced by Western-style concrete houses and high-rise apartments.

Most Lebanese wear Western-style clothes, but some people in rural areas wear traditional Lebanese clothing. Some peasant women, for example, wear colorful, long dresses over ankle-length trousers. Some older Druse men wear jackets woven of many colors, and white headdresses.

The Lebanese enjoy such dishes as *dolmeh*—grape leaves stuffed with rice and ground lamb and spiced

with cinnamon—served with *khobez* (flat, round wheat bread); or *hummus*, a concoction of mashed chickpeas, *tahini* (sesame paste), garlic, and olive oil. Soft drinks are popular, as is Arabic coffee and a strong liquor called *arak*.

Many Lebanese people enjoy both Western and Arabic literature, music, and art. Lebanese artists are known for their beautiful silverware, brassware, jewelry, needlework, and colored glassware.

Service industries—especially banking, finance, and trade—rank as Lebanon's chief source of income. Manufacturing and agriculture are also important. The main farm products are fruits—apples, grapes, cherries, lemons, and oranges. Other farm products include cucumbers, olives, potatoes, tomatoes, and wheat. The chief manufactured products include cement, chemicals, furniture, jewelry, processed foods, and textiles.

Lebanon imports more than it exports. Its main trading partners include China, Syria, the United States, and European countries.

Shi`ah Muslims in Lebanon commemorate the Ashura, the 10th day the month of Muharran on the Islamic calendar. The event marks the anniversary of the Battle of Karbala when Imam Hussain ibn Ali, the grandson of the Islamic prophet Muhammad, and a Shi`ah imam, was killed in battle.

LESOTHO

Lesotho (lay SOO too or luh SOH toh) is sometimes called the "Switzerland of southern Africa" because of its beautiful mountain scenery. The Drakensberg and the Maloti mountains cover most of this tiny nation, which is completely surrounded by the Republic of South Africa. Lesotho's only plains lie in the west, where about two-thirds of the people live.

The people and their work

Lesotho is a poor country, with few industries and jobs. The main economic activity in Lesotho is raising cattle, goats, and sheep. Farmers grow asparagus, beans, corn, peas, sorghum, and wheat, but over-grazing and overcultivation have damaged the soil.

The few Lesotho industries produce clothing, furniture, processed food, and textiles. Lesotho has diamond deposits, but diamond mining was halted in the 1980's when prices for the gems fell.

Most of Lesotho's people belong to a group called the Basotho (also spelled Basuto). Because Lesotho does not have enough jobs, many Basotho people go to South Africa to work. At any one time, almost half of all the men are working in South African mines, factories, farms, or households. Generally, they work on contract for several months to two years, and the law requires them to deposit 60 percent of their wages in the Lesotho Bank. The worker's family may withdraw half of the funds to live on, but the other half must stay in the bank until the worker returns from South Africa. This system enables the government, which owns the Lesotho Bank, to invest funds in development projects.

Most Basotho people live in small rural villages, where family groups build their dwellings around a cattle *kraal,* or pen. The homes usually have mud or sod walls and thatched roofs, but wealthy Basotho may live in stone houses with roofs of tin or tile. Each village has a *khotla,* or meeting place, where men discuss village business. The Basotho raise their crops on the land surrounding the village. All land is owned in common by the people and assigned by local chiefs.

FACTS

Official name:	Kingdom of Lesotho
Capital:	Maseru
Terrain:	Mostly highland with plateaus, hills, and mountain
Area:	11,720 mi² (30,355 km²)
Climate:	Temperate; cool to cold, dry winters; hot, wet summers
Main river:	Orange
Highest elevation:	Thabana Ntlenyana, 11,425 ft (3,482 m)
Lowest elevation:	Junction of the Orange and Makhaleng rivers 4,593 ft (1,400 m)
Form of government:	Constitutional monarchy
Head of state:	Monarch
Head of government:	Prime minister
Administrative areas:	10 districts
Legislature:	Parliament consisting of the Senate with 33 members and the Assembly with 120 members serving five-year terms
Court system:	High Court, Court of Appeal, Magistrate's Court
Armed forces:	2,000 troops
National holiday:	Independence Day - October 4 (1966)
Estimated 2010 population:	2,046,000
Population density:	175 persons per mi² (67 per km²)
Population distribution:	76% rural, 24% urban
Life expectancy in years:	Male, 38; female, 38
Doctors per 1,000 people:	Less than 0.05
Birth rate per 1,000:	27
Death rate per 1,000:	22
Infant mortality:	77 deaths per 1,000 live births
Age structure:	0-14: 39%; 15-64: 56%; 65 and over: 5%
Internet users per 100 people:	4
Internet code:	.ls
Languages spoken:	Sesotho (official), English (official), Zulu, Xhosa
Religions:	Christian (predominant), Muslims, Hindus, indigenous beliefs
Currency:	Loti
Gross domestic product (GDP) in 2008:	$1.63 billion U.S.
Real annual growth rate (2008):	6.8%
GDP per capita (2008):	$726 U.S.
Goods exported:	Mostly: clothing Also: agricultural products, diamonds
Goods imported:	Agricultural products, machinery, manufactured goods, medicines
Trading partners:	African countries, China, Hong Kong, Taiwan, United States

Lesotho, a mountainous country completely surrounded by South Africa, lies about 200 miles (320 kilometers) inland from the Indian Ocean. It was once called Basutoland, and ruled by the United Kingdom.

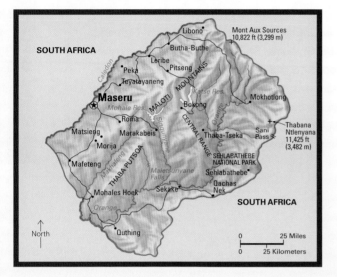

A modern road snakes through a mountain pass in Lesotho. Most of the country is mountainous.

History

The Basotho trace their history to the late 1700's and early 1800's, when tribal wars swept over southern Africa. Many groups at that time were almost completely wiped out. Some of the victims of the fighting fled into the highlands of what is now Lesotho, where they were given protection by an African chief named Moshoeshoe. By 1824, Moshoeshoe had about 21,000 followers, and he united them into the Basotho nation.

From 1856 to 1868, the Basotho were at war with South African settlers of Dutch descent called *Boers*. In 1868, the United Kingdom established the protectorate of Basutoland.

In 1966, Basutoland became the independent kingdom of Lesotho. The Basutoland National Party (BNP) leader Chief Leabua Jonathan became prime minister. Paramount Chief Motlotlehi Moshoeshoe II, great-grandson of Moshoeshoe, became king.

In January 1986, Jonathan was overthrown by a group of army officers, who in 1990 forced King Moshoeshoe II to leave office. They installed his oldest son as King Letsie III. King Letsie III dissolved the government and swore in a provisional council in 1994. When other nations denounced the move, the king agreed to restore the government and resign in favor of his father, the former King Moshoeshoe II. Moshoeshoe II died in 1996, and his oldest son returned to the throne as King Letsie III.

In 1998 elections, a new party, the Lesotho Congress for Democracy (LCD), won 79 of the 80 seats in the Assembly. Violence broke out after opposition parties claimed that the elections were fixed. In an agreement, 40 more seats were added to the Assembly, to be distributed proportionally among the political parties to ensure the inclusion of an opposition. However, in elections held in 2002 and those held in 2007, opposition parties claimed that the proportional seats were incorrectly allocated.

THE LESSER ANTILLES

The West Indies are an island chain dividing the Caribbean Sea from the rest of the Atlantic Ocean. Stretching about 2,000 miles (3,200 kilometers), the chain forms a broad curve from near southern Florida to Venezuela's northern coast.

Three island groups make up the West Indies: the Bahamas in the north; the Greater Antilles, including Cuba, Jamaica, Hispaniola, and Puerto Rico; and the Lesser Antilles. The Lesser Antilles are a chain of small islands extending southeast of Puerto Rico from the Virgin Islands to Aruba.

The islands of the Lesser Antilles are noted for their great natural beauty. Sandy beaches and graceful palm trees line many of the coasts. The northern islands form a double chain—the western inner arc is made up of rugged, volcanic islands, while the outer eastern arc consists of low, flat-topped islands with limestone bases. The inner and outer arcs come together at the butterfly-shaped islands of Guadeloupe. The southern islands, from Trinidad and Tobago to Aruba, are made up of sedimentary rock.

The Windwards and the Leewards

Geographers divide the Lesser Antilles into the Windward Islands, which are exposed to the moist, northeast trade winds, and the Leeward Islands, which include the more sheltered downwind northerly and westerly islands.

The Windward Islands include Dominica, Grenada, Martinique, St. Lucia, St. Vincent, and the Grenadine chain. About 15 main islands and many islets make up the Leeward Islands. They include Anguilla, Antigua and Barbuda, Guadeloupe, Montserrat, Saba, St.-Barthélemy, St. Eustatius, St. Kitts and Nevis, St. Martin, and the Virgin Islands.

Fishing crews prepare their nets before setting sail from a sheltered bay on St. Lucia. A majority of the people of St. Lucia are descended from African slaves. This small island country became independent in 1979 after being ruled by the United Kingdom since 1814.

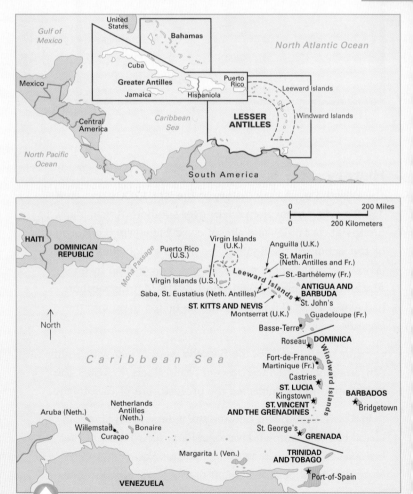

The island chain of the Lesser Antilles forms the eastern boundary of the Caribbean Sea. On many islands, tourism has become an important part of the economy. Several island governments are working to develop new industries that will lessen the islands' dependence on tourism.

A row of palms stand out against a golden sky on an island in the Lesser Antilles. The islands' beautiful landscape and tropical climate attract thousands of vacationers. However, many workers must go abroad in search of work because of the lack of job opportunities on the islands.

Fresh fruit is sold at a "floating market" in the harbor at Willemstad on the island of Curaçao. This island, which is the trade and industrial center of the Netherlands Antilles, is dry and barren, so most food must be imported.

Early history

Ciboney Indians were the earliest known prehistoric inhabitants of the West Indies. Arawak Indians from South America moved to the West Indies between about 200 B.C. and A.D. 1000. They were followed by the more warlike Carib Indians in about 1300. Both groups grew crops. They also hunted, fished, and gathered wild plants for food.

Christopher Columbus discovered the West Indies when he landed on an island in the Bahamas in 1492. Over the next 10 years, he claimed almost all the West Indies islands for Spain. Soon, settlers from England, France, the Netherlands, and Denmark—drawn by the promise of gold and other riches—arrived and claimed some of the smaller islands. The newcomers established sugar cane plantations and imported slaves from Africa to work on them.

By the late 1800's, slavery was abolished on all the islands. Without cheap labor, the plantation system declined, and the European powers lost interest in their colonies. Since 1945, many islands have become independent or have gained more control over their own affairs.

Shirley Heights in Antigua and Barbuda looks down on Galleon Beach and English Harbour. Falmouth Harbour is the bay at the top.

PEOPLE

The Lesser Antilles have been a popular destination ever since Christopher Columbus discovered what he described as "the best, most fertile, most delightful and most charming land in the world." During the 1500's and 1600's, rival European powers fought for possession of the islands. Today, tourists come from all over the world to bask in the glorious sunshine, swim in the sparkling sea, and stroll along the islands' sandy beaches.

In addition to their great natural beauty, the islands have a charm all their own. Although the Lesser Antilles form a single island group, they vary greatly in culture, government, and language. Each island has kept much of the flavor and characteristics of the European country that once ruled it.

Barbados, for example, earned the nickname "Little England" after more than 300 years of British rule. Although the island country has been independent since 1966, Barbadians are proud that their way of life is very much like that in England. The French dependency of Martinique, on the other hand, has Parisian-style boutiques and imports French wines for its people and for the tourist shops.

In Curaçao, a red mailbox gives a glimpse of the island's Dutch heritage. West Indian culture has absorbed many different European, African, and Asian influences, yet it has its own unique style.

Ethnic origins

The islanders trace their heritage to a variety of sources, from Europe to Asia to Africa. Most islanders trace their ancestry to Africans who were captured and taken from their native land to work as slaves on sugar and tobacco plantations. Some islanders have British, Dutch, French, Portuguese, or Spanish ancestors. And some island people are descended from Chinese or East Indian laborers who arrived in the 1800's, after slavery was abolished.

This ethnic mixture has produced a fascinating culture, not only in the Lesser Antilles but throughout the West Indies. The islands' official languages, such as English, Spanish, and Dutch, are often "sprinkled" with African words and phrases. Many islanders use a dialect called *patois,* which is a mixture of African words and mainly English or French. In Aruba, Bonaire, and Curaçao, the people speak *Papiamento,* which is a combination of Dutch, English, Portuguese, and Spanish.

Steel band musicians in Antigua use "pans," or hollowed-out drums, of different heights to achieve a wide range of notes. With 20 or more pans, a modern steel band can play any type of music—from classical to calypso.

Wide, sandy beaches and graceful palm trees lure millions of tourists to the Caribbean islands every year. Vacationers flock to this tropical paradise to escape winter's cold, as well as to enjoy such sports as windsurfing and snorkeling.

Colorful, dramatic costumes are part of the fun at carnival, an annual celebration that takes place on most Caribbean islands.

Calypso and carnival

The islands of the Caribbean have a number of distinctive traditions, including *calypso*—folk music that began among the African slaves on the island of Trinidad. It originated in singing competitions held by slaves during annual carnivals.

Modern steel bands originated in the late 1930's on Trinidad, also to accompany carnival celebrations. Winston "Spree" Simon of Trinidad is generally given credit for making the first "pan." The pans are hollow-topped metal drums made from oil drums. The bottom of the oil drum is cut off, and the top is hammered into a concave shape. A characteristic ringing sound is produced when the drum top is struck with a mallet.

Calypso and steel band performances are especially festive during the carnivals that take place on most islands every year. Each island celebrates in its own special way, but colorful parades, along with plenty of food and drink, are always part of the festivities.

THE LEEWARD ISLANDS

Sheltered from the trade winds and boasting a dry, healthful climate, the Leeward Islands stretch from Puerto Rico to the Windward Islands and form part of the Lesser Antilles. With about 15 islands and many islets, the Leeward Islands cover an area of 1,542 square miles (3,994 square kilometers).

St. Martin/Sint Maarten

St. Martin/Sint Maarten is a hilly island located east of Puerto Rico in the northern part of the arc of the Leeward Islands. The northern section of the island, known as St. Martin, is an overseas *collectivity* (administrative unit) of France. The southern section, known as Sint Maarten, is part of the Netherlands Antilles, a self-governing partner with the Netherlands in the Kingdom of the Netherlands. The governor of the Netherlands Antilles is appointed by the Dutch monarch.

The border between the two areas is an invisible line that visitors often cross without even knowing it. But each side has kept its separate identity, which adds to the island's unique character.

Marigot, the capital and chief city in the northern part of the island, has a distinctly French flavor. Small cafes serve coffee and *croissants* (crescent-shaped rolls), and gourmet restaurants feature freshly caught fish and imported French wines. In the busy Dutch capital of Philipsburg, tourists shop for china, cosmetics, crystal, jewelry, linens, and perfume imported from the Netherlands and other European countries.

Barbuda is one of three islands that make up the country of Antigua and Barbuda. The island attracts visitors with its beautiful beaches, clear water, and warm, sunny climate.

Clouds cover the rocky mountain peaks on Saba, left. Majestic Mount Scenery towers 2,855 feet (870 meters) above this tiny tropical paradise, which is only about 5 square miles (13 square kilometers) in size.

Saba and St. Eustatius

Not far from St. Martin/Sint Maarten are the friendly, slow-paced islands of Saba and St. Eustatius, two small volcanic islands that belong to the Netherlands Antilles. Saba has no beaches, but its dramatic cliffs, deep ravines, and lush tropical vegetation attract many visitors. The capital of Saba, called The Bottom, has all the charm of a Dutch village. The town lies in a green valley that is actually the crater of an extinct volcano.

St. Eustatius, also called Statia, is noted more for its history than its scenery. During the 1700's, St. Eustatius was a neutral free port known as *The Golden Rock,* where merchants, traders, and smugglers bought and sold a variety of goods. St. Eustatius was also the first foreign port in the world to salute the new American flag in 1776.

Pleasure boats lie at anchor off one of St.-Barthélemy's magnificent beaches. The beauty of this remote island has attracted many wealthy vacationers, and some have purchased large private estates on the island.

St.-Barthélemy and Montserrat

The small, mountainous island of St.-Barthélemy, near St. Martin/Sint Maarten, is an elegant, sophisticated French island with charming villages and beautiful beaches. The island's economy is based on farming, fishing, and tourism.

St.-Barthélemy was occupied by the French in 1648, but France turned it over to Sweden in 1784. It once again came under French rule in 1877. In 2007, its inhabitants voted for increased self-rule as an overseas collectivity of France. Previously, the island had been administered as part of the French island group of Guadaloupe.

Lying southwest of Antigua is Montserrat, a self-governing British crown colony. Irish settlers came to Montserrat in 1632, and the United Kingdom has controlled the island since 1783.

Since 1995, a number of volcanic eruptions in the Soufriére Hills in southern Montserrat have caused massive destruction. Many people have been evacuated to the northern part of Montserrat or to nearby islands. An eruption in 1997 destroyed Plymouth, the capital. Another massive eruption hit in 2003.

LIBERIA

Liberia is the oldest republic in sub-Saharan Africa. Founded in 1822, it was settled by freed American slaves. The name *Liberia* comes from a Latin phrase meaning *free land*.

Today, almost all of Liberia's people are divided into two groups: the *indigenous* (native) Africans, whose ancestors lived in the region for hundreds of years; and the Americo Liberians, who are descended mainly from African American settlers who emigrated from the United States.

The indigenous Africans, who make up about 95 percent of the population, belong to 16 different African ethnic groups. The largest groups are the Kpelle and the Bassa. The Americo Liberians make up about 5 percent of the population. They live mainly in the coastal towns and cities, where the standard of living is higher than in rural areas. The Americo Liberians are generally far better off than the indigenous Africans.

Most city dwellers live in small, wooden houses with tin roofs. Many are employed in service industries, which have become increasingly important to Liberia's economy. Others work in factories, producing such goods as soap, beverages, and explosives. Liberian mines produce iron ore.

Rural Liberians, by contrast, live in villages of mud houses with thatched roofs, and almost none have electricity or indoor plumbing. Most rural Liberians are farmers. Their food crops include cassava, rice, sugar cane, and tropical fruits.

The differences between indigenous Africans and Americo Liberians have created difficulties throughout Liberia's history. While the ancestors of the indigenous Africans probably came from Sudanese kingdoms between the 1100's and 1500's, ancestors of the Americo Liberians—mainly freed slaves—began to settle in the region in 1822. Not only did the settlers have trouble finding food, but they often fought with the indigenous Africans over land.

In 1838, the Commonwealth of Liberia was formed, but it was still controlled by the American Colonization Society, a group of white Americans

FACTS

Official name:	Republic of Liberia
Capital:	Monrovia
Terrain:	Mostly flat to rolling coastal plains rising to rolling plateau and low mountains in northeast
Area:	43,000 mi² (111,369 km²)
Climate:	Tropical; hot, humid; dry winters with hot days and cool to cold nights; wet, cloudy summers with frequent heavy showers
Main rivers:	Cavally (also called Cavalla), St. Paul
Highest elevation:	Nimba Mountains, 4,528 ft (1,380 m)
Lowest elevation:	Atlantic Ocean, sea level
Form of government:	Republic
Head of state:	President
Head of government:	President
Administrative areas:	15 counties
Legislature:	National Assembly consisting of the Senate with 30 members serving nine-year terms and the House of Representatives with 64 members serving six-year terms
Court system:	Supreme Court
Armed forces:	2,400 troops
National holiday:	Independence Day - July 26 (1847)
Estimated 2010 population:	4,177,000
Population density:	97 persons per mi² (38 per km²)
Population distribution:	59% urban, 41% rural
Life expectancy in years:	Male, 43; female, 45
Doctors per 1,000 people:	Less than 0.05
Birth rate per 1,000:	48
Death rate per 1,000:	18
Infant mortality:	133 deaths per 1,000 live births
Age structure:	0-14: 47%; 15-64: 51%; 65 and over: 2%
Internet users per 100 people:	0.6
Internet code:	.lr
Languages spoken:	English (official), about 20 ethnic group languages
Religions:	Christian 40%, indigenous beliefs 40%, Muslim 20%
Currency:	Liberian dollar
Gross domestic product (GDP) in 2008:	$877 million U.S.
Real annual growth rate (2008):	7.5%
GDP per capita (2008):	$247 U.S.
Goods exported:	Mostly: rubber Also: cocoa, coffee, diamonds, iron ore
Goods imported:	Chemicals, machinery, petroleum, rice, transportation equipment
Trading partners:	Japan, Malaysia, Singapore, South Korea, United States

Liberia is a republic in western Africa. Its capital, Monrovia, was named for James Monroe, the U.S. president who arranged for its settlement.

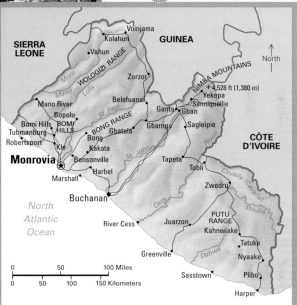

Monrovia is the educational and cultural center of Liberia as well as the country's capital. It stands on the Atlantic coast at the mouth of the St. Paul River.

who had helped the former slaves settle the area. Liberia became independent on July 26, 1847.

The Liberian economy was helped immensely in 1926, when the government leased large amounts of land to the American Firestone Company for rubber plantations. It was helped still more in 1944, when William V. Tubman, an Americo Liberian, became president. Tubman, determined to improve the nation's economy, expanded mining and foreign trade.

Tubman was succeeded by William R. Tolbert, Jr., but under Tolbert, the rich prospered while the poor became poorer. In 1980, a group of indigenous Liberian army officers killed Tolbert and took control.

Samuel K. Doe, an army sergeant, was elected president in 1985. However, many people felt he had fixed the election. Under Doe, Liberia faced major economic problems. Doe also had many of his political opponents jailed or killed. A bloody civil war broke out in the late 1980's, and in 1990, Doe was captured by rebel forces, tortured, and killed.

The rebellion became a civil war between three fighting factions. In 1996, the groups signed a peace agree-

ment. Charles Taylor, one of the rebel leaders, was elected president in 1997. By then, the fighting had severely damaged many towns, especially the capital, Monrovia. The economy had been disrupted, and many people had been forced to leave their homes. Soon, fighting broke out again.

In 2003, United Nations peacekeepers established a transitional government. Liberians elected a new president and legislature in 2005. Ellen Johnson-Sirleaf became the first woman elected president of an African country. She was reelected in 2011. In 2012, an international criminal court near the Hague, the Netherlands, sentenced former President Taylor to 50 years in prison for his role in atrocities committed in neighboring Sierra Leone during that country's civil war in the 1990's.

LIBYA

Libya, an Arab country in North Africa, forms a kind of bridge between Islamic countries. To the west are the *Maghreb* (western) countries of Tunisia, Algeria, and Morocco, which were colonized by France. To the east lies the Middle East—Egypt and the countries of the Arabian Peninsula.

Government

The government of Libya is based on popular assemblies. About 1,000 local groups elect representatives to the General People's Congress (GPC), which officially runs the government. The GPC meets every year to pass laws and select the members of the General People's Committee, which forms national policy. All Libyan citizens 18 years old or older may vote and hold office.

Until 2011, Colonel Mu'ammar Muhammad al-Qadhafi controlled Libya's government. Qadhafi was Libya's head of state, but he had no official title. Qadhafi took over in 1969, after he led a revolt against Libya's King Idris. Under Qadhafi's strong rule, Libya's government held control of most of the country's economic activities. Oil revenues were used to fund new and ambitious social, political, and economic projects.

Qadhafi replaced the political institutions of Libya with the popular assemblies. Yet, despite the appearance of democracy in Libya, Qadhafi tolerated no political opposition. Although the GPC technically chose the members of the General People's Committee, Qadhafi actually controlled these appointments. Political parties were forbidden in Libya after 1952. In 1971, Qadhafi formed the Arab Socialist Union as Libya's only political alliance. However, a number of underground opposition groups grew up. Those groups, with the help of NATO and French forces, overthrew Qadhafi in 2011.

History

Berbers were probably the first inhabitants of Libya. Until the early 1900's, Libya consisted of three separate regions—each with its own distinc-

FACTS

Official name:	**Al Jumahiriyah al Arabiyah al Uzma al Libiyah ash Shabiyah al Ishtirakiyah (Socialist People's Libyan Arab Jamahiriya)**
Capital:	**Tripoli**
Terrain:	**Mostly barren, plains, plateaus, depressions**
Area:	**679,362 mi² (1,759,540 km²)**
Climate:	**Mediterranean along coast; dry, extreme desert interior**
Main rivers:	**N/A**
Highest elevation:	**Bette Peak, 7,500 ft (2,286 m)**
Lowest sea level elevation:	**Sabkhat Ghuzayyil, 154 ft (47 m) below**
Form of government:	**Transitional**
Head of state:	**No official title for head of state**
Head of government:	**Secretary of the General People's Committee (prime minister)**
Administrative areas:	**25 baladiyat (municipalities)**
Legislature:	**General People's Congress with 760 members**
Court system:	**Supreme Court**
Armed forces:	**76,000 troops**
National holiday:	**Revolution Day - September 1 (1969)**
Estimated 2010 population:	**6,518,000**
Population density:	**10 persons per mi² (4 per km²)**
Population distribution:	**78% urban, 22% rural**
Life expectancy in years:	**Male, 73; female, 78**
Doctors per 1,000 people:	**1.3**
Birth rate per 1,000:	**24**
Death rate per 1,000:	**4**
Infant mortality:	**21 deaths per 1,000 live births**
Age structure:	**0-14: 30%; 15-64: 66%; 65 and over: 4%**
Internet users per 100 people:	**5**
Internet code:	**.ly**
Languages spoken:	**Arabic (official), Italian, English, French**
Religions:	**Sunni Muslim 97%, other 3%**
Currency:	**Libyan dinar**
Gross domestic product (GDP) in 2008:	**$102.83 billion U.S.**
Real annual growth rate (2008):	**6.3%**
GDP per capita (2008):	**$16,411 U.S.**
Goods exported:	**Chemicals, crude oil and petroleum products**
Goods imported:	**Electrical equipment, food, machinery, transportation equipment**
Trading partners:	**France, Germany, Italy, Spain, Turkey, United States**

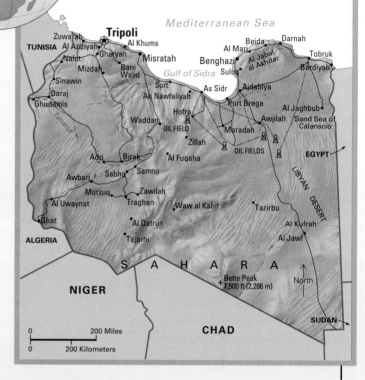

Libya is mostly covered by a vast desert. The nation's capital city of Tripoli is on the Mediterranean coast. Tunisia and Algeria lie to the west, Niger and Chad to the south, and Egypt and Sudan to the east.

Date palms and the sand dunes of the Sahara come up to the shores of Um El Ma lake in the vast desert area in Libya known as Erg Ubari.

tive geography and history. In the 600's B.C., Greeks colonized the northeastern coast and established a province known as Cyrenaica. In the 400's B.C., the Carthaginians built trading centers on the northwestern coast; this region was called Tripolitania. Nomads lived in the southwestern desert known as the Fezzan.

Over the next 1,000 years, different empires took control of one or more of these Libyan regions. Then in A.D. 642, the Arabs invaded Cyrenaica, and in 643, they occupied the city of Tripoli. The Arabs brought their language and the Islamic religion to Libya

The Ottoman Empire, based in what is now Turkey, captured all three regions in the 1500's and controlled the area until Italy conquered the three provinces in 1912. Italy ruled Libya until its defeat in Africa during World War II (1939-1945).

In December 1951, the United Nations (UN) called for Libya's independence. When Libya became a kingdom, Muhammad Idris al Mahdi as-Sanusi, a resistance leader, became king. The discovery of oil in Libya in 1959 changed the nation dramatically. Libya—then one of the most poverty-stricken nations in the Arab world—soon became one of the wealthiest. However, many of Libya's people became discontented because so few of them shared in the oil wealth.

In September 1969, a group of military officers called the Revolutionary Command Council overthrew King Idris. Qadhafi, the group's leader, rose to power. During the 1970's, Libya supported the Palestine Liberation Organization (PLO) and aided rebellions in Chad and Western Sahara.

The leaders of many nations criticized Qadhafi for interfering in the affairs of other countries. In 1992, the United Nations (UN) imposed economic sanctions on Libya for harboring two Libyans suspected of bombing an American airplane in 1988 and a French airplane in 1989, killing 441 people. In August 2003, Libya accepted responsibility for the 1988 bombing. The UN and the United States both lifted sanctions against Libya.

In early 2011, opposition groups in Libya revolted against Qadhafi's rule. Their movement was one of several in a number of Arab nations that came to be known as the Arab Spring. The rebels killed Qadhafi in October 2011, and a National Transitional Council took over as Libya's transitional government.

LAND AND ECONOMY

The Sahara dominates the landscape of Libya, covering about 95 percent of the country. In eastern Libya, the Sahara is called the Libyan Desert.

Huge sand dunes make up most of the Sahara in Libya. The desert terrain gradually rises from north to south, where rugged mountains rise from the desert floor along the southern border. Majestic Bette Peak, Libya's highest point, towers 7,500 feet (2,286 meters) above the desert sands.

The desert has extremely hot daytime temperatures but cools off rapidly at night. The average daytime temperature is 100° F (38° C); the average nighttime temperature is 50° F (10° C). An average of less than 2 inches (5 centimeters) of rain falls each year.

Except for scattered oases, only the land near the Mediterranean Sea in northwestern and northeastern Libya is inhabitable. In north-central Libya, the Sahara reaches to the coast.

Most Libyans live on plains near the Mediterranean Sea. One fertile strip of land stretches along the northwest coast for almost 200 miles (320 kilometers). It is rimmed by hills to the south. Other Libyans live on a smaller plain on the northeast coast between Benghazi and Darnah, or in the highlands just south of there known as Al Jabal al Akhdar, or the Green Mountain region.

Both coastal areas have a Mediterranean climate with warm summers and mild winters. January temperatures in Tripoli, on the northwest coast, average 52° F (11° C); July temperatures average 81° F (27° C). The coast receives more rain than the inland desert— about 16 inches (41 centimeters) per year.

Most Libyan workers are employed in service industries or farm in the coastal areas. But

The Tuareg, a nomadic Berber group, gather feed for their camels. The Tuareg and other nomads roam across the desert in search of water and grazing land for their animals. Scattered oases are the only fertile areas in the desert of Libya.

Libya's most valuable source of income— the oil fields that form the basis of the Libyan economy—is centered in the north-central region, where the Sahara reaches to the Gulf of Sidra.

Petroleum accounts for about 25 percent of the value of Libya's economic production, and for almost all its export earnings. The government, which controls petroleum operations, has used some of the oil wealth to improve farmland and provide services for the Libyan people, and to pay for imported manufactured goods, food, technology, and weapons.

Service industries make up about 40 percent of the value of Libya's economic production. Government agencies rank first among service industries, which also include banks, retail stores, and wholesale companies.

Construction boomed after 1959, when many factories and other buildings were needed for the rapidly developing petroleum industry. Today, construction makes up about a tenth of the value of Libya's economic production.

Camels and donkeys have served as beasts of burden in the Sahara for centuries. Modern Libya, however, has a developing economy that depends heavily on petroleum.

Petroleum counts for about 25 percent of the value of Libya's total economic production, and for almost all the country's export earnings. The national government controls petroleum mining.

Manufacturing also makes up about a tenth of the value of the country's economic production, with refined petroleum products and petrochemicals ranking first. Other goods include cement, processed foods, and steel. Libya's northern cities are the chief manufacturing centers.

Although agriculture accounts for only about 7 percent of the value of economic production in Libya today, about 18 percent of Libya's people are farmers. The main crops include barley, citrus fruits, dates, olives, potatoes, tomatoes, and wheat. Farmers and herders also raise cattle, chickens, and sheep. Libya imports most of its food, however, because only about 5 percent of the land can be farmed.

Libya's national airline, Libyan Arab Airlines, connects Libya with other countries. The country's major seaports are Tripoli, Benghazi, Misratah, and Port Brega. Libya has no railroads, but paved roads link the larger cities of northern Libya and connect them with desert oases.

Rocky plateaus and gravelly plains are typical of most of Libya's landscape. The Sahara covers about 95 percent of the country. The road cutting through the desert in this photo serves an oil field.

PEOPLE

More than 6-1/2 million people live in Libya. About 80 percent of the population live along the Mediterranean coast or in the upland regions just south of it.

The early inhabitants of Libya were Berbers who began moving into North Africa about 3000 B.C., probably from southwestern Asia or Europe. Beginning in the 600's B.C., parts of Libya were then colonized or invaded by a series of forces: the Carthaginians, the Greeks, the Romans, the Vandals, and the Byzantines. In the A.D. 600's, Arabs invaded first northeastern and then northwestern Libya. Their culture, language, and religion were adopted by the native Berbers. Today, almost all of the Libyan people are of mixed Arab and Berber ancestry. Although Arabic is the official language of Libya, many educated Libyans also speak English or Italian.

Islam is the official religion of Libya. According the country's constitution, all Libyan laws must agree with Islamic teachings. Almost all Libyans are *Sunni Muslims*—that is, followers of Islam who belong to the Sunni branch of the faith.

Whitewashed mud-brick houses are typical homes of Libya's rural population. Libya's city dwellers live in modern high-rise apartments.

Nearly 80 percent of Libya's people live in cities. Most of the rural population lives in villages or oases. A small number are nomads who move across the desert in search of water and pasture for their sheep, goats, and camels.

Since the nation's economy, spurred by the oil industry, started to develop in the mid-1900's, many rural Libyans have moved to urban areas. The flood of newcomers has caused serious overcrowding in the cities, especially in the older neighborhoods. This shift in population has brought many changes in the Libyan way of life. Rural Libyans, for example, live in extended families, with grandparents, parents, and children sharing a home. This living arrangement is seldom followed in the crowded cities.

In rural areas, most people live in stone or mud-brick houses that often have only one room for living, cooking, eating, and sleeping. Animals are kept in a nearby shelter. In the cities, high-rise apartment buildings and office buildings line the downtown streets. In fact, Libya's large cities look much like those in North America and Western Europe. In the suburbs, some Libyans live in large single-family homes.

Most rural Libyans wear traditional clothing. The men wear a loose cotton shirt and trousers covered by an outer cloak, and a flat, brimless, tight-fitting cap. The women wear a full-length robe. Urban Libyans, on the other hand, generally wear Western-style clothing. However, some wear traditional dress to show their respect for time-honored values and practices.

The status of Libyan women has changed dramatically since the mid-1900's. In the past, women in Libya received little or no education and were largely confined to their homes. Today, Libyan women have the legal right to participate fully in society. Although many traditional attitudes toward women remain, women make up a growing percentage of the nation's work force today.

Most of Libya's people can read and write. This literacy rate is largely due to the government's education program, which is funded by oil income.

Muslims enter the Karamanli mosque in Tripoli through a colonnaded passageway. Qadhafi's government has promoted traditional Islamic practices along with modern social reforms, such as increased freedom for women.

The Gurgi Mosque, built in 1833, dominates an open-air market in Tripoli's old city. Tripoli is Libya's capital and largest city.

THE SAHARA

Libya has the distinction of being the location of the world's highest official temperature. In 1922, at Al Aziziyah in the Sahara, the temperature reached 136 °F (58 °C). For the Libyan people, the harsh Saharan climate and landscape are a fact of life. But the desert itself is a unique environment where plants and animals have adapted to the extreme conditions.

The Sahara is by far the world's largest desert. It covers about 3 ½ million square miles (9 million square kilometers) of North Africa, stretching more than 3,500 miles (5,630 kilometers) from west to east and 1,200 miles (1,930 kilometers) from north to south. In addition to Libya, it covers much of Morocco, Algeria, Tunisia, Egypt, Sudan, Chad, Niger, Mali, and Mauritania, and all of Western Sahara.

The name *Sahara* comes from the Arabic word *sahra,* which means *desert.* The dry, hot climate of the Sahara is typical of many deserts. The average yearly rainfall is less than 4 inches (10 centimeters), but large areas receive less than 1 inch (2.5 centimeters) of rain per year.

In the central portion of the Sahara, mountains and uplands rise as high as 11,204 feet (3,415 meters). This highland region gets slightly more rain than other areas of the desert, and snow may even cover some peaks in the winter.

Most of the Sahara is made up of rocky plateaus and gravelly plains, but lying within large basins in the desert are vast seas of sand called *ergs.* The shifting sands in these ergs sometimes form towering dunes as high as 600 feet (180 meters).

The plateaus and plains of the Sahara are not entirely barren, however. Plant and animal life does exist, though it may not be as plentiful as in other deserts.

The grasses, shrubs, and trees that grow in parts of the Sahara have adapted to the arid conditions

The Sahara, which covers much of North Africa, is the world's largest desert. It covers about 3 ½ million square miles (9 million square kilometers) and includes mountain ranges, rocky plateaus, gravelly plains, and sandy wastes.

there. Some of the plants are *ephemeral,* or short-lived. Their seeds lie in the ground and do not start to grow until rain falls. Then the plants shoot up quickly and may complete their life cycle in just six to eight weeks.

Plants that live longer than a year have developed various ways to get—and keep—water. Some have long roots that reach deep into the soil and absorb moisture; others take in moisture from the air through their leaves.

Animals also have adapted to the arid Sahara. Barbary sheep live on the rocky plateaus of the desert, while white gazelles and rare antelope called *addax* roam the sand dunes. Horned vipers, spiny-tailed lizards, gerbils, and small foxes called *fennecs* also live in the dunes. Many of the small animals are *nocturnal* animals, which stay in their burrows during the day to avoid the heat, emerging at night to hunt for food.

Camels were introduced into the Sahara more than 2,000 years ago. Like most desert animals, they can go for long periods without drinking water. They get some water from the plants they eat, and they keep water in their bodies because they do not sweat much.

Scattered throughout the Sahara are *oases*—fertile green spots irrigated by water from springs or wells. Plants and animals that require more water—such as huge date palms—

thrive in the oases. Some oases are large enough to support villages of up to 2,000 people.

Thousands of years ago, the Saharan environment had a much wetter climate than it has now. Grasslands covered much of the region, and some areas had lakes and streams. Elephants, giraffes, and other large animals roamed the land.

About 4000 B.C., Africa's climate started to become drier, and the Sahara region began to turn into a desert. Ever since, the desert has been spreading. Through the centuries, people have contributed to this expansion by removing the plants that help to hold down the soil against erosion. The farmers have allowed their herds to over-graze on grasses at the edges of the desert, and they have cut down trees and shrubs there for firewood.

Rock-strewn plateaus and gravelly plains make up most of the Sahara. Formations of granite, sandstone, and other types of rock, sculpted by wind and water, rise from the desert floor throughout the Sahara.

The Saharan people primarily use camels for transportation. Motor vehicles can be driven across the desert along unpaved routes, but it is a difficult and an uncomfortable journey.

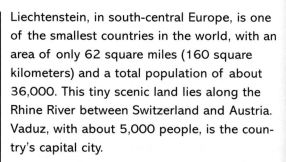

LIECHTENSTEIN

Liechtenstein, in south-central Europe, is one of the smallest countries in the world, with an area of only 62 square miles (160 square kilometers) and a total population of about 36,000. This tiny scenic land lies along the Rhine River between Switzerland and Austria. Vaduz, with about 5,000 people, is the country's capital city.

Liechtenstein is a constitutional monarchy, ruled by a prince—the head of the House of Liechtenstein. The 25 members of the country's *Landtag* (parliament) pass its laws, which must be approved by the prince. A five-member Collegial Board headed by a prime minister handles government operations.

The people of Liechtenstein have many close cultural, political, and economic ties with Switzerland. Liechtenstein uses the Swiss franc. Switzerland operates the country's communication systems and represents Liechtenstein in its diplomatic and trade relations.

Economy

Since about 1950, Liechtenstein has been transformed from an agricultural country to a highly industrialized one. Today, it has one of the world's highest standards of living.

Products made in Liechtenstein include ceramics, electronic equipment, fabricated metal products, food products, and pharmaceuticals. Agricultural products such as barley, corn, potatoes, wheat, and vegetables are grown in the Rhine Valley. Farmers raise beef and dairy cattle on the grassy meadows of the country's mountain slopes. Grapes and other fruits are grown on the upland slopes. Liechtenstein's low tax rates attract many foreign businesses, and the government collects money from thousands of foreign firms based in Liechtenstein.

FACTS

Official name:	Fuerstentum Liechtenstein (Principality of Liechtenstein)
Capital:	Vaduz
Terrain:	Mostly mountainous (Alps) with Rhine Valley in western third
Area:	62 mi² (160 km²)
Climate:	Continental; cold, cloudy winters with frequent snow or rain; cool to moderately warm, cloudy, humid summers
Main rivers:	Rhine, Samina
Highest elevation:	Vorder-Grauspitz, 8,527 ft (2,599 m)
Lowest elevation:	Ruggeller Riet, 1,411 ft (430 m)
Form of government:	Constitutional monarchy
Head of state:	Monarch
Head of government:	Prime minister
Administrative areas:	11 Gemeinden (communes)
Legislature:	Landtag (Diet) with 25 members serving four-year terms
Court system:	Oberster Gerichtshof (Supreme Court), Obergericht (Court of Appeal)
Armed forces:	N/A
National holiday:	Assumption Day - August 15
Estimated 2010 population:	36,000
Population density:	581 persons per mi² (225 per km²)
Population distribution:	86% rural, 14% urban
Life expectancy in years:	Male, 78; female, 83
Doctors per 1,000 people:	N/A
Birth rate per 1,000:	10
Death rate per 1,000:	7
Infant mortality:	4 deaths per 1,000 live births
Age structure:	0-14: 17%; 15-64: 70%; 65 and over: 13%
Internet users per 100 people:	65
Internet code:	.li
Languages spoken:	German (official), Alemannic dialect
Religions:	Roman Catholic 78.4%, Protestant 8.3%, other 13.3%
Currency:	Swiss franc
Gross domestic product (GDP) in 2007:	$4.99 billion U.S.
Real annual growth rate (2007):	3.1%
GDP per capita (2007):	$138,694 U.S.
Goods exported:	Agricultural products, electronics, small specialty machinery, transportation equipment
Goods imported:	Agricultural products, machinery, metal goods, motor vehicles, raw materials
Trading partners:	Austria, France, Germany, Italy, Switzerland, United States

Vaduz is the capital and largest city of Liechtenstein. The city was founded during the Middle Ages, probably in the mid-1100's.

History

Charlemagne controlled the area that is now Liechtenstein in the late 700's and early 800's. After his death, the area was divided into two independent states. Both states later became part of the Holy Roman Empire. By 1712, both states had been acquired by Johann-Adam Liechtenstein, a prince from Vienna, whose descendants still rule Liechtenstein today.

The country has been an independent state since 1719, except for a brief period during the early 1800's when the French empire ruled by Napoleon I controlled it. Liechtenstein has also been a neutral country since 1866 and has had no army since 1868.

In 1924, Liechtenstein agreed to an economic union with Switzerland. The women of Liechtenstein were finally given the right to vote in 1984. In 2003, the people voted to give the prince more authority in Liechtenstein's government.

Liechtenstein is a tiny country in south-central Europe.

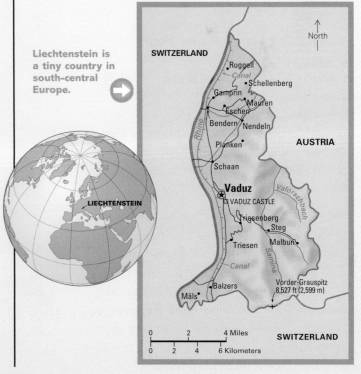

LITHUANIA

Lithuania is situated on the eastern shore of the Baltic Sea. Its landscape consists chiefly of flat or gently sloping land. Some 3,000 small lakes cover about 1½ percent of the region. Beautiful white sand dunes line the coast of the Baltic Sea and stretch for miles along a sparkling strip of land that separates the Kuršiu Marios (a lagoon) from the sea.

About 85 percent of the people of Lithuania are Lithuanians, a nationality group with its own customs and language. The other main groups in the country are Poles and Russians.

Most people live in towns and cities. Service industries employ about half the workers. Most of the others are split between manufacturing and agriculture.

History

The ancestors of present-day Lithuanians have lived in the region at least 2,000 years. Near the end of the 1100's, these people united into a single nation.

During the Middle Ages, the people of Lithuania controlled an empire that extended to the Black Sea in the south and almost as far as Moscow in the east. In 1386, Grand Duke Jogaila (Jagiello in Polish) joined Lithuania with Poland. The union lasted more than 400 years, until the czar of Russia gained control of the Lithuanian part of the region in 1795.

In 1918—during World War I—Lithuania declared its independence. Russia attempted to take over the country but was defeated in 1920. Poland occupied the Lithuanian capital of Vilnius between 1920 and 1939, and in 1940, the Soviet Union annexed the country. Germany occupied Lithuania for several years during World War II (1939-1945), but the Soviet Union took it back in 1944.

FACTS

Official name:	Lietuvos Respublika (Republic of Lithuania)
Capital:	Vilnius
Terrain:	Lowland, many scattered small lakes, fertile soil
Area:	25,212 mi² (65,300 km²)
Climate:	Transitional, between maritime and continental; wet, moderate winters and summers
Main river:	Neman (Nemunas)
Highest elevation:	Juozapines, 958 ft (292 m)
Lowest elevation:	Baltic Sea, sea level
Form of government:	Republic
Head of state:	President
Head of government:	Prime minister
Administrative areas:	10 apskritys (counties)
Legislature:	Seimas (Parliament) with 141 members serving four-year terms
Court system:	Supreme Court
Armed forces:	8,600 troops
National holiday:	Independence Day - February 16 (1918)
Estimated 2010 population:	3,349,000
Population density:	133 persons per mi² (51 per km²)
Population distribution:	67% urban, 33% rural
Life expectancy in years:	Male, 67; female, 79
Doctors per 1,000 people:	4.0
Birth rate per 1,000:	10
Death rate per 1,000:	14
Infant mortality:	6 deaths per 1,000 live births
Age structure:	0-14: 15%; 15-64: 69%; 65 and over: 16%
Internet users per 100 people:	54
Internet code:	.lt
Languages spoken:	Lithuanian (official), Russian, Polish
Religions:	Roman Catholic 79%, Russian Orthodox 4.1%, Protestant 1.9%, other 15%
Currency:	Lithuanian litas
Gross domestic product (GDP) in 2008:	$47.80 billion U.S.
Real annual growth rate (2008):	3.2%
GDP per capita (2008):	$14,167 U.S.
Goods exported:	Clothing, electrical equipment, fertilizers, food, machinery, motor vehicles, petroleum products, plastics, wood and wood products
Goods imported:	Chemicals, crude oil, electronics, iron and steel, machinery, plastics, transportation equipment
Trading partners:	Estonia, Germany, Latvia, Poland, Russia

The largest of the three Baltic States, Lithuania lies in northern Europe along the eastern shore of the Baltic Sea.

Vilnius is the capital and largest city of Lithuania. It lies on the Neris River. The city includes a mix of modern skyscrapers and old buildings, some dating back to the 1400's.

Resistance and independence

The Lithuanians strongly opposed the Soviet take-over. In the late 1980's, Lithuanian nationalism gained massive support throughout the republic. Leaders of the non-Communist *Sajudis* and other groups sought to restore political and economic independence.

In August 1991, conservative Communist leaders in the Soviet Union attempted to overthrow the Soviet central government, but failed. In the political upheaval that followed, Lithuania declared its independence from the Soviet Union.

In September 1991, the Soviet government recognized Lithuania's independence. Afterward, the government of Lithuania expressed support of free enterprise and initiated plans to establish a free market economy. In 2004, Lithuania joined the North Atlantic Treaty Organization (NATO), a defense alliance, and the European Union, which promotes economic and political cooperation. In 2009, voters elected Dalia Grybauskaite as the country's first woman president.

LUXEMBOURG

Luxembourg, one of Europe's oldest and smallest independent countries, lies in northwestern Europe where Germany, France, and Belgium meet. The country covers only 998 square miles (2,586 square kilometers) and has about 495,000 people.

The people of Luxembourg often call their country the "green heart of Europe" because of its beautiful landscape. Rolling green hills and medieval castles perched on steep cliffs attract many tourists. The city of Luxembourg is the country's capital and largest city.

The northern third of Luxembourg is a wooded region—an extension of the Ardennes mountain system of Belgium and Germany. River valleys cut through the region's low hills. The Bon Pays (Good Land) region, which covers the rest of the country, is mainly a hilly or rolling plateau with level areas along its rivers. The Bon Pays is a productive farming region.

Government

Luxembourg is a constitutional monarchy. The grand duke or duchess of the House of Nassau serves as monarch and head of state, but the office is largely ceremonial. The monarchy is inherited by the monarch's oldest son or daughter.

A 60-member parliament called the Chamber of Deputies passes Luxembourg's laws. The people elect the members to five-year terms. With the support of parliament, the monarch appoints a prime minister and other Cabinet ministers to run the government. The monarch also appoints for life a 21-member advisory body called the Council of State.

History

Luxembourg became an independent state in A.D. 963, when Siegfried, Count of Ardennes, gained control of the area and built a castle on the site of the present-day city of Luxembourg. In 1354, Charles IV created the Duchy of Luxembourg, and a period of prosperity began.

FACTS

Official name:	Grand-Duche de Luxembourg (Grand Duchy of Luxembourg)
Capital:	Luxembourg
Terrain:	Mostly gently rolling uplands with broad, shallow valleys; uplands to slightly mountainous in the north; steep slope down to Moselle flood plain in the southeast
Area:	998 mi² (2,586 km²)
Climate:	Modified continental with mild winters, cool summers
Main rivers:	Attert, Alzette, Moselle, Sûre
Highest elevation:	Buurgplatz, 1,835 ft (559 m)
Lowest elevation:	Moselle River, 435 ft (133 m)
Form of government:	Constitutional monarchy
Head of state:	Grand duke or duchess
Head of government:	Prime minister
Administrative areas:	3 districts
Legislature:	Chambre des Deputes (Chamber of Deputies) with 60 members serving five-year terms
Court system:	Cour Superieure de Justice (Superior Court of Justice), Tribunale Administratin (Administrative Court)
Armed forces:	900 troops
National holiday:	National Day - June 23
Estimated 2010 population:	495,000
Population density:	496 persons per mi² (191 per km²)
Population distribution:	82% urban, 18% rural
Life expectancy in years:	Male, 77; female, 83
Doctors per 1,000 people:	2.7
Birth rate per 1,000:	12
Death rate per 1,000:	8
Infant mortality:	5 deaths per 1,000 live births
Age structure:	0-14: 18%; 15-64: 68%; 65 and over: 14%
Internet users per 100 people:	76
Internet code:	.lu
Languages spoken:	Letzeburgesch (official), French (official), German (official), English
Religions:	Roman Catholic 87%, other (including Protestant, Jewish, Muslim) 13%
Currency:	Euro
Gross domestic product (GDP) in 2008:	$54.97 billion U.S.
Real annual growth rate (2008):	3.6%
GDP per capita (2008):	$117,213 U.S.
Goods exported:	Aluminum, chemicals, electronics, machinery, rubber products, steel products, transportation equipment
Goods imported:	Automobiles, food, iron and steel, machinery, petroleum products, plastics
Trading partners:	Belgium, France, Germany, Netherlands

The country later came under a succession of foreign rulers, including Burgundy, Spain, Austria, and France. In 1815, after the defeat of Napoleon I of France, the Congress of Vienna made Luxembourg a grand duchy that was technically ruled by the Netherlands. In 1890, Luxembourg broke away from the Netherlands and named its own monarch.

Germany occupied the country during parts of World War I (1914-1918) and World War II (1939-1945). In the winter of 1944 and 1945, part of the Battle of the Bulge was fought in northern Luxembourg.

After World War II, Luxembourg became one of Europe's most prosperous countries. In 1945, it became a member of the United Nations, and in 1948, with Belgium and the Netherlands, Luxembourg helped establish the economic union of Benelux. It was also a founding member of the North Atlantic Treaty Organization in 1949 and of the European Economic Community, a precursor of the European Union, in 1957.

Today, Luxembourg plays an important role in European affairs. The city of Luxembourg serves as the headquarters of the European Court of Justice and several other international agencies. The country is also an international financial center where foreign banks and corporations have offices.

The European Court of Justice meets in the city of Luxembourg. Several other international organizations also have their headquarters here.

Luxembourg is one of Europe's smallest countries. Its northern region is hilly and wooded, while its southern two-thirds has most of the nation's farmland and industry.

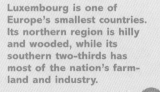

PEOPLE AND ECONOMY

The population of Luxembourg is unevenly spread throughout the country. The most densely populated areas include the capital city of Luxembourg, the industrialized southwest corner of the country, and the farming regions of the Bon Pays.

Most of Luxembourg's people are Roman Catholics. About one-third of Luxembourg's population are immigrants.

Luxembourg has three official languages—French, German, and a German dialect called Letzeburgesch. People use Letzeburgesch widely in everyday speech, though they usually write in French or German. German is used in most elementary schools, and French is used in most high schools. Luxembourg's newspapers are printed in German, while French is used in the courts and parliament.

Luxembourgers have close cultural ties with their neighbors, but their independent spirit is expressed in the words of their national anthem, "*Mir welle bleiwe wat mir sin*" ("We want to remain what we are"). Most Luxembourgers enjoy a high standard of living and have better food and housing than many other Europeans have. In addition, the government provides extensive social security and health-care benefits.

Economy

Luxembourg is one of Europe's leading steel producers but, since World War II, the mines that provided the iron ore to make the steel have decreased in number. This reduction in mines, plus the general decline of steel production in the 1970's, led to the closing of many steel factories. As a result, Luxembourg has diminished its dependence on heavy industry.

Today, Luxembourg has a number of high-technology industries that produce electronic equipment, chemicals, plastics, and tires. Since the 1960's, Luxembourg has also developed many small- and medium-sized service industries. Over the years,

A Luxembourg bank and stock exchange suggest the country's importance as an international center of finance.

A shop offers fruits and vegetables in the historic Old Town area in Luxembourg city.

Traditional architecture, like this bank building, gives Luxembourg an old world feeling. The city is an international financial center and many foreign banks have offices there.

tourism has grown into a major industry. The country has also become an international banking center.

Although about half of the nation's land is farmed, only a small number of Luxembourg's workers are farmers. Barley, oats, potatoes, wheat, and livestock are raised in the Bon Pays region. The area along the Moselle River yields grapes that produce fine wine.

The city of Luxembourg

Many of the foreign banks in Luxembourg are based in the country's capital city. Luxembourg also serves as the headquarters for many European international agencies.

The capital occupies a picturesque position on a rocky plateau overlooking the valleys formed by the Alzette and Petrusse rivers. The Grand Ducal Palace in Luxembourg, built in the 1500's, is the residence of the country's monarch. Other landmarks include the Gothic Cathedral of Notre Dame, which dates from the early 1600's, and the town hall, built in the early 1800's.

The Grand Duchess Charlotte Bridge spans the Alzette River between the historic center of Luxem-bourg and Kirchberg, the city's modern section. A district of wide boulevards and new buildings, Kirchberg was constructed in the 1960's to accommodate the numerous European institutions located in Luxembourg. Today, the institutions headquartered in Luxembourg include the *secretariat* (administrative staff) of the European Parliament, the European Court of Justice, the European Court of Auditors, and the European Investment Bank.

MACEDONIA

Macedonia is a mountainous land in the Balkan Peninsula in southeastern Europe. Formerly one of the six republics of Yugoslavia, Macedonia withdrew from the federation and declared its independence in 1991.

Most of the people in Macedonia belong to the Macedonian nationality group and speak their own Slavic language, which is similar to Bulgarian. Many of Macedonia's cultural traditions, including music, arts, and crafts, have remained free from outside influences. As a result, Macedonian songs, dances, embroidery, carpet weaving, and woodcarving have a style all their own. Even so, the Macedonians' claim to a separate, national identity has been challenged. From earliest times, various ethnic groups have laid claim to this mountainous region situated in the heart of the Balkan Peninsula.

The name *Macedonia* originally referred to a region that included parts of Greece and Bulgaria as well as present-day Macedonia. After about the 800's B.C., the Macedonians came under the influence of the Greeks. The son of King Philip II of Macedonia, Alexander the Great, conquered the Persian Empire in 331 B.C. and founded a vast empire on its ruins.

Macedonia was a Roman province from the 140's B.C. to A.D. 395, when the region became part of the Byzantine Empire. Macedonia was included in the first Bulgarian Empire in the 800's and in the Serbian Empire in the early 1300's. In 1371, the Ottoman Turks began their conquest of the region and ruled Macedonia for over 500 years.

Under Ottoman rule, various groups fought for dominance in Macedonia. The Greeks claimed the entire southern region, the Serbs claimed the northern region around Skopje, their ancient capital, and the Bulgarians claimed all of Macedonia except for the southern region.

The First Balkan War (1912-1913) freed Macedonia from the Ottomans. The area was finally divided between Greece, Serbia, and Bulgaria after the Second Balkan War in 1913. The peace treaties

FACTS

Official name:	Republika Makedonija (Republic of Macedonia)
Capital:	Skopje
Terrain:	Mountainous territory covered with deep basins and valleys; three large lakes, each divided by a frontier line; country bisected by the Vardar River
Area:	9,928 mi² (25,713 km²)
Climate:	Warm, dry summers and autumns and relatively cold winters with heavy snowfall
Main river:	Vardar
Highest elevation:	Mount Korab, 9,068 ft (2,764 m)
Lowest elevation:	Vardar River, 230 ft (70 m)
Form of government:	Parliamentary democracy
Head of state:	President
Head of government:	Prime minister
Administrative areas:	84 opstini (municipalities)
Legislature:	Sobranje (Assembly) with 120 members serving four-year terms
Court system:	Supreme Court
Armed forces:	10,900 troops
National holiday:	Ilinden Uprising Day - August 2 (1903)
Estimated 2010 population:	2,057,000
Population density:	207 persons per mi² (80 per km²)
Population distribution:	68% urban, 32% rural
Life expectancy in years:	Male, 72; female, 77
Doctors per 1,000 people:	2.6
Birth rate per 1,000:	11
Death rate per 1,000:	9
Infant mortality:	13 deaths per 1,000 live births
Age structure:	0-14: 19%; 15-64: 70%; 65 and over: 11%
Internet users per 100 people:	43
Internet code:	.mk
Languages spoken:	Macedonian (official), Albanian (official), Turkish, Roma, Serbian
Religions:	Macedonian Orthodox 64.7%, Muslim 33.3%, other Christian 0.4%, other 1.6%
Currency:	Macedonian denar
Gross domestic product (GDP) in 2008:	$9.57 billion U.S.
Real annual growth rate (2008):	4.6%
GDP per capita (2008):	$4,674 U.S.
Goods exported:	Clothing, food, iron and steel, petroleum products, tobacco, wine
Goods imported:	Automobiles, chemicals, crude oil, food, iron and steel, machinery
Trading partners:	Bulgaria, Germany, Greece, Italy, Russia, Serbia

A country of towering mountains and broad plains, Macedonia is bordered by Kosovo, Serbia, Bulgaria, Greece, and Albania. Skopje is the capital and largest city.

Grapes grow in a vineyard near Skopje. Wine is an important product in Macedonian agriculture.

that followed World War I (1914-1918) divided Macedonia among three nations. The largest region became part of the new Kingdom of the Serbs, Croats, and Slovenes, which later changed its name to Yugoslavia. Smaller sections of Macedonia went to Greece and Bulgaria.

During World War II (1939-1945), Axis forces invaded and occupied Yugoslavia. Macedonia was partitioned between Bulgaria and Albania, both allies of the Axis powers. The section given to Albania became part of Greater Albania, a state created by Italian dictator Benito Mussolini. After World War II, when Yugoslavia became a federal republic under Communist rule, the section of Macedonia in Yugoslavia became the Republic of Macedonia, one of six Yugoslav republics. Funding from Yugoslavia's government helped build new roads, the tourist trade, and heavy industry.

Macedonia declared its independence in 1991, but tension surrounded the newly independent nation. Greece opposed recognition of the new country because it regarded the use of the name *Macedonia* as a claim to some of its territory. Also, Macedonia feared it might be

drawn into the conflict between other former Yugoslav states. The United Nations sent troops to protect the country in late 1992.

In 1993, Macedonia and Greece reached a compromise allowing Macedonia to join the United Nations under the temporary name of the Former Yugoslav Republic of Macedonia. However, in 2008, Macedonia was denied membership in the North Atlantic Treaty Organization (NATO) because the conflict with Greece over its name had not been resolved.

In February 2001, Albanian rebels began fighting for greater equality for Albanians in Macedonia. After negotiations failed, the Macedonian government attacked rebel-held villages. Later that year, after a peace accord had been signed and the rebels had been disarmed, Macedonia's Assembly approved a constitution that granted the Albanians greater rights.

Many Macedonian people make their living as farmers, growing apples, grapes, tobacco, vegetables, and wheat. Farmers also raise cattle, hogs, poultry, and sheep. The republic is rich in mineral resources, including chromium, copper, iron ore, lead, manganese, uranium, and zinc.

MADAGASCAR

The country of Madagascar is made up of one large island off the east coast of Africa and a number of small nearby islands. The large island, also called Madagascar, is the fourth largest island in the world.

Cool, temperate highlands make up much of the island of Madagascar. Central Madagascar consists of plateaus and hills that rise 2,000 to 4,000 feet (610 to 1,200 meters) and some mountains that are even higher. In the north, Maromokotro rises more than 9,000 feet (2,800 meters) above sea level.

Much of the highland region has been *deforested* (cleared of its trees), and therefore much of the soil has eroded. This region has the densest population, however, and the capital city of Antananarivo is located in the highlands. Because of its altitude, temperatures at Antananarivo range from 50° to 67° F (13° to 19° C).

The mountains separate northern Madagascar, which has some of the country's richest soil, from the rest of the island. Southern Madagascar is mainly desert, and people of isolated southern tribes often wear little clothing in the hot, dry climate.

Western Madagascar has wide plains, some fertile river valleys, and a fairly sheltered coast. Eastern Madagascar, on the other hand, is a narrow plain, and offshore reefs and storms make the east coast dangerous for ships. Both coasts are warm and humid.

About three-fourths of Madagascar's people make their living as farmers and herders. Rice is their chief food crop. Cassava, bananas and other fruits, and vegetables such as sweet potatoes are also grown for their own use. Cattle, which are raised for both beef and milk, are the country's most important livestock.

A fisherman angles for his dinner in a peaceful Madagascar setting. Fish is an occasional dish for the islanders. But rice, vegetables, and fruit form the basis of the people's diet.

Cloves, coffee, and vanilla are among Madagascar's most valuable exports. The country is one of the world's leading producers of cloves and vanilla

The country has a few valuable mineral resources. Bauxite, chromite, coal, graphite, and some semiprecious stones are mined.

Madagascar's few industries process the country's agricultural products—hides, meat, sisal, and sugar—for export. During the 1970's, military leaders took control of certain kinds of businesses. But since 1983, the government has reduced its role in the national economy.

Most of the roads that link the chief towns and cities of Madagascar are unpaved, and many are badly rutted and impassable during the rainy season. In the desert of southern Madagascar, people often use cattle, such as zebu, to haul heavy wooden carts loaded with goods.

Grassy hills make up much of the highland landscape of central Madagascar. The highlands were once forested, but the trees were cut down, and the soil has eroded.

Mahajanga on the west coast and Toamasina on the east coast are the leading seaports. Ships that need to sail along the dangerous east coast can use the Ampanalana Canal, which runs between Mahavelona and Farafangana.

Tourism is not a major source of income in Madagascar, but the island has much to attract visitors. For example, Madagascar has distinctive plants and animals that are found nowhere else except on the nearby Comoros Islands. The island also offers travelers a fascinating glimpse of a unique culture. Local people practice traditional religions that include the worship of ancestors and spirits, cattle sacrifices, and ceremonies at the tombs of family members.

Woven mats are offered for sale at a street market. Market days are a popular part of life in Antananarivo, the capital city, and other Madagascar towns.

Balconied apartments and a church stand side by side in a highland town. Many houses in the country are several stories high and built of brick, with tile or thatched roofs.

MADAGASCAR TODAY

Madagascar's population is made up mostly of farmers or herders of either African or Indonesian descent. About half of the people worship ancestors and spirits according to traditional African religious beliefs. About 40 percent of the people practice Christianity, and most of the rest are Muslims. Madagascar has three official languages—English, French, and Malagasy.

Government

In August 1992, Madagascar's voters approved a new constitution. The Constitution provided for a two-tier legislature, made up of a National Assembly and a Senate. The National Assembly is elected under a system of proportional representation to serve four-year terms. The president is elected to a five-year term. The prime minister, the head of government, is appointed by the president.

Historical background

Madagascar was settled by Indonesians who sailed across the Indian Ocean from the east—a migration that started before the time of Christ and continued until the A.D. 1400's. They settled in the central highlands of the large island. Immigrants from the African mainland and the Arabian Peninsula settled along the coasts.

Madagascar was a favorite base for pirates in the 1600's and 1700's, including the notorious Scottish pirate known as Captain Kidd.

Many kingdoms developed on what is now Madagascar. But in the early 1800's, the Merina kingdom, whose people were of Indonesian descent, gained control of most of the island. Radama I, who became king in 1810, outlawed the foreign slave trade, but kept many of his own people in slavery.

FACTS

Official name:	Republique de Madagascar (Republic of Madagascar)
Capital:	Antananarivo
Terrain:	Narrow coastal plain, high plateau and mountains in center
Area:	226,658 mi² (587,041 km²)
Climate:	Tropical along coast, temperate inland, arid in south
Main rivers:	Betsiboka, Mangoky
Highest elevation:	Maromokotro, 9,436 ft (2,876 m)
Lowest elevation:	Indian Ocean, sea level
Form of government:	Republic
Head of state:	President
Head of government:	Prime minister
Administrative areas:	6 faritany (provinces)
Legislature:	Assemblee Nationale (National Assembly) with 127 members serving four-year terms and Senat (Senate) with 100 members serving four-year terms
Court system:	Cour Supreme (Supreme Court), Haute Cour Constitutionnelle (High Constitutional Court)
Armed forces:	13,500 troops
National holiday:	Independence Day - June 26 (1960)
Estimated 2010 population:	21,200,000
Population density:	94 persons per mi² (36 per km²)
Population distribution:	70% rural, 30% urban
Life expectancy in years:	Male, 59; female, 62
Doctors per 1,000 people:	0.3
Birth rate per 1,000:	38
Death rate per 1,000:	10
Infant mortality:	70 deaths per 1,000 live births
Age structure:	0-14: 44%; 15-64: 53%; 65 and over: 3%
Internet users per 100 people:	1.7
Internet code:	.mg
Languages spoken:	English, French, Malagasy (all official)
Religions:	Indigenous beliefs 52%, Christian 41%, Muslim 7%
Currency:	Ariary
Gross domestic product (GDP) in 2008:	$9.25 billion U.S.
Real annual growth rate (2008):	7.0%
GDP per capita (2008):	$493 U.S.
Goods exported:	Clothing, cloves, coffee, petroleum products, shellfish, vanilla
Goods imported:	Cotton, food, machinery, petroleum products, textile yarn, transportation equipment
Trading partners:	China, France, South Africa, United States

English and French traders and missionaries brought European influences to the island. After 1869, the French expanded their political influence on the island. Conflicts broke out between the French and the Merina. The French forces gained control, and France made all of Madagascar a French colony in 1896.

France granted the people of Madagascar some self-rule after World War II (1939-1945). Full independence was finally granted in 1960. However, French influence remained strong in the country, which was called the Malagasy Republic.

In May 1972, demonstrations caused elected President Philibert Tsiranana to resign. A series of military rulers took over the government as well as important parts of the country's economy. In late 1975, the military government under Didier Ratsiraka changed the name of the nation to Madagascar.

In 1977, the nation became a republic again as the people elected a legislature. In 1982, they elected Ratsiraka president. They reelected him in a one-party election in 1989. In 1991, protests against the government and general strikes led to the dissolution of the government. Although Ratsiraka remained in office, he was forced to share power with members of the opposition. In 1993, Albert Zafy, the leader of the opposition, was elected to replace Ratsiraka.

In 1996, Zafy resigned after the National Assembly impeached him on charges that he had engaged in unconstitutional acts. Ratsiraka was reelected president in a special election. After a violently disputed election that led to a vote recount, Marc Ravalomanana, former mayor of Antananarivo, succeeded Ratsiraka as president in 2002.

In early 2009, public resentment against Ravalomanana led to rioting. Andry Rajoelina, the mayor of Antananarivo, led calls for Ravalomanana to resign. A group of military officers loyal to Rajoelina seized the president's office, and Ravalomanana stepped down. The military gained control of the country and installed Rajoelina as president.

Madagascar is an African country with one big island and many tiny ones. The largest island, also called Madagascar, is the world's fourth largest island.

Mud brick houses are spread out in Highland Madagascar. The region is dominated by grasslands, rice paddies, farms, and stands of pine or eucalyptus trees.

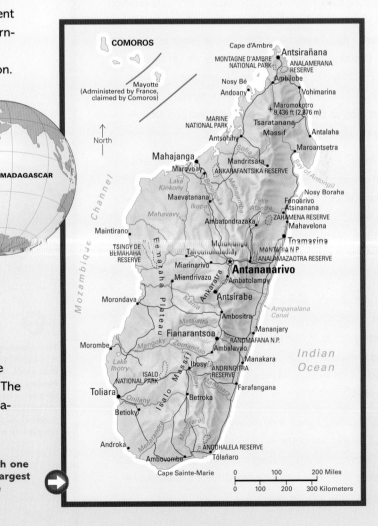

WILDLIFE

The huge island of Madagascar is home to unusual wildlife. In fact, many of Madagascar's animals and plants are found nowhere else in the world except the nearby Comoros Islands. This makes the island a unique resource for biologists and other scientists. However, Madagascar is also home to more than 21 million people, and that number is expected to increase rapidly in the near future. As a result, much of this remarkable wildlife is at risk.

Madagascar was once part of the African mainland. About 125 million years ago, the piece of land that became Madagascar broke away and drifted north and east. The water that separates the island from the African mainland, now a passage 240 miles (386 kilometers) wide, prevented most mainland animals from spreading to Madagascar and most Madagascar animals from spreading to the mainland.

In the process of *evolution,* groups of animals change over time as they adapt to changes in their environment. The animals on Madagascar changed in isolation and developed in different ways from the animals on mainland Africa. For example, the absence of competition from monkeys and large predators allowed animals called *lemurs* to evolve from an animal that died out almost everywhere else.

The size of the island and the variety of weather conditions there permitted the development of numerous unique species of plants and animals. A listing of Madagascar's wildlife includes about 1,000 species of orchids, almost all of them native only to Madagascar; hundreds of species of moths and butterflies; half of the world's species of chameleons; and about 20 species of lemurs.

Scientists classify lemurs as primates, together with monkeys, apes, and human beings. On Madagascar, lemurs range in size from the 2-ounce (57-gram) gray mouse lemur—the world's smallest primate—to the black-and-white indri, weighing about 20 pounds (9 kilograms).

All but the ring-tailed lemur travel in trees rather than on land. The indri and the sifaka can cover more than 30 feet (9 meters) in a single leap from one tree trunk to another. Some lemurs are nocturnal; others are *diurnal*—that is, active during the day.

A variety of lemurs occupy a number of habitats in Madagascar—from the southern desert to the warm, humid coastal areas to the cool, forested highlands. Lemurs vary greatly in size, color, and appearance. Some, for instance, resemble monkeys, while others are more like mice or squirrels.

Verreaux's sifaka
Propithecus verreaux

Ring-tailed lemur
Lemur catta

The elephant bird was a giant flightless bird that once lived on Madagascar. The largest elephant bird stood about 10 feet (3 meters) high. The species is now extinct.

The ring-tailed lemur is one of the most common species of lemur.

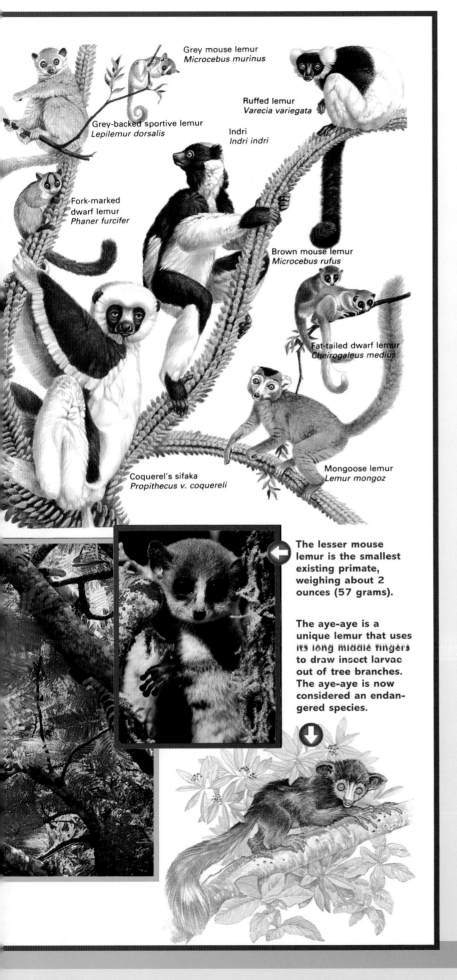

Grey mouse lemur
Microcebus murinus

Ruffed lemur
Varecia variegata

Grey-backed sportive lemur
Lepilemur dorsalis

Indri
Indri indri

Fork-marked
dwarf lemur
Phaner furcifer

Brown mouse lemur
Microcebus rufus

Fat-tailed dwarf lemur
Cheirogaleus medius

Coquerel's sifaka
Propithecus v. coquereli

Mongoose lemur
Lemur mongoz

The lesser mouse lemur is the smallest existing primate, weighing about 2 ounces (57 grams).

The aye-aye is a unique lemur that uses its long middle fingers to draw insect larvae out of tree branches. The aye-aye is now considered an endangered species.

Some lemurs—such as the ring-tailed and ruffed lemurs—resemble monkeys. Others—for example, the lesser mouse lemur—are more like mice. The aye-aye lemur plays the ecological role that woodpeckers play elsewhere, eating insect larvae that it digs out of tree branches.

Madagascar's lemurs have few natural enemies because the island has few large predators. Today, however, many species are endangered, mainly because people have cut down so many trees to build villages, to clear farmland, or to harvest timber. The rain forest on the east side of the island is shrinking. There and in other regions of Madagascar, the lemurs' habitat is disappearing.

Without its forest or grass cover, *erosion*—the wearing away of the fertile top layer of soil—is occurring rapidly. If this destruction of vegetation is left unchecked, not only lemur species but also other unique animals may become extinct.

Human destruction of animal habitats has already caused the extinction of several of Madagascar's animals, including a lemur the size of an orangutan, giant tortoises with shells 4 feet (1.2 meters) long, a pygmy hippopotamus, and the elephant bird.

The elephant bird was huge—up to 10 feet (3 meters) high and weighing about 1,000 pounds (450 kilograms). Seven species of the elephant bird were widespread on Madagascar when people first arrived about 2,000 years ago. These birds probably became extinct about 1,000 years ago. Old legends tell of a giant bird called a roc, and some people think that the legends were based on the elephant bird.

The people and government of Madagascar have long recognized the importance of the island's wildlife both to science and to their own economy. The hunting of lemurs has been illegal since 1927, and the country has many wildlife preserves.

Since the 1980's, more attention has been given to the problem. In 1984, the government established a National Conservation Strategy. Its goals include educating the population about the need for conservation, restoring woodlands, eliminating soil erosion, and protecting endangered animals.

MALAWI

Malawi *(mah LAH wee)*, a small nation in southeastern Africa, is a poor country, but one that is rich in natural beauty. Several lakes, including deep blue Lake Nyasa, lie in the Great Rift Valley that runs the length of Malawi from north to south. West of Lake Nyasa, the land rises steeply to a plateau. Grasslands and *savannas* (grassy plains with scattered trees) cover much of the region, but hardwood forests stretch across the northwest.

The country's landscape is partly responsible for its poverty. Malawi's economy is based on agriculture, yet its mountains, forests, and infertile pastures cover so much of the land that only about one-third of the area can be farmed. Also, frequent droughts and floods destroy a significant portion of crops—especially in the south—each year. Malawi has no important mineral deposits and very little industry. A few factories produce bricks, cement, cotton goods, and processed foods. The government has tried to encourage foreign investment and aid.

Although little of the land is farmed, Malawi has areas of rich volcanic soil—perfect for growing tea, one of the nation's most important export crops. The tea is grown on highland plantations owned by Europeans. Malawi farmers also grow a variety of other crops, including corn, cotton, peanuts, sorghum, sugar cane, and tobacco. Many farmers raise livestock too, and some people fish for a living. Women raise most of the food crops and men raise crops for sale, but this situation is changing.

Women have a special position in Malawi society. In most Western traditions, the father is the head of the family, and descent is determined through him. But most people in Malawi determine descent through the mother. Couples often establish their households near the wife's family.

Most of Malawi's people are Africans who belong to Bantu groups. The leading Bantu ethnic groups include the Chewa (Cewa), Lomwe, Ngoni (Angoni), Nyanja, Sena, Tonga, Tumbuka, and Yao. Chichewa and English are the official languages of

FACTS

Official name:	Republic of Malawi
Capital:	Lilongwe
Terrain:	Narrow elongated plateau with rolling plains, rounded hills, some mountains
Area:	45,747 mi² (118,484 km²)
Climate:	Sub-tropical; rainy season (November to May); dry season (May to November)
Main rivers:	Shire, Bua
Highest elevation:	Sapitwa, 9,843 ft (3,000 m)
Lowest elevation:	Junction of the Shire River and Mozambique boundary, 121 ft (37 m)
Form of government:	Republic
Head of state:	President
Head of government:	President
Administrative areas:	28 districts
Legislature:	National Assembly with 193 members serving five-year terms
Court system:	Supreme Court of Appeal, High Court, magistrate's courts
Armed forces:	5,300 troops
National holiday:	Independence Day (Republic Day) - June 6 (1964)
Estimated 2010 population:	14,735,000
Population density:	322 persons per mi² (124 per km²)
Population distribution:	82% rural, 18% urban
Life expectancy in years:	Male, 45; female, 45
Doctors per 1,000 people:	Less than 0.05
Birth rate per 1,000:	41
Death rate per 1,000:	16
Infant mortality:	80 deaths per 1,000 live births
Age structure:	0-14: 46%; 15-64: 51%; 65 and over: 3%
Internet users per 100 people:	2
Internet code:	.mw
Languages spoken:	English (official), Chichewa (official), regional languages
Religions:	Christian 79.9%, Muslim 12.8%, other 7.3%
Currency:	Malawian kwacha
Gross domestic product (GDP) in 2008:	$4.27 billion U.S.
Real annual growth rate (2008):	6.5%
GDP per capita (2008):	$313 U.S.
Goods exported:	Clothing, cotton, sugar, tea, tobacco
Goods imported:	Fertilizers, machinery, motor vehicles, petroleum products
Trading partners:	Mozambique, South Africa, United Kingdom, United States

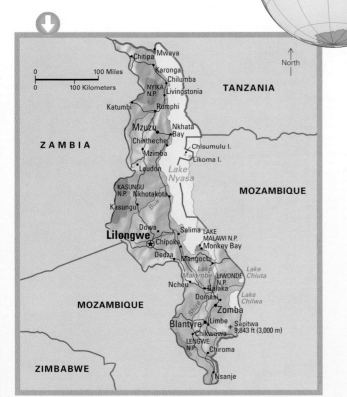

Malawi is a country in southeastern Africa. It is 520 miles (837 kilometers) long but only 50 to 100 miles (80 to 160 kilometers) wide. Although land-locked, it lies on the western shore of Lake Nyasa, which is also known as Lake Malawi.

Fishermen prepare to launch their canoes on Lake Chilwa. Freshwater fishing on Malawi's lakes, especially Lake Nyasa, contributes to the diet of the people of this poor country, where only about a third of the land is suitable for farming. Fishing has also become an important industry in Malawi.

the country, but most people in central and southern Malawi speak Nyanja and Yao. Tumbuka is spoken by most people in the north.

Bantu-speaking people began living in the region about 2,000 years ago, and some formed kingdoms—including the Kingdom of Malawi, which was established during the 1500's. In the 1830's, two other Bantu groups, the Ngoni and the Yao, invaded the area. The Yao were slave traders who sold African slaves to the Arabs.

When the Scottish missionary David Livingstone reached the area in 1859, he found it torn by local wars and the suffering caused by the slave trade. To help bring peace, the Free Church of Scotland set up a mission in the area. To replace the slave trade, Scottish businessmen tried to introduce businesses there. In 1889, the British made treaties with the local chiefs, and two years later the United Kingdom proclaimed the area the Protectorate of Nyasaland.

In 1958, Hastings Kamuzu Banda, a physician educated in the United States, became the leader of an independence movement in the protectorate. In 1964, Nyasaland gained independence as the nation of Malawi. A new constitution, adopted in 1966, made Malawi a republic, and Banda was declared president.

In 1993, Banda was forced to hold a referendum on one-party rule, and voters approved the legalization of all political parties. In 1994, he was defeated in the country's first multiparty elections. Bakili Muluzi, leader of the United Democratic Front (UDF), became Malawi's new president. He was reelected in 1999.

In 2004, Bingu wa Mutharika of the UDF was elected president. He was reelected in 2009 but died in office in April 2012. Vice President Joyce Banda (no relation to Kamuzu Banda), a longtime women's rights activist and founder of the People's Party, became Malawi's first woman president.

MALAYSIA

Malaysia is a tropical land rich in natural resources. One of the world's largest producers of natural rubber, tin, and palm oil, Malaysia also has deposits of petroleum and natural gas, bauxite, copper, gold, and iron ore. Large amounts of timber come from the nation's dense rain forests. Because of its abundant resources, Malaysia has one of the strongest economies in Southeast Asia.

About 28 million people live in Malaysia. Malaysia's population is racially and ethnically diverse. Malays make up more than half of the country's population. The Chinese and Indians also form major ethnic groups. Malaysia's ethnic groups speak different languages or dialects, and, in many areas, have different ways of life. Although Malays are the most powerful group in Malaysian politics, the Chinese control much of the nation's economy. Social, economic, and political differences between the Chinese and Malays have led to friction—and sometimes violence.

Malaysia consists of two regions about 400 miles (640 kilometers) apart, separated by the South China Sea. Peninsular Malaysia, the smaller region, lies on the southern part of the Malay Peninsula. The other part consists of two states called Sarawak and Sabah along the northern and northwestern coasts of the island of Borneo and the small island territory of Labuan off the coast of Sabah. Peninsular Malaysia has many bustling cities, their narrow streets crowded with motor vehicles. The region also has large rural areas where people live in thatch-roofed houses built on stilts. Sarawak and Sabah is mainly rural.

Many Malays in the rural areas of the peninsula live in settlements called *kampongs* and work as farmers. Malays who live in cities usually have jobs in industry or in government. Most of Malaysia's Chinese people live in the cities and work in stores, banks, or offices. Wealthy and middle-class Chinese live in high-rise apartments in downtown areas or in comfortable suburban homes. The people of Sarawak and Sabah generally live in small rural settlements. Several families often live together in *long houses* along rivers. Many of these farmers are barely able to produce enough food for their families.

Kuala Lumpur, the capital and largest city of Malaysia, attracts many tourists. The eastern part of the city has high-rise buildings, small shops, a busy outdoor market, and many beautiful *mosques* (Muslim houses of worship). It is also home to the Petronas Twin Towers, which are among the tallest buildings in the world.

Malaysia has a good road system. Most people in Malaysia travel by bus or shared taxi. Railroads link Kuala Lumpur with Singapore and with Bangkok, Thailand. Kuala Lumpur, Kota Kinabalu, Kuching, and Pinang Island have international airports.

MALAYSIA TODAY

Beginning in the 1500's, the area that is now Malaysia was controlled, in turn, by the Portuguese, the Dutch, and the British. These European nations wanted colonies in Southeast Asia—as in other parts of the world—for economic benefits. They hoped to expand their industry and trade by gaining sources of raw materials and markets for their goods. They also wanted strategic locations from which to control trade.

The road to independence

At the same time European powers struggled for economic control of the area, they brought economic development by introducing Western agricultural, industrial, and medical techniques. For example, the first seedlings for rubber trees were brought from the United Kingdom in the 1870's; roads, railroads, hospitals, and schools were built toward the end of the 1800's; and efforts to conquer malaria began in the early 1900's. Still, after World War II (1939-1945) and the Japanese occupation of Malaysia, the people began to demand better economic and social conditions and started to work toward independence.

In 1948, the states on the Malay Peninsula, plus Pinang, united to form the Federation of Malaya, a partially independent territory under British protection. During the late 1940's and 1950's, rebel groups on the peninsula fought the British. The conflict ended when the Federation of Malaya gained complete independence in 1957.

In 1963, Malaya, Singapore, and what is now Sarawak and Sabah united and formed the new independent nation of Malaysia. Singapore, however, withdrew from Malaysia in 1965 to become an independent country.

FACTS

Official name:	Malaysia
Capital:	Kuala Lumpur
Terrain:	Coastal plains rising to hills and mountains
Area:	127,355 mi² (329,847 km²)
Climate:	Tropical; annual southwest (April to October) and northeast (October to February) monsoon
Main rivers:	Kelantan, Perak, Pahang, Kinabatangan, Rajang
Highest elevation:	Mount Kinabalu, 13,431 ft (4,094 m)
Lowest elevation:	Indian Ocean, sea level
Form of government:	Constitutional monarchy
Head of state:	King
Head of government:	Prime minister
Administrative areas:	13 negeri-negeri (states), 1 wilayah persekutuan (federal territory)
Legislature:	Parlimen (Parliament) consisting of Dewan Negara (Senate) with 70 members serving three-year terms and the Dewan Rakyat (House of Representatives) with 222 members serving five-year terms
Court system:	Federal Court
Armed forces:	109,000 troops
National holiday:	Independence Day (Malaysia Day) - August 31 (1957)
Estimated 2010 population:	27,942,000
Population density:	219 persons per mi² (85 per km²)
Population distribution:	68% urban, 32% rural
Life expectancy in years:	Male, 71; female, 76
Doctors per 1,000 people:	0.7
Birth rate per 1,000:	21
Death rate per 1,000:	5
Infant mortality:	10 deaths per 1,000 live births
Age structure:	0-14: 31%; 15-64: 64%; 65 and over: 5%
Internet users per 100 people:	63
Internet code:	.my
Languages spoken:	Bahasa Malaysia (official), English, Chinese dialects, Tamil, indigenous languages
Religions:	Muslim 60.4%, Buddhist 19.2%, Christian 9.1%, Hindu 6.3%, other (including Confucianism and Taoism) 5%
Currency:	Ringgit
Gross domestic product (GDP) in 2008:	$214.70 billion U.S.
Real annual growth rate (2008):	5.1%
GDP per capita (2008):	$7,800 U.S.
Goods exported:	Electrical and electronic products, palm oil, petroleum and liquefied natural gas, rubber and rubber products, wood products
Goods imported:	Chemicals, electronics, iron and steel, machinery, petroleum and petroleum products, plastics, transportation equipment
Trading partners:	China, Japan, Singapore, United States

Since independence

In 1969, bloody riots broke out after an election on Peninsular Malaysia. The government declared a state of emergency, suspending the Constitution and Parliament until 1971.

After the riots, Malaysia's political leaders tried to build national unity and determined to improve the economic conditions of the Malays. They launched an economic plan to achieve a better balance of wealth among racial groups.

In 1981, Mahathir bin Mohamad became prime minister of Malaysia. Malaysia's economy grew rapidly under Mahathir during the 1980's and early 1990's. In the late 1990's, an economic crisis spread throughout Southeast Asia. The growth of Malaysia's economy slowed somewhat, but Malaysia took measures to put its economy back on track.

In 2003, Mahathir stepped down as prime minister, and his deputy prime minister, Abdullah bin Ahmad Badawi, took over as prime minister. In 2009, Abdullah was succeeded by his deputy, Najib Razak.

Today, Malaysia is a constitutional monarchy. A Parliament makes the country's laws. A prime minister serves as the top government official and selects a Cabinet to help carry out the operations of the government. The king, called the *yang di-pertuan agong,* serves as head of state, but his duties are largely ceremonial.

Kuala Lumpur is the capital and largest city of Malaysia. It lies along both banks of the Klang River on Peninsular Malaysia. Its mixture of Moorish architecture, Dutch and English colonial architecture, and modern high-rise buildings are testaments of the city's colorful history.

Malaysia is made up of two main regions separated by the South China Sea. Peninsular Malaysia, the southern part of the Southeast Asian mainland, has the smaller land area. Sarawak and Sabah, on the northwest coast of Borneo, is the larger part of Malaysia.

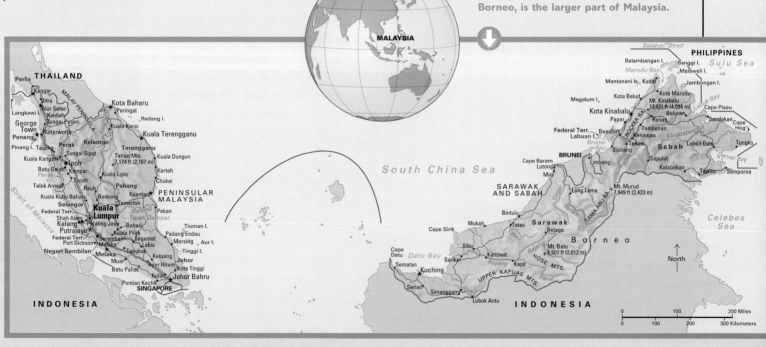

ENVIRONMENT

Peninsular Malaysia comprises the cities of Kuala Lumpur and Putrajaya and 11 small states, with a total area of 50,810 square miles (131,598 square kilometers). Two much larger states—Sarawak and Sabah—lie on the island of Borneo. Sarawak covers 48,050 square miles (124,449 square kilometers). Sabah—including the small island of Labuan, which is administered separately as part of the Federal Territory of Malaysia—covers 28,460 square miles (73,711 square kilometers).

Malaysia holds a strategic position along the Strait of Malacca, a major commercial route between the Indian and Pacific oceans. Malaysia's location—which has shaped the country's cultural identity, economy, history, and religion for centuries—guarantees the nation a key role in the affairs of modern Southeast Asia.

Both parts of Malaysia have tropical climates. Coastal temperatures usually stay between 70° and 90° F (21° and 32° C). About 100 inches (250 centimeters) of rain falls annually in Peninsular Malaysia, while Sarawak and Sabah get about 150 inches (380 centimeters) each year.

Both parts of Malaysia have *monsoons*—winds that blow regularly in the same direction during definite seasons. Monsoons from the northeast pass through Southeast Asia from November to March, ushering in cooler weather. However, beginning in April, monsoons from the southwest bring extremely hot temperatures. From May to October, wet monsoons bring heavy rains from the south seas. Many of these monsoons cause floods, and some are so destructive that they ruin crops and livestock and disrupt the nation's economy.

A great variety of animals roam the Malaysian rain forests, including civets, deer, elephants, monkeys, tapirs, tigers, and wild oxen. The interior landscape includes lush groves of camphor, ebony, fig, mahogany, rubber, and sandalwood trees, while mangrove and palm trees line the swampy coastal area.

Tropical rain forests blanket Mount Kinabslu in Sabah, the highest peak in Malaysia at 13,431 feet (4,094 meters). From its peaks, climbers can see the Philippines across the South China Sea.

Graceful palm trees sway above a traditional village on Penninsular Malaysia's swampy northeast coast. The wooden houses are built on stilts to protect them from flooding.

Peninsular Malaysia

Mountains covered with dense tropical rain forests run along the center of Peninsular Malaysia from north to south. Rugged limestone hills on both sides of the mountain range slope down to low, swampy plains on the coasts.

Most of Peninsular Malaysia's cities and major seaports, including George Town, Kuala Lumpur, and Melaka, are located along the Strait of Malacca. The lowland that covers parts of the region east of the mountains is

This peaceful beach lies on the island of Kuah in the Langkawi island group. Malaysia holds a strategic position along the strait of Malacca, a major commercial route between the Indian and Pacific oceans.

only about 5 miles (8 kilometers) wide in some areas and flooded with swamps and lagoons in other areas, making it a difficult region to live in or to develop.

Tropical rain forests cover much of the area east of the mountains. Major rivers of Peninsular Malaysia include the Kelantan, Perak, and Pahang.

Sarawak and Sabah

This eastern region of Malaysia covers most of the northern part of Borneo. Much of the coastal area along the South China Sea is low and swampy, while inland areas are mountainous and covered with rain forests. Mount Kinabalu, the highest peak in Malaysia, rises 13,431 feet (4,094 meters) in Sabah.

The area's extensive river systems include the Kinabatangan, the longest river in Sabah, and the Rajang. Shallow-draft vessels, such as rafts and scows, can travel up to 100 miles (160 kilometers) inland on these rivers. The entrances to many rivers and ports, however, are obstructed by deposits of soil, sand, or clay.

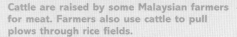

Cattle are raised by some Malaysian farmers for meat. Farmers also use cattle to pull plows through rice fields.

Batu Caves north of Kuala Lumpur are formed out of limestone. One of these caves, known as the "cathedral," serves as the setting for an annual Hindu ceremony.

PEOPLE

The Malays are the largest ethnic group in Malaysia. Most Malays speak Bahasa Malaysia, the country's official language. In addition, most are Muslims—followers of Islam, the country's official religion.

Many of the Malay people live in rural areas on the peninsula. Many Malay men and women, especially in rural areas, wear a *sarong,* a traditional length of cloth wrapped around the body as a skirt. Others, however, wear Western clothing.

The ancestors of the Malays migrated to Southeast Asia from southern China thousands of years ago. Malay people value social harmony, courtesy, and respect for authority. They are known as *bumiputras,* or sons of the soil, and their importance to the nation has been recognized in the Constitution. For example, only a Malay can become *yang diper-tuan agong* (king and head of state) or prime minister.

The Chinese are Malaysia's second largest ethnic group. Chinese people began to arrive on the peninsula in large numbers in the 1850's to work in the tin mines. As their

An Iban, or Sea Dayak, holds the skull of an enemy killed by one of his ancestors. He stands outside a village long house in which many families live, each in a separate room.

numbers grew, so did their need for services, and adventurous Chinese started businesses that catered to the needs of new arrivals. Gradually, they began to control the nation's economy. The Chinese also developed their own school system, focusing on traditional Chinese subjects. Today, most Chinese in Malaysia still use the Chinese language and follow Buddhism, Confucianism, or Taoism.

The critical differences between the Malays and the Chinese involving language, religion, race, and social position have caused racial tensions, which led to rioting in 1969 and 1987. The Malays resent the superior

Two Malay boys cycle to a kite-flying contest on the east coast of Peninsular Malaysia. The bamboo-and-paper kites used in the contest can reach a height of more than 1,475 feet (450 meters).

economic and social position of the Chinese, while the Chinese believe that the government favors the Malays.

Indians are the third major ethnic group. In Malaysia, the term *Indian* includes people from Pakistan and Sri Lanka, as well as those from India. Many Indians are employed on plantations, or work as merchants, money lenders, or white-collar workers.

A group of people called the *Dayaks* live mainly in Sarawak. The *Sea Dayaks,* or *Ibans,* who make up about 30 percent of Sarawak's population, live along the seacoast and rivers. The *Land Dayaks*—about 8 percent of the population—live inland and call themselves by the name of their village or locality. Most Dayaks are farmers or plantation workers, and their major crop is rice. A majority of the people in this group follow traditional religions, but some are Christians or Muslims.

Ceramic tiles such as those that decorate the entrance to this house in Melaka, are a legacy of Dutch rule. The Dutch took Melaka from the Portuguese in 1641 but lost it to the British in the late 1700's.

Bukit Bintang (Star Hill) is a shopping and entertainment district in Kuala Lumpur. The area includes shopping centers, cafes, clubs, and shops.

ECONOMY

From the mid-1970's to the mid-1990's, Malaysia had one of the strongest economies in Southeast Asia. The Malaysian economy slowed somewhat in the late 1990's, but Malaysia took measures that put its economy back on track. The Malaysian economy depends heavily on the production of petroleum, rubber, timber, and tin, but the country also produces a variety of farm crops and manufactured goods.

Vital markets

In the 1970's, Malaysia was primarily an exporter of raw commodities such as timber, rubber, tin, and palm oil. It still produces these goods, but they play a smaller role in Malaysia's economy.

Much of the country's wealth now comes from manufacturing. The Malaysian electronics industry has been a major success, and Malaysia is a leading producer of integrated circuits and other semiconductor devices. Electronic products are now one of the country's leading export products. Malaysia has also established its own automobile industry.

Malaysia still produces tin; *bauxite* (aluminum ore); copper; gold; iron ore; and *ilmenite,* an ore that contains a valuable metal called *titanium.* In addition, petroleum and natural gas production has increased in Malaysia since the 1970's, and petroleum is now one of the country's chief exports.

The country's vast rain forests yield many valuable products, including aromatic woods, such as camphor and sandalwood, and beautiful hardwoods, such as ebony, mahogany, and teak. However, there has been worldwide concern about the destruction of these rain forests.

The powerful water buffalo makes large-scale rice farming possible in the states of Sarawak and Sabah and other parts of Asia. Although new varieties of rice and improved irrigation techniques have been introduced, Malaysia still cannot produce all the rice it needs to feed its people.

An oil refinery in the state of Terengganu opened in 2008 to produce and trade petroleum and petrochemical products. Petroleum is Malaysia's chief export.

A truck carries giant logs in the state of Sabah. Timber was a major export commodity in the mid-1900's, but the country derives much of its wealth today from manufacturing.

Rice, the nation's chief food crop, is grown on small farms throughout Malaysia. However, even with the introduction of new varieties of high-yield rice and improvements in drainage and irrigation, Malaysia cannot grow enough rice to feed its people. The nation's small farms also produce cacao, coconuts, pepper, pineapples, and vegetables. Some farmers raise cattle, chickens, and hogs for meat.

Economic planning

The continued prosperity of Malaysia's economy depends on its ability to strengthen its export markets. Malaysia has greatly increased its manufacturing to lessen its economic reliance on agriculture and mining

In 1970, the government of Malaysia instituted its New Economic Policy (NEP), a 20-year program intended to increase the participation of the Malays in the economy. The program has been only partially successful because of shortages of money for investment.

Malaysia belongs to the Association of Southeast Asian Nations (ASEAN), an organization of Southeast Asian countries that promotes economic, cultural, and social cooperation among its members. The organization also works to reduce trade barriers. In 1976, the member nations of ASEAN agreed to share basic products during shortages and to gradually remove trade restrictions, especially taxes on imports.

Along with other members of ASEAN, Malaysia has tried to attract international businesses. Foreign businesses in Malaysia receive generous tax breaks, duty-free export zones, and a relatively cheap labor force.

HISTORY

The community marketplace is one of Malaysia's great attractions—a meeting place for Chinese, Indians, and Malays, with elements of both the traditional and modern. Traditional Malaysian products include the famous *batik* cloth, elaborate metalwork, handcrafted bamboo items, and the marvelous kites that are flown in competitions. Adding color to the crowd are such exotic sights as snake charmers, dancing bears, and fortunetellers, as well as vendors of traditional Chinese folk medicines selling dried antler or preserved turtles.

The marketplace is a fitting introduction to a country whose history has been shaped by trade and by its location on the trade routes linking India and China. Chinese and Indian merchants used the peninsula as a stopping place for their ships 2,000 years ago. Here they found shelter from the monsoon winds and bought exotic goods ranging from gold and spices to aromatic woods and rhinoceros horn.

The impact of trade

Trade brought wealth to the region, and settlements sprang up along the coast. Some became thriving commercial areas, including Melaka, which developed into a major trading center in the early 1400's. In 1409, Melaka was declared a kingdom by the emperor of China.

Melaka owed much of its importance to its location and its ideal port. Melaka's rulers controlled the trade through the Strait of Malacca, and its harbor provided a safe place for ships to anchor. Melaka's rulers wisely kept their toll and customs charges reasonable. The "golden age" of Melaka lasted only a century, but it provided cultural heroes and enduring standards of ideal behavior for the Malays.

By 1509, the strategic importance of Melaka had attracted the attention of Portugal, and in 1511 its forces captured the town. To withstand rival powers, the Portuguese built a massive fort called *A Famosa* (The Famous One), which with-

stood enemy assaults for 130 years. In 1641, however, the Dutch stormed the fort and took Melaka, which they held for about 150 years.

In the late 1700's, traders from Great Britain (later called the United Kingdom) began setting up trading posts on the peninsula and nearby islands. Soon, British forces captured Melaka from the Dutch. They bombed A Famosa, and today only its great carved gateway stands as a reminder of the city's historic past.

In 1826, the British formed the Colony of the Straits Settlements, which included Melaka, the island of Pinang, and the island of Singapore. During the 1800's and early 1900's, the British

A Malay woman puts the finishing touches on a wau kite. These kites play an important part in Malaysian traditions and are often flown at festivals.

The State Mosque stands in Kuching on the shore of the Sarawak River in the state of Sarawak. Islam is the religion of almost all Malays.

gained control of the Malay states on the peninsula, as well as what is now Sarawak and Sabah. Like the Dutch and Portuguese before them, the British were more interested in gaining a strategic trade location than in acquiring territory. Their presence had a lasting impact on the country's economy.

Cultural imports

The Indian traders who visited the area 2,000 years ago had a tremendous effect on Malaysian culture. They brought political ideas and practices, art forms, and popular legends. Indian traders also introduced Hinduism, Buddhism, and Islam.

Everywhere in Malaysia today, there are reminders of other civilizations. Using Indian ideas of political organization, Southeast Asians in early trading communities began to organize settlements and villages into city-states and kingdoms. Over time, villagers who became citizens of these kingdoms and city-states were governed by rulers. These rulers claimed the profits of trade and justified the new arrangements by citing Hindu and Buddhist religious doctrines. Islam, which was spread throughout the Malay Peninsula and to other parts of Southeast Asia by Muslim merchants and scholars, is now Malaysia's state religion.

MALDIVES

The Maldives is a small, independent country that consists of about 1,200 small coral islands off the southwest coast of India. The islands form a chain 475 miles (764 kilometers) long and 80 miles (129 kilometers) wide in the Indian Ocean. None of the islands is larger than 5 square miles (13 square kilometers), and some are little more than small platforms about 6 feet (1.8 meters) above sea level. The Maldives's total land area is 115 square miles (298 square kilometers), making it the smallest independent country in Asia.

History

Little is known of the Maldives before the arrival of European traders in the 1500's. The Portuguese were the first to stake their claim on the islands, but the Dutch took control from 1656 to 1796. In 1887, the Maldives became a British protectorate. The Maldivians governed themselves, while the British conducted their foreign affairs.

The Maldives gained complete independence from the United Kingdom on July 26, 1965. In 1985, the Maldives and six other countries established the South Asian Association for Regional Cooperation (SAARC). This organization, which deals with social and economic issues, also helps the Maldives ensure their political neutrality.

In December 2004, a tsunami killed more than 80 people in the Maldives and caused enormous amounts of damage to property and natural resources.

Land and climate

The islands of the Maldives are grouped in clusters called *atolls*. Barrier reefs around the atolls protect the islands from the open sea. The climate is hot and humid. Daytime temperatures average about 80° F (27° C).

The islands are quite beautiful, with clear lagoons and white sand beaches. The land is covered with grasses and low-growing tropical plants. Coconut palms and fruit trees also grow on the islands. Tourists come from all over the world to see the coral and the dazzling fish that inhabit the islands' many reefs.

FACTS

Official name:	Dhivehi Raajjeyge Jumhooriyyaa (Republic of Maldives)
Capital:	Male
Terrain:	Flat, with white sandy beaches
Area:	115 mi² (298 km²)
Climate:	Tropical; hot, humid; dry, northeast monsoon (November to March); rainy, southwest monsoon (June to August)
Main rivers:	N/A
Highest elevation:	8 ft (2.4 m) on Wilingili Island
Lowest elevation:	Indian Ocean, sea level
Form of government:	Republic
Head of state:	President
Head of government:	President
Administrative city areas:	19 atholhu (atolls), 1 capital
Legislature:	Majlis (People's Council) with 77 members serving five-year terms
Court system:	Supreme Court
Armed forces:	N/A
National holiday:	Independence Day - July 26 (1965)
Estimated 2010 population:	322,000
Population density:	2,800 persons per mi² (1,081 per km²)
Population distribution:	73% rural, 27% urban
Life expectancy in years:	Male, 72; female, 75
Doctors per 1,000 people:	0.9
Birth rate per 1,000:	17
Death rate per 1,000:	4
Infant mortality:	23 deaths per 1,000 live births
Age structure:	0-14: 27%; 15-64: 68%; 65 and over: 5%
Internet users per 100 people:	24
Internet code:	.mv
Languages spoken:	Dhivehi (official), English
Religion:	Sunni Muslim
Currency:	Rufiyaa
Gross domestic product (GDP) in 2008:	$1.26 billion U.S.
Real annual growth rate (2008):	5.7%
GDP per capita (2008):	$4,023 U.S.
Goods exported:	Fish and fish products
Goods imported:	Construction materials, food, machinery, petroleum products, wood
Trading partners:	Singapore, Sri Lanka, Thailand

A view from the air shows the ring-shaped form of the Maldives's coral atolls. The bright white sand is a stunning contrast to the brilliant blue of the surrounding tropical waters. Scientists are concerned about the possible rise in sea level caused by global warming. Some experts believe that the Maldives may be underwater early in the next century. Many low-lying nations share this problem.

The islands that make up the Maldives are mostly uninhabited. About 17 percent of the people live in the capital city of Male, on Male Island. It is the country's political, cultural, and commercial center. Male has many mosques and a national museum that displays items from Arab, Dravidian, and Sri Lankan cultures.

People

The Maldivians live on only about 200 of the country's 1,200 islands. Most are descendants of Sinhalese people who came from Sri Lanka. Others claim the people of southern India and Arab traders and sailors as their ancestors. Almost all of the Maldivians are Sunni Muslims.

Many of the Maldivian men make their living as fishermen. Each day, thousands of men go out to sea in boats made of coconut or other timber. They use rods and reels to catch bonito, tuna, and other fish. Most of the fish is prepared for export. The people eat some fish as part of their diet, along with coconuts, papayas, pineapples, pomegranates, and sweet potatoes.

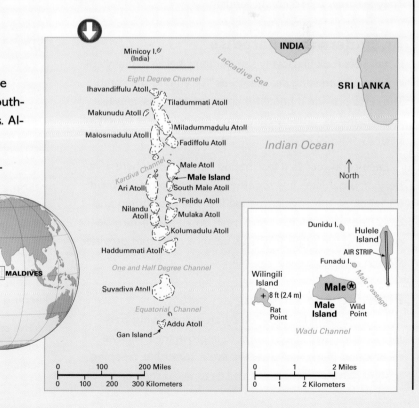

BENEATH THE MALDIVES

Coral islands are formed by the shells of tiny marine animals. The tropical waters of the Indian Ocean are an ideal environment for the formation of coral islands. The Maldives include some of the world's largest coral atolls. The atolls are home to a great variety of plant and animal life, including more species of plants and animals than any habitat on Earth except tropical rain forests.

How coral is formed

Coral is a limestone formation formed in the sea by millions of tiny animals. Individual coral animals are called *polyps*. They belong to the same animal group as hydras, jellyfish, and sea anemones. Most polyps have a cylinder-shaped body that is about 1 inch (2.5 centimeters) long. At one end is a mouth surrounded by small *tentacles* (feelers). The other end attaches to hard surfaces on the sea floor.

Most coral polyps live together in colonies. These formations can be seen in a variety of colors, including shades of tan, orange, yellow, purple, and green. When the animals die, they leave limestone "skeletons" that form the foundations of coral reefs. Sometimes these coral masses build up to the point where they rise above the water. They are then called coral islands.

An underwater paradise

Coral reefs look like lovely sea gardens, because many colorful and interesting sea creatures live among the coral. The reefs provide a home for sponges, sea fans, mussels, sea anemones, tube-dwelling worms, and a wide variety of brightly colored algae.

Each coral reef is a fascinating *ecosystem*, where a variety of organisms live together. Plankton provides food for much of the smaller marine life, such as shrimp and crab. These crustaceans and other small fish in turn become food for larger fish. This balance of nature provides enough food for every species.

Fighting for survival

In order to avoid being eaten by predators, living creatures constantly look for ways to improve their survival techniques. Many reef dwellers live a secret life, creeping around narrow cracks and crevices to avoid their enemies.

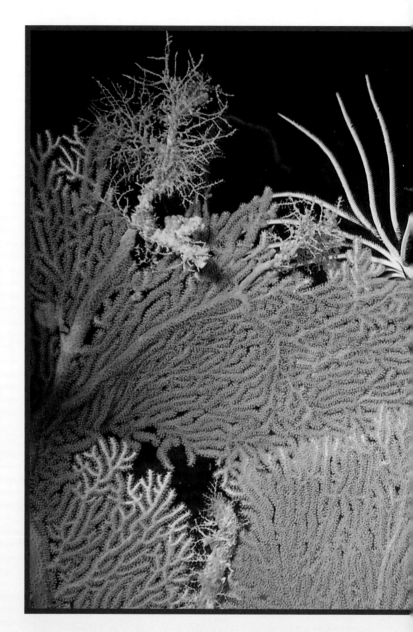

Some animals try to fool predators by changing their shape or color to blend in with the surroundings, or by developing bright colors and patterns. Still others form an alliance with another species. The clown fish, for example, finds safety among the sea anemone's stinging tentacles. Of course, their enemies also adapt themselves, thus keeping nature in balance.

The cracks, overhangs, and caves of the coral reef provide an ideal home for many kinds of fish. Some live by themselves, some live in pairs, and some live in large

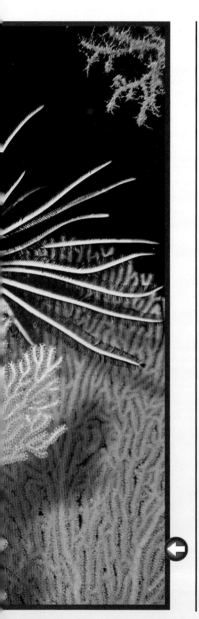

A flash photograph shows the natural colors of a crinoid, also known as a sea lily, as it perches on the leafy branches of a gorgonian coral. Millions of years ago, the crinoid was a thriving species, but only a few survive today.

A beautifully patterned starfish nestles on a coral formation. The starfish is a spiny sea animal with thick, armlike extensions on its body. Most species look like five-pointed stars but some have 40 "arms" or more.

The clown fish, found mainly in the Indian Ocean, uses large sea anemones for shelter. The stinging tentacles of the sea anemone can be fatal to other fish, but the clown fish comes and goes unharmed.

In the underwater world of the Maldives, a diver observes red sponges colonizing a group of dead coral. A sponge has ostia (pores) that allow water to enter its body. The water carries tiny plants and animals for the sponge to eat.

groups called *shoals*. Each group defends its territory against competitors for food.

Some fish are scavengers, cleaning food debris from the sea floor or attacking parasites attached to larger fish. Other species hide in cracks and openings until their prey comes too close. This technique is used by robber fish, moray eels, and many types of perch.

Larger fish in the open seas sometimes visit the coral reefs. Huge shoals of mackerel often appear, along with larger, more solitary fish like sharks and barracudas.

MALI

Mali is a large, landlocked country in western Africa. Today, it is a poor, thinly populated nation where droughts have killed many people and animals. However, Mali was once the site of powerful African empires.

A former colony of France, Mali is now an independent republic. According to its constitution, voters elect a president for a maximum of two terms. The president appoints a prime minister, who is the head of the government. The voters also elect the members of the National Assembly, the country's lawmaking body.

For many years, Mali had a one-party political system. Only candidates from the Mali People's Democratic Union could run for office, and the military controlled the party. However, in 1992, a new constitution allowing for multiparty elections was adopted.

Like other developing nations, Mali faces major problems. Many of its people are uneducated, and most of the adults cannot read and write. In addition, poor health conditions prevail in Mali, and only a few hundred doctors live there. Malaria is a major cause of death among Mali's children.

Although Mali is economically poor, it has a rich cultural heritage. In the past, three great black empires ruled parts of what is now Mali. The Ghana Empire flourished from about the A.D. 300's to the mid-1000's. It was known as "the land of gold" because traders brought gold into the empire from the south to exchange for salt and other goods.

The Mali Empire lasted from about 1240 to 1500. It was the wealthiest and most powerful state in western Africa, and its cities were centers of the caravan trade. King Mansa Musa, who ruled from 1312 to 1337, invited Islamic scholars to the empire, and the city of Timbuktu became a center of Muslim learning.

The Songhai Empire began in the 700's and flourished alongside the Mali Empire. After about 1400, it began to conquer some of Mali's outlying areas. By 1500, it controlled most of the Mali Empire. Under Songhai rulers, Timbuktu reached its peak as a center of wealth and learning. After Songhai was overrun by Moroccan invaders in 1591, many small kingdoms ruled the region. In 1895, France gained control of the area.

FACTS

Official name:	Republique de Mali (Republic of Mali)
Capital:	Bamako
Terrain:	Mostly flat to rolling northern plains covered by sand; savanna in south, rugged hills in northeast
Area:	478,841 mi² (1,240,192 km²)
Climate:	Subtropical to arid; hot and dry February to June; rainy, humid, and mild June to November; cool and dry November to February
Main rivers:	Sénégal, Niger
Highest elevation:	Hombori Tondo, 3,789 ft (1,155 m)
Lowest elevation:	75 ft (23 m), at the western border
Form of government:	Republic
Head of state:	President
Head of government:	Prime minister
Administrative areas:	8 regions
Legislature:	Assemblee Nationale (National Assembly) with 147 members serving five-year terms
Court system:	Cour Supreme (Supreme Court)
Armed forces:	7,400 troops
National holiday:	Independence Day - September 22 (1960)
Estimated 2010 population:	13,489,000
Population density:	28 persons per mi² (11 per km²)
Population distribution:	69% rural, 31% urban
Life expectancy in years:	Male, 51; female, 56
Doctors per 1,000 people:	0.1
Birth rate per 1,000:	48
Death rate per 1,000:	15
Infant mortality:	102 deaths per 1,000 live births
Age structure:	0-14: 48%; 15-64: 48%; 65 and over: 4%
Internet users per 100 people:	1
Internet code:	.ml
Languages spoken:	French (official), Bambara, numerous African languages
Religions:	Muslim 90%, indigenous beliefs 6%, Christian 4%
Currency:	Communaute Financiere Africaine franc
Gross domestic product (GDP) in 2008:	$8.78 billion U.S.
Real annual growth rate (2008):	4.2%
GDP per capita (2008):	$596 U.S.
Goods exported:	Cotton, food
Goods imported:	Food, machinery, petroleum products, pharmaceuticals, transportation equipment
Trading partners:	China, Côte d'Ivoire, France, Senegal, South Africa

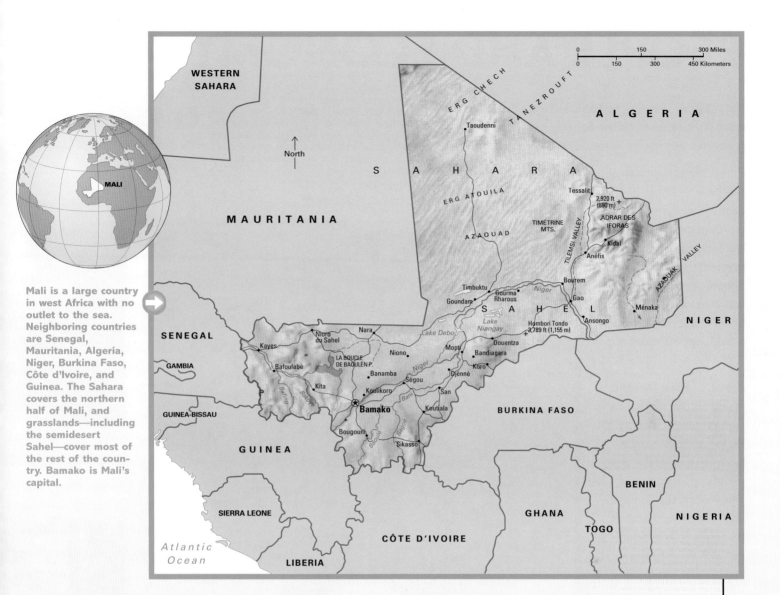

WESTERN
SAHARA

MALI

North

MAURITANIA

ALGERIA

SAHARA

ERG CHECH

TANEZROUFT

ERG ATOUILA

AZAOUAD

Taoudenni

Tessalit

2,920 ft
(890 m)

ADRAR DES
IFORAS

TIMÉTRINE
MTS.

Kidal

TILEMSI VALLEY

Anéfis

AZAOUAK VALLEY

Timbuktu
Goundam

Gourma
Rharous

Niger

Bourem

Gao

Ménaka

NIGER

SAHEL

Lake Debo

Lake
Niangay

Hombori Tondo
3,789 ft (1,155 m)

Ansongo

Mali is a large country in west Africa with no outlet to the sea. Neighboring countries are Senegal, Mauritania, Algeria, Niger, Burkina Faso, Côte d'Ivoire, and Guinea. The Sahara covers the northern half of Mali, and grasslands—including the semidesert Sahel—cover most of the rest of the country. Bamako is Mali's capital.

SENEGAL

Nioro
du Sahel

Nara

Niono

Mopti

Douentza

Bandiagara

GAMBIA

Kayes

Bafoulabé

LA BOUCLE
DE BAOULÉN P.

Banamba

Niger

Ségou

Djénné

Koro

Bafing

Sahel

Kita

Koulikoro

San

Bani

GUINEA-BISSAU

Bamako

Koutiala

BURKINA FASO

Bougouni

Bagoé

Baoulé

Sikasso

GUINEA

BENIN

SIERRA LEONE

GHANA

NIGERIA

Atlantic
Ocean

LIBERIA

CÔTE D'IVOIRE

TOGO

The French colony, called French Sudan, became part of French West Africa. In 1959, French Sudan and Senegal united to form the Federation of Mali. Senegal dropped out of the federation in August 1960, and on Sept. 22, 1960, Mali became an independent nation.

Modibo Keita, Mali's first president, tried to develop the economy, partly by establishing close ties with Communist countries. But Mali went into debt, and in 1968, a group of military leaders overthrew Keita. One officer, Moussa Traoré, took control and was later elected president. In March 1991, Traoré was overthrown in a military coup, whose leaders later established a multiparty democracy.

In 1992, voters approved a new constitution. They also elected a new civilian president—Alpha Oumar Konaré of the Alliance for Democracy in Mali (ADEMA)—and a new National Assembly. Konaré was reelected in 1997. In 2002, Amadou Toumani Touré, an independent who had

helped lead the overthrow of Traoré in 1991, was elected president. He was reelected in 2007.

In March 2012, a military junta overthrew Touré and suspended the constitution, accusing the government of failing to subdue Tuareg nomads, who have sought since the 1960's to establish an independent homeland in Mali's northern Sahara region. The Tuareg rebels, aided by foreign Islamic groups, took advantage of the coup to seize control of three northern provinces and declared independence. They called their new homeland Azawad.

After several weeks, sanctions applied by the international community forced the coup leaders and the president to reach an agreement. Touré resigned, and Dioncounda Traore, the former speaker of parliament, became interim president. However, clashes between presidential guards and junta loyalists continued.

PEOPLE AND ECONOMY

Africa's great desert, the Sahara, covers the entire northern half of Mali. The Sahel, a semidesert grassland, lies south of the Sahara in central Mali.

The Sahel has been especially dry since 1968. The severe droughts of the 1970's and 1980's destroyed much of the region's plant and animal life, including crops and livestock. Thousands of people died of starvation, and thousands of others poured into Mali's urban areas, seeking water and food.

Mali's urban areas lie mainly in the southern portion of the country, a region of rolling grassland. Most of Mali's people live in villages and cities along the Sénégal and Niger rivers or their branches. The interior delta of the Niger is Mali's most fertile area.

The vast majority of Mali's people are black Africans, but they belong to different ethnic groups. The Mandinka—made up mainly of the Bambara, Malinke, and Soninke—make up about half of Mali's population. The Fulani make up the next largest ethnic group. The Fulani have both black and white ancestors. Other groups include the Dogon, Songhai, and Voltaic.

Most of Mali's black population lives in small rural villages in southern Mali. Many of the Fulani live in dome-shaped, thatched huts. Those who herd cattle live in low huts made of straw mats or branches. Still other blacks live in houses made of mud bricks.

The Niger River is Mali's lifeline. Its network of branches and lakes in southern Mali provides well-watered, fertile land, as well as a bountiful catch of carp, catfish, and perch for the country's fishing industry.

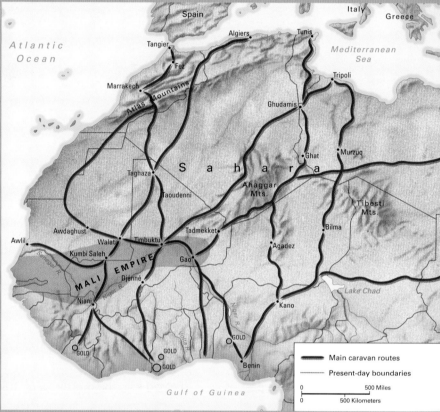

The main caravan routes across the Sahara were well established by A.D. 1000. Southbound caravans carried salt as well as cloth, glass beads, and other products. Northbound caravans carried gold, kola nuts, leather, pepper, and slaves. The great black empires that once ruled Mali became rich and powerful because they controlled important trade routes.

A tailor carries out his trade on a narrow street in Bamako, the capital and largest city of Mali. Only about 30 percent of Mali's people live in such urban areas.

Timbuktu rose up at the "meeting point of camel and canoe," about 8 miles (13 kilometers) from the Niger River, near the southern edge of the Sahara on one of the caravan routes. Parts of the old city now lie under desert sands.

Most Mali farmers can raise only enough food for their own use. They usually work on village-owned plots, using old-fashioned hand tools. They grow cassava, corn, millet, rice, sorghum, and yams.

Whites make up a small percentage of the population. They include Arabs, Europeans (mainly French), Moors (of Arab and Berber descent), and Tuareg (of Berber descent). Many of the Arabs and Moors and almost all the Tuareg people are nomads. They herd cattle, goats, sheep, camels, and donkeys across the Sahel and Sahara in search of water and pasture. The nomads travel in groups led by *marabouts* (holy men). They live in tents made of camel hair and eat mainly dates and millet.

Most of the Europeans live in modern houses in Bamako and other cities. Many own businesses or have jobs in government, the professions, stores, banks, or offices.

Mali is an agricultural country, and more than three-fourths of its workers farm or herd for a living. Yet only about a fifth of the land is suitable for farming. The government has sometimes discouraged farming by keeping food prices low, and droughts have damaged crops and reduced the amount of pasture.

Some farmers raise cotton, peanuts, and sugar cane as cash crops. Cotton is Mali's chief export, but sharp drops in world cotton prices have hurt the country's economy. Fishing is an important industry in the south.

Mali has few mineral resources. The country's mined products include diamonds, gold, and salt. The rising cost of importing petroleum has also damaged Mali's economy.

LIVING AFRICAN ARTS

The arts have been highly developed in Africa for thousands of years. The oldest known African artwork—dating from before 5000 B.C.—is the prehistoric rock painting found in the Sahara and elsewhere. Today, art is part of Africans' everyday life, as well as an essential element in African rituals.

Islamic designs are characteristic of the art of northern Africa. Because Islam forbids artists to create images of living things, Islamic artists developed an abstract, flat style of depicting people, animals, and birds. The figures look more like geometric symbols than lifelike pictures. Such designs decorate the walls of many magnificent mosques in the region, as well as the fine jewelry, metalware, pottery, rugs, and other handicrafts produced by North African artists.

Farther south, in western Africa, traditional African music, dance, and sculpture have their own distinctive beauty. But because many Africans south of the Sahara are Muslims as well, the Arab Islamic style has sometimes influenced their art. Arab religious chants and musical instruments used in northern Africa have also spread southward to influence the music of people in Mali, Senegal, Niger, and Chad.

Traditional black African music is part of almost every aspect of life in western Africa, especially religious ceremonies, festivals, and social rituals. Many Africans believe that music is a link with the spirit world.

The instrument most strongly identified with African music is the drum. Some drums are made of animal skins and played with the hands. Others are hollow logs played with sticks. The complex rhythms of African music are created by combining different patterns of drumbeats. Sometimes iron bells or handclaps are used to create rhythms.

Other instruments include harps, horns, flutes, lyres, zithers, and xylophones. In Senegal, stringed instruments called *kora* are made from huge gourds.

Songs are a part of religious ceremonies and celebrations as well as a means of telling stories or teaching. The *dweli* (singers) of the Malinke people in Mali pass along their tribal history in songs.

The complicated rhythms, choral singing, and flattened, or *blue*, notes heard in African American blues songs and church music reflect African traditions. African music has also influenced Western popular music, jazz, West Indian calypso, and Latin American dance music.

Because dancing developed in Africa as a part of village life, African dancing is nearly always a group activity. In most village dances, everyone joins in the dance—men, women, and children. Sometimes they form a circle, clap their hands, and

Dogon dancers perform the dama, a dance that embodies the beliefs and history of the Mali people. The dancers wear stilts because the Dogon believe that long ago they came from a land of long-legged herons.

call out to dancers within the circle. For important ceremonies, professional dancers may perform, using traditional symbolic movements.

One of the most famous African dances is the splendid *dama* performed by the Dogon people of Mali. The dance lasts for hours. The dancers wear elaborate masks that symbolize the Creator and the works of creation.

They dance to direct the spirits of the dead to join their ancestors and to show the link between humans and God. Every important event in African life—birth, death, marriage, coming of age, and the planting and harvesting of crops—includes dancing.

Traditional crafts such as sculpting are also involved with African rituals. Ethnic groups such as the Bambara and Dogon are noted for their wonderful carved masks and the striking figures of their ancestors. The antelope masks of the Bambara are worn in harvest ceremonies, and Dogon masks are worn at such ceremonies as the dama festival.

Few people outside Africa knew about African sculpture until the 1900's, but it has since become a major influence on Western artists.

Djenné Mosque in Mali shows a blend of Islamic religious influence and an architectural style typical of the Sahara region. Many buildings in rural Africa are constructed of adobe, which keeps out the intense heat.

Musicians play under the palm trees of Dakar, Senegal. Drums are the most important instrument in African music, which for many Africans is a link with the spirit world.

MALTA

The Republic of Malta consists of the inhabited Mediterranean islands of Malta, Gozo, and Comino, as well as the smaller, uninhabited islands of Cominotto and Filfla. Malta is located about 60 miles (97 kilometers) south of Sicily.

For centuries, the strategic location of the islands of Malta has made them a stopping place for sailors on the Mediterranean Sea. According to tradition, Saint Paul the Apostle was shipwrecked near Malta about A.D. 60 and converted the inhabitants to Christianity as recently as World War II (1939-1945), Malta was used as a naval base by the Allied forces.

For almost 150 years, until it was granted independence in 1964, Malta was a British crown colony. Today, it is an independent republic within the British Commonwealth.

Malta is one of the most densely populated countries in the world. The population is concentrated on the northeast coast of the main island of Malta, around two natural harbors, Marsamxett and Grand Harbour.

People

With Italy to the north and Libya to the south, Malta is neither European nor African. Its people are determined to remain neutral in their political affairs and keep friendly ties with all their neighbors. Perhaps their tolerant spirit comes from their mixed ancestry and their blend of cultural heritages.

The Maltese generally have the black hair, dark eyes, and medium height of most Mediterranean people. The Maltese language combines a West Arabic dialect with some Italian words. Although the Arabs held Malta for only 220 years, many of the region's place names and family names reflect the days of Arab rule. However, almost all the islanders are Roman Catholics.

About two-thirds of Malta's people work in service industries. Only a small percentage of the Maltese people are farmers, and Malta must import most of its food.

FACTS

Official name:	Repubblika ta' Malta (Republic of Malta)
Capital:	Valletta
Terrain:	Mostly low, rocky, plains; many coastal cliffs
Area:	122 mi² (316 km²)
Climate:	Mediterranean with mild, rainy winters and hot, dry summers
Main rivers:	N/A
Highest elevation:	Ta'Dmejrek, near Dingli, 829 ft (253 m)
Lowest elevation:	Mediterranean Sea, sea level
Form of government:	Republic
Head of state:	President
Head of government:	Prime minister
Administrative areas:	None
Legislature:	House of Representatives usually consisting of 65 members serving five-year terms
Court system:	Constitutional Court, Court of Appeal
Armed forces:	2,000 troops
National holiday:	Independence Day - September 21 (1964)
Estimated 2010 population:	412,000
Population density:	3,377 persons per mi² (1,304 per km²)
Population distribution:	95% urban, 5% rural
Life expectancy in years:	Male, 77; female, 81
Doctors per 1,000 people:	3.9
Birth rate per 1,000:	10
Death rate per 1,000:	8
Infant mortality:	4 deaths per 1,000 live births
Age structure:	0-14: 17%; 15-64: 69%; 65 and over: 14%
Internet users per 100 people:	49
Internet code:	.mt
Languages spoken:	Maltese (official), English (official)
Religions:	Roman Catholic 98%, other 2%
Currency:	Euro
Gross domestic product (GDP) in 2008:	$8.34 billion U.S.
Real annual growth rate (2008):	2.5%
GDP per capita (2008):	$20,386 U.S.
Goods exported:	Machinery, manufactured goods
Goods imported:	Automobiles, food, machinery, manufactured goods, petroleum products
Trading partners:	France, Germany, Italy, Singapore, United Kingdom, United States

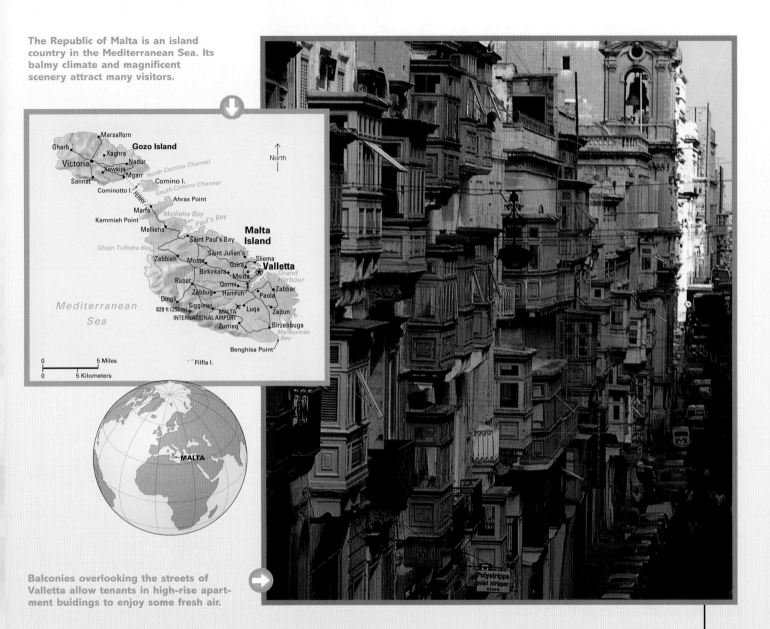

The Republic of Malta is an island country in the Mediterranean Sea. Its balmy climate and magnificent scenery attract many visitors.

Balconies overlooking the streets of Valletta allow tenants in high-rise apartment buidings to enjoy some fresh air.

History

Malta's history goes back to prehistoric times. The small Cave of Ghar Dalam on the island of Malta contains the remains of settlements dating from 7,000 years ago. About 1000 B.C., the Phoenicians colonized the islands, and their temples, tombs, and other relics still stand on Malta.

Greek, Carthaginian, Roman, and Arab conquerors followed the Phoenicians into Malta. During the Middle Ages, control of Malta passed to the Norman kings of Sicily. Finally, in 1530, the Holy Roman Emperor Charles V gave Malta to the Knights of the Order of Saint John of Jerusalem (sometimes called the Hospitallers), and in 1565,

the Knights fought off an invasion by the Ottoman Empire. Over the next 200 years, the Knights brought much wealth to Malta.

The rule of the Knights came to an end when Napoleon I seized the islands on his way to Egypt in 1798. In 1800, the British helped the Maltese drive out the French, and the Maltese then offered control of the islands to the British. The United Kingdom developed important military headquarters there, and British troops remained on the island until 1979. In 2004, Malta became a member of the European Union.

MARSHALL ISLANDS

The Marshall Islands are a group of low-lying islands and coral *atolls* in the central Pacific Ocean. Atolls are ring-shaped reefs that enclose a lagoon. The islands became an independent country in 1986. The Marshall Islands lie east of the Caroline Islands and northwest of the Gilberts, in the part of the Pacific referred to as Micronesia.

Land

The Marshall Islands lie in two parallel chains about 130 miles (209 kilometers) apart. The eastern group is called the *Radak,* or *Sunrise Chain*. The western group is called the *Ralik,* or *Sunset Chain*. Each chain extends about 650 miles (1,050 kilometers) in a curve from northwest to southeast. About 1,150 islets lie along the reefs that form the atolls.

The climate is tropical, but ocean breezes cool the air. Rainfall is light on the northern islands, but heavier in the south. Only a few kinds of plants, such as coconut palms and banana and papaya plants, grow in the coral sand that covers the land.

People and history

The people of the Marshall Islands are Micronesians. About 67,000 people live on the islands. The Marshall Islanders are noted for their handicrafts.

The islands were named for John Marshall, a British sea captain who explored the islands in 1788. Germany gained possession of the islands in 1886 and bought them from Spain, along with the Mariana and Caroline islands, in 1899. Japanese forces occupied the Marshalls during World War I (1914-1918), and Japan was allowed to rule the islands after the war under a mandate of the League of Nations. In 1933, however, Japan left the League and took over the Marshalls, closing the islands to Europeans and building war bases there.

 FACTS

Official name:	Republic of the Marshall Islands
Capital:	Majuro
Terrain:	Low coral limestone and sand islands
Area:	70 mi² (181 km²)
Climate:	Wet season from May to November; hot and humid; islands border typhoon belt
Main rivers:	N/A
Highest elevation:	33 ft (10 m), on Likiep
Lowest elevation:	Pacific Ocean, sea level
Form of government:	Parliamentary democracy
Head of state:	President
Head of government:	President
Administrative areas:	33 municipalities
Legislature:	Nitijela (Parliament) with 33 members serving four-year terms
Court system:	Supreme Court, High Court
Armed forces:	The United States is responsible for the Marshall Islands' defense
National holiday:	Constitution Day - May 1 (1979)
Estimated 2010 population:	67,000
Population density:	957 persons per mi² (370 per km²)
Population distribution:	70% urban, 30% rural
Life expectancy in years:	Male, 67; female, 70
Doctors per 1,000 people:	0.5
Birth rate per 1,000:	34
Death rate per 1,000:	5
Infant mortality:	24 deaths per 1,000 live births
Age structure:	0-14: 40%; 15-64: 58%; 65 and over: 2%
Internet users per 100 people:	4
Internet code:	.mh
Languages spoken:	Marshallese (official), English (official)
Religions:	Protestant 54.8%, Assembly of God 25.8%, Roman Catholic 8.4%, other 11%
Currency:	United States dollar
Gross domestic product (GDP) in 2008:	$160 million U.S.
Real annual growth rate (2008):	-0.3%
GDP per capita (2008):	$2,353 U.S.
Goods exported:	Coconut oil, fish
Goods imported:	Food, machinery, petroleum products
Trading partners:	Australia, Japan, United States

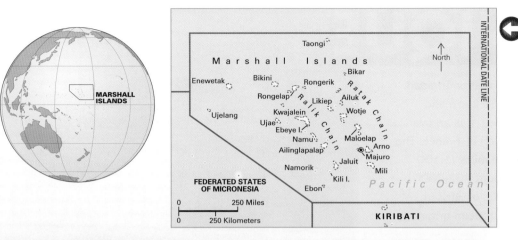

The Marshall Islands consist of coral atolls and islands that lie in two parallel chains about 130 miles (209 kilometers) apart.

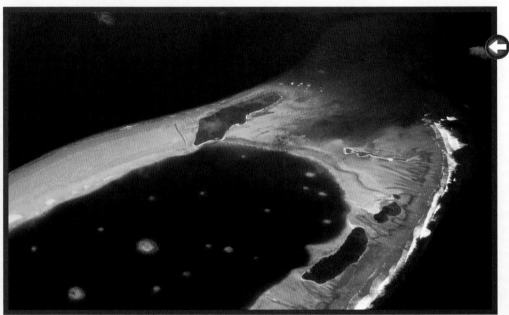

An atoll sits in the Pacific Ocean near Majuro, the capital of the Marshall Islands. The country consists of 29 atolls and five tiny islands scattered over about 780,000 square miles (2,020,000 square kilometers) of ocean.

During World War II (1939-1945), American forces took possession of the Marshalls. In 1947, the islands became part of the United Nations Trust Territory of the Pacific Islands, administered by the United States. In that year also, the U.S. government decided to test nuclear weapons on Enewetak, an isolated atoll in the Marshalls. It was already testing nuclear devices on the Bikini atoll. In both cases, the island's inhabitants were moved to other atolls. Tests were conducted until the late 1950's.

Because of radiation contamination, the United States conducted cleanup operations, but Bikini and some islands of Enewetak will remain unfit for human habitation for hundreds of years. Inhabitants of Enewetak's southern islands were finally allowed to return in 1980. In 1985 all residents of Rongelap atoll were forced to relocate to Mejato atoll after tests showed high levels of radiation.

In 1986, the United States granted the Marshalls a form of self-government called *free association*. Under this system, the people control their internal and foreign affairs, and the United States is obligated to defend the islands in emergencies.

United States military concerns continue to dominate the Marshalls, as Kwajalein atoll serves as an essential element of the Pacific Barrier radar system. Certain Kwajalein islands are used as targets for missiles test-fired from California.

In 1994, several members of the Marshall Islands legislature demanded that the U.S. government release information on the effects of nuclear tests on the area. Lawmakers suggested that the information remains classified so that the United States does not have to pay adequate compensation to residents, who have the highest rate in the world for some cancers.

MARTINIQUE

Martinique is the second largest island, after Trinidad, in the Lesser Antilles. It lies north of St. Lucia and south of Dominica in the Caribbean Sea. It is an overseas *department* (administrative district) of France. The oval-shaped island covers 425 square miles (1,100 square kilometers). Martinique has about 402,000 people. Most islanders are descendants of African slaves, though some people are of European origin.

In addition to its delightful French atmosphere, Martinique boasts beautiful mountains, tropical rain forests, scenic coasts, sunny beaches, and charming villages. The island attracts hundreds of thousands of tourists a year. Most of these visitors come from France.

An island of mountains

Martinique has three volcanic, forest-covered mountain regions in the north, center, and south. The tallest mountain on the island is Mount Pelée, which rises to 4,583 feet (1,397 meters). Flatter areas in the south are covered by huge plantations where bananas, pineapples, and sugar cane are grown.

An unusual landscape called the *Savane des Petrifactions,* or the Petrified Savanna, lies in the far south of the island, near the village of Ste.-Anne. The Petrified Savanna appears to be a forest of petrified wood, but it is actually a series of lava flows.

Martinique's coastal plains are narrow, and beautiful beaches—some consisting of white sand and some of black volcanic sand—face the Caribbean Sea. The eastern coast, which faces the Atlantic Ocean, has a wild, natural beauty with dramatic bays and rough seas.

History

Christopher Columbus reached Martinique in 1502, on his fourth voyage to the New World. But it was not until 1635 that the French began to colonize the island. French settlers established coffee and sugar-cane plantations and used slave labor to work them. Great Britain (now called the United Kingdom) occupied the island for short periods before French rule was officially recognized in the early 1800's.

The cloud-covered peak of Mount Pelée rises high above the small town of St.-Pierre. This town was once a city known as Little Paris of the West Indies—the capital city of Martinique. The city was destroyed when Mount Pelée erupted in 1902, and about 28,000 people died. Only one person survived.

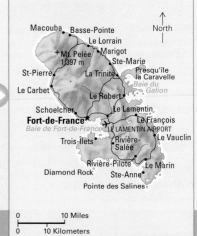

Martinique is a mountainous island in the Lesser Antilles. While sugar cane is the chief crop, bananas, cotton, pineapples, and tobacco are also grown. Rum distilling is an important manufacturing activity.

The French government made Martinique an overseas department in 1946. In 1958, Martinique chose to remain an overseas department. The island sends three deputies to the French National Assembly. In a 2009 referendum, the people of Martinique rejected additional self-rule.

Through substantial financial aid, France has done much to develop Martinique and to bring a modest level of prosperity to Martinique's people. France and Martinique maintain close ties, and much of the island's trade is with France.

Fort-de-France

Fort-de-France, the capital and chief commercial and cultural center of Martinique, is also home to about one-fourth of the island's population. The city lies on a large bay on the west coast and also serves as a busy port of call for cruise ships.

Fort-de-France's central area has elegant colonial buildings that are similar to those in the old French Quarter of New Orleans. Large, handsome homes, set amid splendid gardens, reflect the wealth of the former plantation owners. La Savane square is a popular gathering spot.

A hardware store owner waits for customers. The sign above the store is written in French, Martinique's official language. Many people also speak Creole, a French patois (dialect).

Villagers haul their fishing nets ashore on a sandy beach along Martinique's west coast, which faces the Caribbean Sea. The waters of the Caribbean are warm and relatively calm, but off the eastern coast, the waters of the Atlantic are often cold and rough.

MAURITANIA

Mauritania, a country on the western bulge of the African continent, was once a French colony. In French, its name is République Islamique de Mauritanie (Islamic Republic of Mauritania).

Mauritania is often described as a bridge linking northern Africa and western Africa, and its flag, a yellow crescent and star on a green background, reflects this connection. The color green and the star and crescent stand for Mauritania's ties to Islamic northern Africa. The color yellow stands for the country's ties to the African nations south of the Sahara.

Conflict between the northern African and western African cultures has troubled Mauritania. The government has also been plagued by *desertification*—the nation's continuing loss of land to the growing Sahara, which now covers about two-thirds of Mauritania. Severe droughts and human activity along the edges of the desert have contributed to the expansion of the desert.

The growing desert and the clashing cultures have long played a role in Mauritanian life. Early black people farmed the region and lived alongside hunters, herders, and fishers. But as the climate became drier and the land turned to desert, these people began to move south. Beginning in the A.D. 200's, Berbers from the north forced more farmers to move south.

From the A.D. 300's until the 1500's, three great west African powers controlled parts of Mauritania—the Ghana, Mali, and Songhai empires. During this time, Arabs began their conquest of North Africa.

The Arabs—and Arab influence—slowly moved south toward Mauritania. The Berbers, driven farther and farther south, forced most of the black people to the Sénégal River. The Berbers were eventually dominated by the Arabs, and their descendants became known as Moors.

Major European contact began in the 1600's. For the next 200 years, France, Great Britain (now called the United Kingdom), and the Netherlands all competed for the valuable gum arabic trade in Maurita-

FACTS

Official name:	Al Jumhuriyah al Islamiyah al Muritaniyah (Islamic Republic of Mauritania)
Capital:	Nouakchott
Terrain:	Mostly barren, flat plains of the Sahara; some central hills
Area:	397,956 mi² (1,030,700 km²)
Climate:	Desert; constantly hot, dry, dusty
Main river:	Sénégal
Highest elevation:	Kediet Ijill, 3,002 ft (915 m)
Lowest elevation:	16 ft (5 m) below sea level
Form of government:	Republic
Head of state:	President
Head of government:	Prime minister
Administrative areas:	12 regions, 1 capital district
Legislature:	Legislature consisting of the Majlis al-Shuyukh (Senate) with 56 members serving six-year terms and the Majlis al-Watani (National Assembly) with 95 members serving five-year terms
Court system:	Cour Supreme (Supreme Court), court of appeals
Armed forces:	15,900 troops
National holiday:	Independence Day - November 28 (1960)
Estimated 2010 population:	3,384,000
Population density:	9 persons per mi² (3 per km²)
Population distribution:	59% rural, 41% urban
Life expectancy in years:	Male, 59; female, 62
Doctors per 1,000 people:	0.1
Birth rate per 1,000:	34
Death rate per 1,000:	9
Infant mortality:	75 deaths per 1,000 live births
Age structure:	0-14: 40%; 15-64: 56%; 65 and over: 4%
Internet users per 100 people:	1.4
Internet code:	.mr
Languages spoken:	Arabic (official), Pulaar, Soninke, Wolof, French, Hassaniya
Religions:	Muslim 99%, other 1%
Currency:	Ouguiya
Gross domestic product (GDP) in 2008:	$3.22 billion U.S.
Real annual growth rate (2008):	3.5%
GDP per capita (2008):	$962 U.S.
Goods exported:	Fish and fish products, iron ore, petroleum
Goods imported:	Food, machinery, petroleum products, transportation equipment
Trading partners:	China, France, Italy, Spain

nia. France made the region a protectorate in 1903, and Mauritania became a French colony in 1920.

In 1958, Mauritania became a self-governing republic in the French Community. Mokhtar Ould Daddah was elected prime minister in 1959. Ould Daddah favored independence, and on Nov. 28, 1960, Mauritania became a free nation.

Mauritania has had many problems since independence. First, Morocco laid claim to the region. Then Mauritania fought a nationalist movement in Western Sahara for control of part of that area. In 1978, Ould Daddah was overthrown by military leaders, partly because he was unable to end the war with Western Sahara. In 1979, the military rulers gave up Mauritania's claim to Western Sahara. The military ruled until 1992.

In 1992, multiparty elections were held, and Maawiya Ould Sid Ahmed Taya, who had served as president of the military government, was elected president. Taya was reelected in 1997 and 2003. In 2005, a group of army officers overthrew Taya and temporarily ruled Mauritania. Since then, the government has alternated between military control and democratically elected leaders.

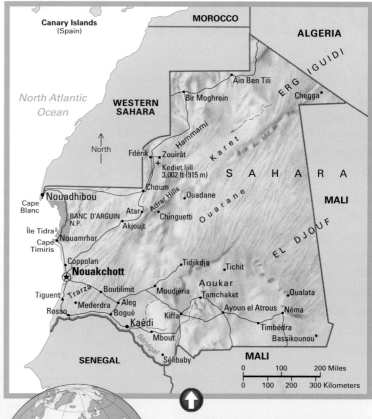

Mauritania, once a French colony, extends from the Atlantic Ocean east into the Sahara, which covers most of the country. Neighboring nations include Senegal, Mali, and Algeria.

The Grand Mosque, also known as the Saudi Mosque, is Mauritania's most important mosque. It stands in the center of Nouakchott, the capital of Mauritania.

PEOPLE AND ECONOMY

One thing that almost all Mauritanians have in common is their religion—about 99 percent of the people are Muslims. However, Islam is not enough to bring the two main ethnic groups in the country together. Each follows a different way of life.

The majority of the Mauritanian people are Moors, descendants of Arabs and Berbers. Most Moors speak Arabic, the country's official language. Some are nomads, who move through the desert with their animals in search of water and pasture. Others live in the cities or villages. Since severe droughts began in the 1960's, the Sahara has been spreading, and a growing number of nomads have flocked to the urban areas.

The Moors themselves are divided into two main groups, *white Moors* (also called Bidan) and *black Moors* (also called Haratine). The terms *white* and *black* here refer to social status and family lineage rather than to skin color. The white Moors have the higher status. Traditionally, the white Moors have been divided into two classes: warriors and religious leaders. Until the early 1900's, the warriors were a noble class who strove for political dominance. Religious leaders have raised cattle, sheep, and other livestock. They traditionally have advised the warriors and also paid the warriors for security services.

After the Moors, black Africans make up the second major group of the Mauritanian population. They may belong to any of several ethnic groups. The largest black ethnic group is the Toucouleur. The Fulani, the Soninké, the Wolof, and the Bambara are some other

Open-pit iron ore mines near Zouirât and Fdérik contain large, high-grade deposits of Mauritania's most important mineral resource. The ore is exported mainly to France, Germany, and Italy.

Fishing is an important source of export earnings in Mauritania, where the catch includes both ocean and freshwater fish.

A market in Nouakchott is strewn with baskets of goods. A young city, the capital was founded in 1957 by the French as a colonial seat. Today, the city is a magnet for Mauritanians fleeing the drought-stricken interior.

groups. Most black Mauritanians are farmers who live along the Sénégal River in the south of the country. Their round, mud-brick huts stand along twisting village pathways.

The nation's educational system is poor. Less than half of Mauritania's children complete primary school, and less than a fifth attend high school.

An underdeveloped economy

Incomes in Mauritania are low, and most workers make barely enough to support their families. About half of the people are farmers and livestock herders. Farmers grow corn, dates, millet, rice, and sorghum. Important livestock products include beef and dairy cattle, goats, and sheep. Herders also raise camels.

Only a small percentage of land receives enough rain to grow crops, and Mauritania must import much of its food. In the 1970's and 1980's, a severe drought destroyed food crops and killed livestock in the country. As the drought continued, cities became vastly overcrowded with rural refugees.

Some of Mauritania's people make their living by fishing. The government has expanded the fishing industry, and it is now an important part of the economy.

Iron ore deposits near Fdérik are Mauritania's most important mineral resource. The ore accounts for much of the country's export income. Gum arabic, which comes from the sap of acacia trees, is exported for use in making perfumes, medicine, candies, and glue.

Mauritania depends on economic aid from other countries, especially France, to balance its budget. Poor communications and transportation have hurt the country's economic development.

MAURITIUS

The island nation of Mauritius lies in the Indian Ocean, about 500 miles (800 kilometers) east of Madagascar and 2,450 miles (3,943 kilometers) southwest of India. Mauritius consists of one main island—also called Mauritius—and several other islands or island groups, including Rodrigues, Agalega, and the Cargados Carajos Shoals. Mauritius also claims the Chagos Archipelago, an island group about 1,300 miles (2,100 kilometers) northeast of the island of Mauritius that is controlled by the United Kingdom.

Mauritius is a republic. Voters elect most of the members of the National Assembly. To guarantee fair representation, an election commission also chooses four members from minority groups that are not adequately represented, and four members on the basis of their minority group and political party.

Mauritius was formed by volcanoes that left the land covered with rocks and a thick layer of lava. Coral reefs surround all but the southern part of the island. A misty plateau rises in the center of Mauritius, and black volcanic peaks tower above the sugar cane fields that cover about half the island.

Mauritius has a strong economy. Much of the country's income comes from the sugar industry. About 90 percent of its farmland is planted with sugar cane, and sugar is one of the country's leading exports. People grow vegetables for their own use, but most of their food must be imported.

Since the 1970's, textile production, tourism, and financial services have grown in importance. More workers are employed in textile production than in any another industry in Mauritius. Banks and other financial companies handle the business needs of many foreign investors. And hundreds of thousands of tourists visit the island for its lovely beaches.

Almost 70 percent of the people of Mauritius are Indians. About 30 percent are *Creoles*—people of mixed European and African descent or mixed European and Indian descent. The rest of the people are Chinese or Europeans. Most of the Europeans are of French descent.

FACTS

Official name:	Republic of Mauritius
Capital:	Port Louis
Terrain:	Small coastal plain rising to discontinuous mountains encircling central plateau
Area:	788 mi² (2,040 km²)
Climate:	Tropical, modified by southeast trade winds; warm, dry winter (May to November); hot, wet, humid summer (November to May)
Main rivers:	Black, Grand
Highest elevation:	Piton de la Rivière Noire, 2,711 ft (826 m)
Lowest elevation:	Indian Ocean, sea level
Form of government:	Republic
Head of state:	President
Head of government:	Prime minister
Administrative areas:	9 districts, 3 dependencies
Legislature:	National Assembly with up to 70 members serving five-year terms
Court system:	Supreme Court
Armed forces:	None
National holiday:	Independence Day - March 12 (1968)
Estimated 2010 population:	1,292,000
Population density:	1,640 persons per mi² (633 per km²)
Population distribution:	58% rural, 42% urban
Life expectancy in years:	Male, 70; female, 77
Doctors per 1,000 people:	1.1
Birth rate per 1,000:	14
Death rate per 1,000:	7
Infant mortality:	13 deaths per 1,000 live births
Age structure:	0-14: 23%; 15-64: 70%; 65 and over: 7%
Internet users per 100 people:	30
Internet code:	.mu
Languages spoken:	English (official), Creole, Bhojpuri, French
Religions:	Hindu 48%, Roman Catholic 23.6%, Muslim 16.6%, other Christian 8.6%, other 3.2%
Currency:	Mauritian rupee
Gross domestic product (GDP) in 2008:	$8.65 billion U.S.
Real annual growth rate (2008):	5.2%
GDP per capita (2008):	$6,780 U.S.
Goods exported:	Clothing and textiles, electronics, fish, sugar
Goods imported:	Chemicals, food, machinery, manufactured goods, petroleum products
Trading partners:	China, France, India, United Kingdom, United States

Modern skyscrapers dominate the skyline of Port Louis, the capital of the nation of Mauritius and its leading port. The city is located on the island of Mauritius in the Indian Ocean.

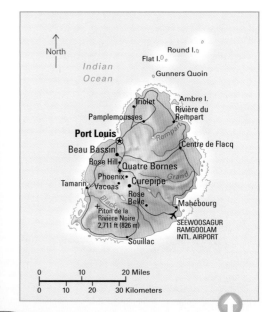

The country of Mauritius consists of the islands of Mauritius, Rodrigues, Agalega, and the Cargados Carajos Shoals. Rodrigues lies about 350 miles (563 kilometers) east of Mauritius Island, Agalega about 580 miles (933 kilometers) north, and the Cargados Carajos Shoals about 250 miles (402 kilometers) north.

English is the official language, but French may be used by government officials, and most of the people speak Creole, a French dialect. Some Indians speak one or more of six Indian dialects, and the Chinese speak one of two Chinese dialects.

Almost half of Mauritians are Hindus. Christians and Muslims make up most of the rest of the population. Dotting the island are Hindu temples, Christian churches, Muslim mosques, and Buddhist pagodas.

This mix of peoples, languages, and faiths reflects the history of Mauritius. The Dutch claimed the island in 1598 and named it after Prince Maurice of Nassau. France later ruled the island and founded Port Louis, now its capital. Both the Dutch and the French brought African slaves.

The British took control in 1810 and freed the slaves 23 years later. Almost half a million Indian workers came to replace the slave laborers over the next 75 years. Chinese traders also settled on the island.

Mauritius became independent in 1968. The nation was a constitutional monarchy until 1992, when it became a republic. A president serves as head of state, and a prime minister leads the government.

A spectacular display of sea shells from the Indian Ocean fills the craft of a Mauritian boatman, who hopes to sell them to tourists as souvenirs.

MEXICO

The fascinating country of Mexico lies in the extreme north of Latin America—just south of the United States. The great majority of its people are *mestizos*—people of mixed European and *indigenous* (native) ancestry—and almost all of them speak Spanish. Mexico itself is an enchanting blend of Spanish and indigenous—also called Amerindian or Indian—cultures.

Mexico's cultural mix is a result of its long and colorful history. Hundreds of years ago, Mexico was the home of great indigenous civilizations. They built cities and temples. They developed a calendar, a counting system, and a form of writing. But the last of these Indian empires fell to Spanish invaders in 1521. For the next 300 years, Mexico was a Spanish colony. The Spaniards introduced new agricultural methods and new forms of government. They also took Mexico's land and mineral riches, and the Indians were left poor, uneducated, and without political power. Mexico is now an independent nation, and its mestizo population takes great pride in its Indian ancestry.

Mexico is a large country. In the Western Hemisphere, only the United States and Brazil have more people than Mexico. Only Canada, the United States, Brazil, and Argentina have more land. Mexico is a land of towering mountains, high plateaus, dry deserts, and coastal rain forests. Few other countries have landscapes and climates so varied and lying so close to one another. Some mountain peaks in tropical southern Mexico are permanently snow-capped. The Rio Grande forms about two-thirds of the border between Mexico and the United States.

Crops are grown on only about 15 percent of Mexico's land. The rest of the country is too dry or mountainous or otherwise unsuitable. However, Mexico is a leading producer of coffee and corn. It is also rich in minerals—silver, copper, and gold. Its petroleum industry is especially important to the country and to the world. Manufacturing is important too.

A social and economic revolution began in Mexico in 1910. The government took over huge, privately owned farms and divided them among millions of landless farmers. Since the 1940's, the government has encouraged manufacturing and petroleum production. But these changes have not kept up with the nation's rapid population growth. Many Mexican people live in poverty. Each year, many leave the rural areas to seek work in the cities or in other countries, especially the United States. The population of Mexico City has swelled, making it one of the largest cities in the world. For many Mexicans, it seems that the revolution that began in 1910 is still going on.

MEXICO TODAY

Mexico's flag features three colored stripes: green for independence, white for religion, and red for union. The country is made up of 31 states and a federal district.

Mexico's constitutional government

The Mexican government is based on the Constitution of 1917. The Constitution calls for three branches of government—executive, legislative, and judicial.

Most of the power is held by the executive branch, especially the president. Mexico has no vice president. If the president does not finish a term of office, the Congress chooses a temporary president. A president is normally elected to one six-year term.

The Congress is composed of two houses. The Senate has 128 members. The Chamber of Deputies has 500 members—300 elected from electoral districts, and 200 allocated on the basis of each party's popular vote. A member of Congress cannot serve two consecutive terms.

The highest court in the judicial branch is the Supreme Court of Justice. The president appoints the 21 justices for life, with approval of the Senate.

Mexico's Constitution also sets up the state governments. Each of the 31 states has an elected governor and legislature.

The Constitution gives the federal government great power over the economy, education, and affairs of state. The government has used its power to take privately owned estates and divide them among poor farmers. It has taken over some of the nation's key industries, such as railroads, banking, and the petroleum industry. The government has also established a national school system and built many hospitals.

For many years, Mexico's major political party was the Partido Revolucionario Institucional (Institutional Revolutionary Party), or PRI. Controversy engulfed PRI

FACTS

Official name:	Estados Unidos Mexicanos (United Mexican States)
Capital:	Mexico City
Terrain:	High, rugged mountains; low coastal plains; high plateaus; desert
Area:	758,450 mi² (1,964,375 km²)
Climate:	Varies from tropical to desert
Main rivers:	Balsas, Rio Grande, Yaqui
Highest elevation:	Pico de Orizaba, 18,410 ft (5,610 m)
Lowest elevation:	Near Mexicali, 33 ft (10 m) below sea level
Form of government:	Federal republic
Head of state:	President
Head of government:	President
Administrative areas:	31 estados (states), 1 distrito federal (federal district)
Legislature:	Congreso de la Union (National Congress) consisting of the Camara de Senadores (Senate) with 128 members serving six-year terms and the Camara Federal de Diputados (Federal Chamber of Deputies) with 500 members serving three-year terms
Court system:	Corte Suprema de Justicia (Supreme Court of Justice)
Armed forces:	255,500 troops
National holiday:	Independence Day - September 16 (1810)
Estimated 2010 population:	110,155,000
Population density:	145 persons per mi² (56 per km²)
Population distribution:	76% urban, 24% rural
Life expectancy in years:	Male, 73; female, 79
Doctors per 1,000 people:	2.0
Birth rate per 1,000:	20
Death rate per 1,000:	5
Infant mortality:	19 deaths per 1,000 live births
Age structure:	0-14: 30%; 15-64: 64%; 65 and over: 6%
Internet users per 100 people:	21
Internet code:	.mx
Languages spoken:	Spanish (official), Nahuatl, Maya, Zapotec, regional indigenous languages
Religions:	Roman Catholic 76.5%, Protestant 6.3%, other 17.2%
Currency:	Mexican peso
Gross domestic product (GDP) in 2008:	$1.088 trillion U.S.
Real annual growth rate (2008):	1.4%
GDP per capita (2008):	$9,810 U.S.
Goods exported:	Crude oil, electronics, food, machinery, motor vehicles
Goods imported:	Chemicals, electrical equipment, industrial machinery, transportation equipment
Trading partners:	Canada, China, Germany, Japan, United States

Mexico is made up of 31 states and a federal district. Mexico shares its long northern border with the United States and extends 1,250 miles (2,012 kilometers) south to Central America. Airlines, highways, and railroads connect Mexico's major cities, but some farmers still carry goods to market on their heads or by burro.

in the 1990's, however. In March 1994, a gunman killed a PRI presidential candidate. The government said that the gunman acted alone, but most Mexicans doubted this. In September 1994, a top PRI official was shot to death. His brother, Assistant Attorney General Ruíz Massieu, investigated the killing but resigned, claiming PRI officials were trying to hide the party's role in the crime. Ruíz himself was later arrested and accused of obstructing the probe. Despite the turmoil, in late 1994 PRI member Ernesto Zedillo Ponce de León was elected president.

In 1997, the PRI lost its majority in the Chamber of Deputies for the first time. In 2000, Vicente Fox Quesada, of the Partido Acción Nacional (National Action Party), or PAN, was elected president of Mexico. He became the first non-PRI candidate to be elected to that office in 71 years. In 2006, Felipe Calderón, also of the National Action Party, won the presidential election by less than 1 percent.

Problems

In the early 2000's, violence connected with Mexican drug cartels (associations formed by suppliers) escalated. Several thousand people died as a result of fighting among the cartels and between the cartels and Mexican authorities. The violence was particularly bad on Mexico's northern border. By early 2009, President Calderón had deployed tens of thousands of soldiers and federal police to combat the violence.

LAND AND CLIMATE

Mexico has six main land regions. Within these regions are many smaller areas that differ greatly in altitude, climate, landforms, and plant life. The result is a land of constant variety.

The Plateau of Mexico is by far the largest of the land regions, covering most of the interior of the country. It also has the most varied landscape.

The Mesa Central, or Central Plateau, is the heart of Mexico. Averaging about 7,000 feet (2,135 meters) above sea level, this highland area gets enough rain to produce crops. The Aztec Indian capital of Tenochtitlán once stood at its southern edge, in the beautiful Valley of Mexico. Today, Mexico City rises on the same site.

The Volcanic Axis marks the southern edge of the Plateau of Mexico. This chain of volcanoes includes Pico de Orizaba (Citlaltépetl), the highest point in Mexico at 18,410 feet (5,610 meters). Southeast of Mexico City, the volcanoes Ixtacihuatl and Popocatépetl soar more than 17,000 feet (5,180 meters).

Rimming the eastern and western edges of the Plateau of Mexico are two mountain ranges—the Sierra Madre Oriental and the Sierra Madre Occidental. The Sierra Madre Oriental is actually a series of ranges. The Sierra Madre Occidental is steep and rugged.

The Mesa del Norte, or Northern Plateau, stretches from the Mesa Central to the United States. As it extends north and east, it drops in altitude from 9,000 feet (2,745 meters) to less than 4,000 feet (1,200 meters). The low mountains that rise above its plains contain some of the richest silver deposits in the world.

The five other main land regions of Mexico lie along the coasts. The Pacific Northwest is generally dry. The Peninsula of Lower California, called Baja California, is mostly rolling or mountainous desert. Fertile river valleys lie

An aerial view of the Valley of Mexico shows the mountains rising above Mexico City. In the foreground are the cones of extinct volcanoes. Some other volcanoes in Mexico are still active.

Lacandón Indians pole through a marshy area in a rain forest in the Chiapas Highlands, where rivers have cut broad, deep valleys through the mountains. Indians farm on the high flatlands.

along the mainland coast of the Gulf of California.

The Southern Uplands and Chiapas Highlands line Mexico's southern coast. A hot, dry valley lies along the Balsas River in the Southern Uplands. On the Oaxaca Plateau in the east, ancient Indians built a religious center, and the Aztecs once mined gold. The rugged Sierra Madre del Sur rises along the coast.

In the Chiapas Highlands, blocklike mountains tower more than 9,000 feet (2,745 meters). Indians who speak Maya and other ancient languages live on the high, flat tablelands.

The Gulf Coastal Plain and the Yucatán Peninsula lie along Mexico's eastern coast. The plain's dry northern section supports only low thorny

A cable bridge spans a river in the Sierra Madre. The Sierra Madre is divided into three ranges: Oriental (east), Occidental (west), and del Sur (south). They form a horseshoe shape around the Plateau of Mexico. Roads and railroads climb the Sierra Madre Oriental to the plateau. The Sierra Madre Occidental is so steep that such routes were not built until the 1900's.

A hunter sits outside the entrance to a cave in the state of Chihuahua, a dry highland region in northern Mexico.

bushes and trees, but rainfall increases toward the south, and the land there grows rich with rain forests and farmland. At the plain's southeastern edge, the Yucatán Peninsula begins. The Yucatán is a low limestone plateau with no rivers. Rainfall reaches the sea through underground channels cutting through the limestone.

The climate of Mexico varies greatly. The northern half of the country is generally dry, though the mountains receive more rainfall than other sections. Above 2,000 feet (610 meters), summers are hot and winters are mild. Nights are much cooler than days. The coastal lowlands are hot and humid.

In the southern, tropical half of Mexico, altitude has created three main climate zones. The *tierra caliente* (hot land), which rises up to 3,000 feet (915 meters) above sea level, has long, hot, humid summers and mild winters. The *tierra templada* (temperate land), which extends from the *tierra caliente* up to 6,000 feet (1,830 meters), has mild to warm temperatures. In the *tierra fria* (cold land), which lies above the *tierra templada*, the highest peaks are always snow covered. In tropical Mexico, short but heavy afternoon showers are common in summer.

FORCES OF NATURE

Mexico is located on the eastern edge of the *Ring of Fire,* a belt circling the Pacific Ocean where many earthquakes and volcanic eruptions occur. It also lies in the path of hurricanes that form in the warm, tropical air over the Atlantic Ocean. As a result, these natural disasters are painfully familiar to the Mexican people.

Earthquakes

On Sept. 19, 1985, the ground began to quake in Mexico City. For three minutes, the central area of the city shook violently, and dozens of high-rise buildings tumbled. By the time the earthquakes were over on September 20, about 10,000 people had been killed.

Earthquakes occur mainly along the edges of rigid sections of Earth's crust called *plates.* Scientists believe that these plates slide slowly on a layer of puttylike hot rock beneath the plates. Pressure builds where the edges of these plates grind against each other. When the pressure grows too great, rocks break and Earth's surface shifts, or quakes.

Mexico City is located near the border between two plates. The 1985 earthquake was particularly devastating because Mexico City is built on a dry lake bed, and the spongy ground beneath the city provides little support for structures.

Volcanoes

The collision of two of Earth's plates can also force rock down, where it is melted by the planet's inner heat. The pressure on this melted rock is so great that it is sometimes forced up, escaping from underground as *lava* and creating a volcano.

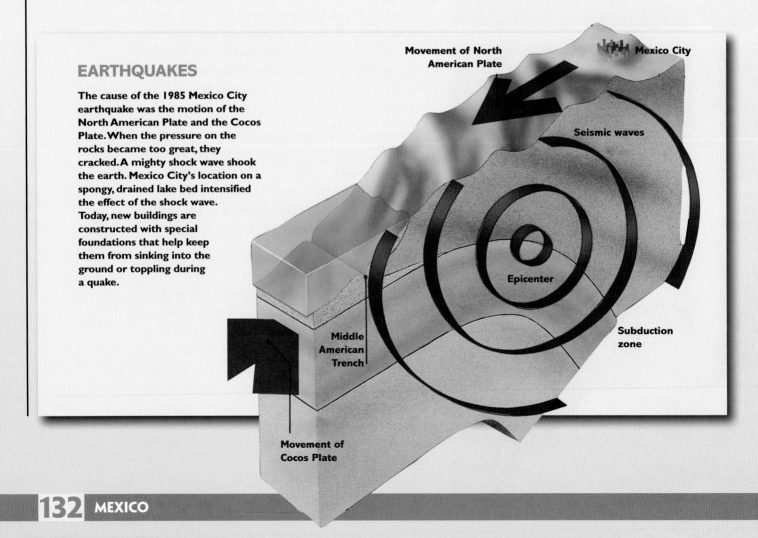

EARTHQUAKES

The cause of the 1985 Mexico City earthquake was the motion of the North American Plate and the Cocos Plate. When the pressure on the rocks became too great, they cracked. A mighty shock wave shook the earth. Mexico City's location on a spongy, drained lake bed intensified the effect of the shock wave. Today, new buildings are constructed with special foundations that help keep them from sinking into the ground or toppling during a quake.

Movement of North American Plate

Mexico City

Seismic waves

Epicenter

Subduction zone

Middle American Trench

Movement of Cocos Plate

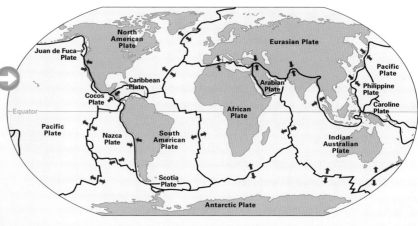

On Feb. 20, 1943, one such volcano, Paricutín, was formed in Mexico. The most recent volcano to form in the Western Hemisphere started as a crack that appeared in a cornfield. Steam, smoke, and lava began to pour out of the opening. By the end of one week, the lava had formed a 460-foot (140-meter) high cone around the opening. Eventually, the volcano destroyed the nearby villages of Paricutín and San Parangaricútiru.

Even more disastrous was the eruption of the volcano El Chichón in Mexico in 1982. This eruption killed 187 people and released a cloud of dust and sulfur dioxide gas high into the atmosphere.

Hurricanes

In September 1988, Hurricane Gilbert crossed the Caribbean Sea and slammed into Mexico. Hurricane Gilbert hit the tourist towns of Cancún and Cozumel along the Yucatán Peninsula.

Such storms develop over the warm waters of the North Atlantic or eastern Pacific in the summer and fall. The air over the warm water heats up, rises, and creates a low-pressure area. Winds begin to circle this area, increasing in speed. If their speed reaches 75 miles (120 kilometers) per hour or more, the storm is an official hurricane. The winds of Hurricane Gilbert reached a sustained speed on the ground of 137 miles (220 kilometers) per hour.

Much of Mexico City lay in ruin after the 1985 earthquake, which measured 8.1 on the Richter scale. About 10,000 people died, and hundreds of buildings collapsed.

ECONOMY

In several important ways, the Mexican economy changed greatly in the 1900's. Before the Mexican Revolution of 1910, the huge estates of wealthy landowners spread over many acres of the country. These estates, called *haciendas,* were owned by Spaniards or *creoles,* people of Spanish ancestry born in the New World.

Since 1910, the government has broken up most of the haciendas and given the land to the peasants. Since the 1940's, it has promoted manufacturing. Service industries, especially those involved in trade and tourism, now contribute much to the country's total production.

Manufacturing

The rapid expansion in Mexico's manufacturing industries since the 1940's has affected the nation's entire economy. Factories need raw materials to use in manufacturing, so the production of these materials increased. Banking and other services expanded to meet the needs of industry. The government spent heavily to construct housing around industrial centers. Power plants were built to provide energy for the new industries, and highways and railroads were constructed to carry their products.

Mexico City is the nation's leading manufacturing center. Its metropolitan area manufactures about half the country's products. Guadalajara, Juárez, Monterrey, and Tijuana are also important centers. Mexico's chief products include chemicals, iron and steel, motor vehicles, petroleum, processed foods, and tobacco.

Mexico has long been famous for the skill of its craft workers. Silver jewelry is made in Taxco, glassware and pottery in Guadalajara and Puebla, and handwoven blankets and baskets in Oaxaca and Toluca. Many of these handicrafts are sold to tourists.

Agriculture and forestry

Since the revolution, the government has distributed millions of acres of land to the peasants. About half of the total cropland is now managed under the traditional system of the *ejido,* in which farmland belongs to all the people of a community. On the ejidos, farmers either work on individual sections by themselves, or they work

An assembly plant in Toluca near Mexico City makes automobiles for home consumption and for export. Mexico City is Mexico's leading industrial center. Businesses in the city and its suburbs make about half the country's manufactured good.

the whole area as a group. Today, most ejidos are farmed in individual sections. The rest of the nation's cropland consists of small family farms and the remaining haciendas.

Mexico's variety of climates leads to a variety of crops. Corn is Mexico's basic food, so more land is used for corn than for any other crop. Corn is used to make thin, round flat bread called *tortillas*, which are eaten plain or made into tacos, enchiladas, or tostadas.

Other major crops include bananas, coffee, lemons, mangoes, onions, oranges, potatoes, sorghum, sugar cane, tomatoes, and wheat. Mexican farmers also produce avocados, chili peppers, and tropical fruits and winter vegetables for export to the United States. Beef cattle are raised in the dry north, and dairy cattle graze in central Mexico.

Forests cover about a fifth of Mexico's land area. The forests provide hardwoods, such as ebony and mahogany for making furniture; pine trees for making wood pulp and paper; and sapodilla trees, which yield *chicle*—a juice used to make chewing gum.

Mining

Gold and silver attracted Spaniards to Mexico in the 1500's. Silver mining has since been one of the nation's chief industries. Most of Mexico's silver mines are in the central regions of the country.

The country is also a major producer of petroleum, with an annual output of more than 1 billion barrels. Oil wells operate chiefly in the states of Campeche, Tabasco, and Veracruz, along the coast and in the Gulf of Mexico. In the late 1970's, after Mexico became a major oil exporter, the government greatly increased spending on public works and industry to create more jobs.

Mexico also mines large quantities of copper, gypsum, lead, salt, sulfur, and zinc. Other valuable minerals include antimony, bismuth, fluorite, and manganese. Large iron ore deposits support the nation's steel industry.

A Maya Indian woman tends tomatoes and melons on the Yucatán Peninsula. The Mexican government promotes modern farming methods with education, financial aid, and irrigation and transportation systems. However, primitive methods are still used in many areas, especially on the ejidos.

Coffee fields surround farm buildings on a plantation in the southern state of Chiapas. Most of the modern farming in this region takes place in deep, broad river valleys.

PEOPLE

Centuries ago, the indigenous people of Mexico developed several advanced civilizations. These civilizations built large cities, developed a calendar, invented a counting system, used a form of writing, and established vast empires. The last indigenous empire in Mexico—the Aztec Empire—fell to Spanish invaders in 1521. Mexico was a Spanish colony for the next 300 years, until it gained independence in 1821.

During the Spanish colonial period, a third group of people developed in Mexico. These people had both indigenous and European ancestors—and, in some cases, African ancestors as well. These Mexicans of mixed ancestry became known as *mestizos*. Today, the great majority of Mexicans are mestizos. To be a mestizo is to be part of Mexico's history, and many mestizos are very proud of their indigenous ancestors.

More than three-fourths of Mexico's people belong to the Roman Catholic Church. Mexico also has some Protestants, Jews, and other religious groups. Almost all Mexicans speak Spanish, the official language of the country. Most indigenous Mexicans speak Spanish

At an outdoor market, an Indian woman sells herbs, spices, and vegetables. Going to market is an important activity for rural people. They spend the day chatting with friends and doing business.

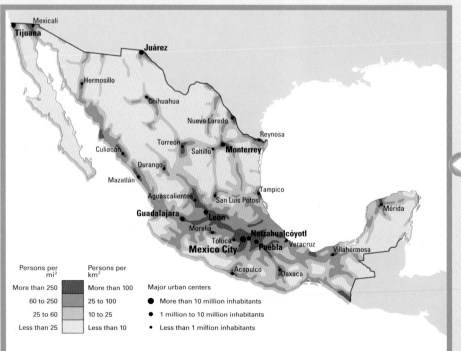

Persons per mi²
- More than 250
- 60 to 250
- 25 to 60
- Less than 25

Persons per km²
- More than 100
- 25 to 100
- 10 to 25
- Less than 10

Major urban centers
- ● More than 10 million inhabitants
- ● 1 million to 10 million inhabitants
- • Less than 1 million inhabitants

The population of Mexico is increasing rapidly every year. Many of the people still live in poverty. Many of the rural poor move to cities, hoping to find work.

Campesinos wear local dress as they meet on the steps of a church in Chiapas. Many people in this area are descended from the Mayas.

along with their own ancient language, but millions of them primarily use their indigenous language in daily life. Major Amerindian languages include Maya, Mixtec, Nahuatl, Otomí, Tarascan, and Zapotec.

Being indigenous in Mexico does not depend chiefly on ancestry. It is mostly a matter of lifestyle, language, and viewpoint. For example, Mexicans are considered indigenous if they speak an Amerindian language or wear clothing typical of indigenous people.

Many indigenous villages lie in the interior regions of Yucatán or in rugged areas of central and southern Mexico. There, the people still live much as their ancestors did. About 75 percent of all Mexicans, however, live in cities or towns. Mexico City, one of the largest cities in the world, has more than 8 million people.

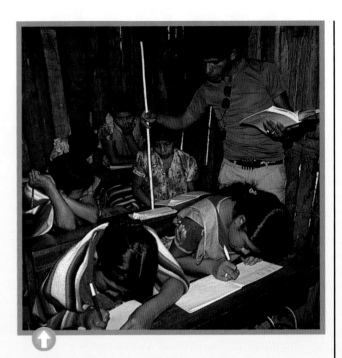

A Mexican teacher leads a class for refugees from Guatemala. Mexico has admitted a great number of refugees from Central America, where war and poverty affect many people.

Many of Mexico's cities and towns began as indigenous communities. Over the years, the Spaniards made them more like Spanish towns, with central *plazas* (public squares) and homes with patios. Today, in many ways, life in Mexico's larger cities is much like life in cities in the United States. Many city dwellers live in rows of homes built in the Spanish-colonial style, and suburbanites often live in modern apartment buildings and houses. The poorest Mexicans live in slum shacks or near-empty rooms. Many of these people came to the city to find jobs, but there is not enough work for the huge population.

In rural areas, many Mexican farmers live near their fields in small villages, where houses stand along simple dirt roads or cobblestone streets. In most villages, a Roman Catholic church stands in the plaza, along with a few stores and government buildings. Almost every village has a market place.

The total population of Mexico is currently more than 110 million people, and the number is increasing rapidly. Today, the government faces challenges in providing jobs, housing, transportation, and schools for its growing population.

MEXICO CITY

Mexico City is one of the largest cities in the world. More than 8 million people live in Mexico City, and about 18 million live in the city and its surrounding area. The city is the capital of Mexico as well as its center of industry, education, transportation, and tourism.

Mexico City covers the same area as the Federal District of Mexico. But only the northern part of the Federal District is an urban area. The National Palace in the heart of the city houses the offices of Mexico's president and other officials.

The city's thousands of factories account for about half of the value of all the goods manufactured in Mexico. Important products include automobiles, chemicals, iron and steel, and textiles.

Mexico City has more institutions of higher education than anywhere else in the country. The country's oldest and largest university is the National Autonomous University of Mexico. It was founded in 1551, and in 1954 its new campus was completed in the capital.

Almost all roads in Mexico lead to Mexico City. It is the center of the country's railroad network and of international air travel.

Tourists flock to Mexico City. The city is a fascinating contrast of old and new—of indigenous, Spanish, and modern Mexican cultures. Aztec ruins still stand in some areas, along with beautiful palaces and houses of the Spanish colonial period. Modern skyscrapers and houses are sometimes decorated with brightly painted murals.

The city has many neighborhoods, called *colonias*. Many have parklike plazas. These public squares are centers of neighborhood life, where people gather to listen to band concerts and enjoy fiestas.

Constitution Plaza, called the Zócalo, is Mexico City's chief plaza, the site of the National

A street vendor sells refreshments in busy Mexico City. Because of the country's economic problems, a growing number of urban Mexicans are forced to earn their living in such low-paying jobs.

Cathedral, National Palace, and Supreme Court of Justice. The heart of Mexico City extends west from the Zócalo to the Paseo de la Reforma, one of the most beautiful boulevards in the world. Nearby stands the majestic Palace of Fine Arts, with its theater and art galleries.

People have lived in what is now Mexico City for thousands of years. About the middle of the 1300's, the Aztec Indians founded their capital, Tenochtitlán, on this site, which was then an island in Lake Texcoco. The Aztecs built raised roads and elevated ramps to connect the city with the mainland.

Spanish invaders came to Tenochtitlán in 1519. Their leader, Hernán Cortés, destroyed the city almost completely in 1521 and built Mexico City, the capital of Spain's colony, on the ruins. After 30,000 people died in floodwaters in 1629, the Spaniards built a large canal to drain Lake Texcoco and carry off rain water. Mexico City remained under Spanish rule for 300 years, and it became the largest city in the New World.

Slum areas, the result of long-standing housing shortages, crowd the outskirts of Mexico City. In these areas, poor families live in wood or sheet-metal shacks that lack running water and electricity.

Although Mexico City has been a large, bustling city for a long time, new problems arose in the 1970's as a result of a massive population increase. The city continues to face a variety of challenges today. For instance, more jobs are needed for the many rural Mexicans who have come to the city seeking work. Housing is needed for the large numbers of poor people who live in slum shacks. And the city must deal with traffic problems, as well as the serious air pollution caused by automobiles and factories.

The "floating gardens" of Lake Xochimilco are in the southeast part of the capital. Flower-bedecked boats glide along canals in this popular weekend spot.

Mexico City is 7,525 feet (2,309 meters) above sea level. The historic center is actually in the northern part of the city. Southern Mexico City is mountainous and, thus, less built up.

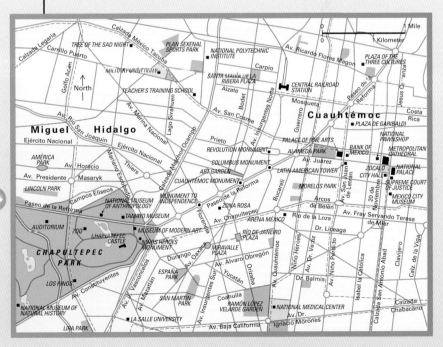

HISTORY

About 7000 B.C., the Indians in what is now the Puebla region of Mexico made a major discovery—they learned how to grow plants for food. Over time, the Indian hunters became farmers and settled in villages. Eventually, the villages grew into towns.

The years from A.D. 250 to 900, when great Indian civilizations thrived in Mexico, is called the Classic Period. During that time, the Mayas built huge pyramids and temples, developed mathematics, and studied astronomy. The Zapotec flattened a mountaintop and built a religious center there. They also made the first written records in the region.

The Aztecs built the last and the greatest Indian empire during the mid-1400's. Their capital, Tenochtitlán, stood on an island in Lake Texcoco. Here, in 1518, the Aztec Emperor Montezuma II heard reports of strangers on the coast. Because the strangers had guns and horses, which the Indians had never seen before, Montezuma thought they were gods. However, they were actually Spaniards exploring the "New World" and looking for gold.

In February 1519, Hernán Cortés founded Veracruz, the first Spanish settlement in Mexico. He then marched toward Tenochtitlán and seized Montezuma for ransom. Cortés and his men had to flee when the Aztecs revolted, but he returned in 1521 and conquered the city. Cuauhtémoc, the last Aztec emperor, was tortured. He is now a Mexican hero.

For the next 300 years, Mexico was a Spanish colony. Europeans established haciendas and mined silver. Mestizos labored in the cities. The Indians lived much as they always had, but sometimes they were forced to work on the haciendas. They also were made to accept the Roman Catholic religion, which they mixed with their traditional forms of worship.

In 1810, Miguel Hidalgo y Costilla, a creole priest, began Mexico's war for independence from Spain. Most of Hidalgo's followers were untrained mestizos and Indians, and almost all of them were captured or killed.

The king of Spain, annoyed by the uprising, began to tax the creoles, most of whom had not wanted independence. The king also organized a large army in Mexico. The creoles turned against the Spanish king and joined forces with an army officer, Agustín de Iturbide. By 1821, Mexico had won its independence.

Iturbide was named emperor, but he was driven from power one year later. Although a republic was established in 1824, the mid-1800's were a time of great trouble in Mexico. Army generals often took control. One of them—Antonio López de Santa Anna—was president 11 times from 1833 to 1855. Santa Anna ruled as a dictator. During this time, Mexico fought wars with Texas and then with the United States. The United States took a vast area of land from Mexico.

Santa Anna seized power for the last time in 1853. Two years later, Benito Juárez, a Zapotec Indian, and other liberals took over and started reforms. They tried to break up the estates of the Roman Catholic Church and end its political power. A revolt followed, but Juárez remained in power.

The ruins of Teotihuacán, near Mexico City, include the Avenue of the Dead and the Pyramid of the Moon. The city was built during Mexico's Classic Period (A.D. 250-900).

TIMELINE

c. 7000 B.C.	Farming develops.
c. 2000 B.C.	Villages are established in the Valley of Mexico and in the south.
c. 1200 B.C.	Olmec civilization arises.
c. A.D. 250-900	Great Indian civilizations thrive during the Classic Period.
c. 900-1200	Toltec Empire flourishes.
mid-1300's	Aztecs found Tenochtitlán (now Mexico City).
late 1400's	Aztec Empire reaches its peak.
1517	Spaniards discover Mexico.
1519-1521	Hernando Cortés conquers Aztec Empire for Spain.
1810	Miguel Hidalgo y Costilla starts fight for independence.
1821	Mexico wins independence.
1824	Mexico becomes a republic.
1836	Texas wins independence from Mexico.
1846-1848	War with the United States. Defeated Mexico loses much land.
1855	Benito Juárez begins governmental and social reforms
1863	French troops occupy Mexico City.
1864	Maximilian of Austria becomes emperor of Mexico.
1867	Juárez returns to power.
1876-1880 and 1884-1911	Porfirio Díaz rules as dictator.
1910	Francisco I. Madero leads a revolution that overthrows Díaz.
1914	U.S. forces occupy Veracruz.
1917	Constitution is adopted.
1920's	Period of economic and social reforms begins.
1934	President Cárdenas starts land distribution.
1938	Government takes foreign oil properties.
1942-1945	Mexico enters World War II on Allied side. Industries expand to supply war goods.
1953	Women receive right to vote in all elections.
1968	Summer Olympic Games held in Mexico City.
1970's	Vast petroleum deposits discovered.
1985	Earthquakes in Mexico City kill thousands.
1994	The North American Free Trade Agreement (NAFTA) goes into effect.
2000	First non-PRI president in 71 years is elected.

Hernán Cortés (1485-1547)

Francisco "Pancho" Villa (1878-1923)

Lázaro Cárdenas (1895-1970)

The Republic of Mexico was established in 1824. It covered much of what is now western and southwestern United States. In the mid-1800's, Mexico lost vast territories to the United States and sold the United States additional lands.

France invaded Mexico and ruled for a time, but in 1867 Juárez again returned as president and ruled until his death in 1872. Next came the long reign of the dictator Porfirio Díaz. Mexico's economy improved under Díaz, but only his wealthy supporters benefited. Most Mexicans remained poor.

The Mexican Revolution of 1910 overthrew Díaz, aided by the U.S. seizure of Veracruz in 1914. Revolutionaries Francisco "Pancho" Villa and Emiliano Zapata turned against the new government because they wanted greater reform. A new constitution, adopted in 1917, gave the government control over education, farm and oil properties, and the Roman Catholic Church. It also limited Mexico's president to one term and recognized labor unions.

In the 1900's, Mexico's presidents carried out the revolutionary programs to various degrees. Lázaro Cárdenas was especially successful in redistributing the land to the poor. He also took over the property of foreign oil companies. In the 1940's, during World War II, President Manuel Ávila Camacho encouraged industrial growth.

For many years, Mexico's major political party was the Partido Revolucionario Institucional (Institutional Revolutionary Party), or PRI. During the first decade of the 2000's, however, two members of the Partido Acción Nacional (National Action Party), or PAN, held the presidency. Vicente Fox Quesada became president in 2000, and Felipe Calderón followed in 2006.

TOURISM

Mexico's economy benefits greatly from tourism. Every year, millions of foreign visitors come to Mexico to see the cultural treasures of the Indian ruins, the Spanish colonial architecture, and the modern performing and fine arts. They also come to enjoy Mexico's magnificent beaches, volcanic mountains, and desert landscapes.

Mexico City

Mexico City is the nation's center of tourism. In addition to the city's historic monuments and government buildings, tourists may visit the majestic Palace of Fine Arts. In this marble palace, the National Theater presents concerts, dance programs, operas, and plays.

North of Mexico City's downtown area is the Plaza of Three Cultures. In this single spot, tourists can see examples of the three cultures that combined to make Mexico. Ruins of ancient Aztec temples stand next to the remains of a colonial Spanish church built in 1524. Nearby, a huge government housing project reflects modern Mexican architecture.

The Basilica of Our Lady of Guadalupe is Mexico's most famous religious shrine, and pilgrims come to worship there throughout the year. The shrine stands in northern Mexico City at the foot of a hill where, according to Roman Catholic legend, the Virgin Mary appeared to a poor Indian man in 1531.

North of Mexico City are the handsome Spanish colonial churches of Acalmán and Tepoztlan. Also, many people visit the ancient Indian pyramids and temples at San Juan Teotihuacán, Tenayuca, and Tula.

The Yucatán Peninsula

Tourists interested in ancient Indian culture visit the Yucatán Peninsula to see the ruins of an ancient Mayan religious center at Chichén Itzá. Many visitors take day trips to the site from Cancún or Cozumel Island—two resorts on the Caribbean coast. These beach resorts, which sprang up in

The ancient Maya city of Palenque emerges from the tropical rain forest in Chiapas. This site, like the ancient religious center of Chichén Itzá in Yucatán, enchants tourists from all over the world.

Enterprising Mexicans carry colorful clothing for sale to tourists on an Acapulco beach. Many tourists come to Acapulco to enjoy water sports, sunbathing, and night life.

the 1970's when the government started to promote tourism, attract northerners seeking warmth and sunshine in the winter months.

Pacific coast resorts

Beautiful scenery and a warm, sunny climate make Acapulco one of the world's most popular vacation spots. This resort city lies on forested hills along a deep, natural harbor on Mexico's Pacific coast. Sunbathers, swimmers, boaters, deep-sea anglers, and water skiers all come to Acapulco. The city has many beaches and hundreds of hotels.

Visitors are thrilled to see daring divers plunge more than 120 feet (37 meters) from La Quebrada cliffs into the waters of a rocky cove. The water is too shallow except when large waves surge in, so the divers must time their dives carefully. People also enjoy Acapulco's fine restaurants and nightclubs.

Other beach resorts on the Pacific coast attract many tourists from the United States and Canada, especially during the winter months. These resorts include Ensenada, Manzanillo, Mazatlán, Puerto Vallarta, and Zihuatanejo.

Tijuana is on Mexico's far northwest coast just south of the U.S. border. A small village until about 1940, Tijuana began to grow rapidly thanks to its booming tourist trade. Today, it is a modern city with luxury hotels, nightclubs, gift shops, bullfights, and horse races.

Fiestas

Tourists are attracted to the culture and lifestyle of Mexico as well as to its spectacular ruins and sunny beaches. Mexicans celebrate many holidays with colorful festivals, known as *fiestas*. Most fiestas begin before daylight with a shower of rockets, exploding fireworks, and ringing bells.

During fiestas, people pray and burn candles to the saints in churches decorated with flowers and colored tissue paper. They also dance and hold parades. Festive crowds gather in the market places and public squares. Bullfights and carnival rides are popular, especially in the larger towns.

← Sugar candy skulls, along with toy coffins and papier-mâché skeletons, are part of Mexico's All Souls' Day celebration. On November 2, the dead are honored with colorful celebrations, often held in graveyards.

↑ The Ballet Folklórico of Mexico has achieved international fame. The company performs many folk dances in an exciting spectacle of color and sound at the Palace of Fine Arts.

ART AND CULTURE

The arts have been important in Mexican life since the days of the ancient Indian cultures. The Mayas built beautiful limestone temples and painted colorful murals on their walls. The Aztecs composed music and poetry. Many Mexican artists today use beautiful old Indian designs in their jewelry, pottery, blankets, and baskets.

Architecture

The ancient Indians devoted most of their architectural skills to religious construction. They built stone temples and flat-topped pyramids and decorated them with murals and sculptures. Symbols in their painting and sculpture often represented the feathered-serpent god Quetzalcoatl and other gods.

The early mission churches, built soon after the Spanish conquest, were simple in design. But the National Cathedral, built in 1573, started a more ornamental style. Churches built during the 1700's, such as the Church of Santa Prisca in Taxco, were even more highly decorated.

Today's Mexican architects combine ancient Indian designs with modern construction methods. Their work includes the beautiful buildings of the National Autonomous University and the National Museum of Anthropology in Mexico City.

Totonac Indians perform the Volador, one of the oldest Mexican dances. "Flying" Indians descend slowly on ropes wound around the top of a high pole. The dance's religious significance dates from Aztec times.

Painting

During the Spanish colonial period, artists created murals in churches and painted portraits of government officials. But the most famous Mexican painting is the work that was done in the decades following the Mexican Revolution of 1910. Beginning in the 1920's, José Orozco, Diego Rivera, and David Siqueiros painted the story of the revolution on the walls of public buildings. Since the 1960's, however, many younger Mexican painters have turned away from revolutionary themes and followed styles from other countries.

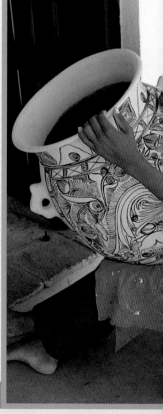

The marimba is a popular instrument in Mexico. It produces a rich, mellow sound. Some marimbas are so large that four or five musicians can play them at one time.

Literature

Colonial writers in Mexico included Juan Ruiz de Alarcón, who wrote outstanding drama, and the poet Sor Juana Inés de la Cruz. Probably the first Latin American novel was *The Itching Parrot*, published in 1816 by José Joaquin Fernández de Lizardi. As in art, revolutionary themes became important after 1910. Novelists of that time included Mariano Azuela and Martín Luis Guzmán. More recent writers have included Carlos Fuentes, Mexico's best-known fiction writer, and Octavio Paz, a leading poet and essayist.

Music

Early Indians made music with drums, flutes, gourd rattles, and sea shells. This ancient music is still heard in some parts of Mexico. Folk songs called *corridos* have also long been popular. They tell about such things as the Mexican Revolution and Mexican bandits and sheriffs. Modern Mexican composers such as Carlos Chávez and Silvestre Revueltas have used themes from Indian music or corridos in their own work.

Today, strolling musical groups called *mariachis* perform on the streets and in cafes. The music of xylophonelike instruments called *marimbas* is also popular. Folk dances, especially the lively Mexican hat dance, are still much enjoyed.

A masked dancer performs in a folk dance. Folk dances are a colorful part of local fiestas and are also performed by the professional dance company Ballet Folklórico in Mexico City.

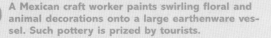

A Mexican craft worker paints swirling floral and animal decorations onto a large earthenware vessel. Such pottery is prized by tourists.

Moldova is a country in southeastern Europe. It is bordered by Romania on the west and by Ukraine on the other three sides. From 1940 to 1991, Moldova was a republic of the Soviet Union. With the collapse of the Soviet Union in 1991, the republic declared its independence.

The history of Moldova is closely linked to that of the Moldavia district in northeastern Romania. These two regions, historically known together as Moldavia, had a long history of invasion and warfare, due to their strategic location between Asia and southern Europe. From about 700 B.C. until about A.D. 200, the region that is now Moldova was under the control of the Scythians and later the Sarmatians. From about A.D. 200 until the 1200's, the Goths, the Huns, the Avars, and finally the Mongols invaded and ruled the area.

The main part of Moldavia was an independent state from the middle 1300's until the early 1500's, when the Ottomans gained control of the region. In 1791, eastern Moldavia came under Russian rule, and Russia acquired more Moldavian territory in 1793. In 1812, the Russians received all of *Bessarabia*—the area of Moldavia between the Prut and Dniester rivers. The Turks kept the rest of Moldavia, which later passed to Romania.

In 1918, Romania seized Bessarabia. However, Romania was forced to surrender the area to the Union of Soviet Socialist Republics (U.S.S.R.) in the 1940's, when most of Moldavia became a republic of the Soviet Union.

In the late 1980's, an independence movement developed in the Soviet republic. The nationalist Moldavian Popular Front gradually drove the Communist Party from power and, in 1990, the nationalists took over the government. The new government favored close cultural links with Romania.

Moldova declared its independence in the midst of political upheaval in the Soviet central government following an attempted coup in August 1991.

FACTS

Official name:	Republica Moldova (Republic of Moldova)
Capital:	Chisinau
Terrain:	Rolling steppe, gradual slope south to Black Sea
Area:	13,066 mi² (33,840 km²)
Climate:	Moderate winters, warm summers
Main rivers:	Dniester, Prut
Highest elevation:	Mount Balanesti, 1,407 ft (429 m)
Lowest elevation:	Dniester River at southeastern border, 7 ft (2 m)
Form of government:	Republic
Head of state:	President
Head of government:	Prime minister
Administrative areas:	32 raions (regions), 3 municipalities, 1 autonomous territorial unit, 1 territorial unit
Legislature:	Parlamentul (Parliament) with 101 members serving four-year terms
Court system:	Supreme Court, Constitutional Court
Armed forces:	6,000 troops
National holiday:	Independence Day - August 27 (1991)
Estimated 2010 population:	3,784,000
Population density:	290 persons per mi² (112 per km²)
Population distribution:	59% rural, 41% urban
Life expectancy in years:	Male, 66; female, 73
Doctors per 1,000 people:	2.7
Birth rate per 1,000:	11
Death rate per 1,000:	12
Infant mortality:	13 deaths per 1,000 live births
Age structure:	0-14: 18%; 15-64: 71%; 65 and over: 11%
Internet users per 100 people:	19
Internet code:	.md
Languages spoken:	Moldovan (official), Russian, Gagauz
Religions:	Eastern Orthodox 93.3%, Baptist 1%, other 5.7%
Currency:	Moldovan leu
Gross domestic product (GDP) in 2008:	$6.12 billion U.S.
Real annual growth rate (2008):	7.3%
GDP per capita (2008):	$1,538 U.S.
Goods exported:	Clothing, fruit and nuts, machinery, vegetables, wheat, wine
Goods imported:	Machinery, motor vehicles, petroleum products, pharmaceuticals, plastics
Trading partners:	Germany, Italy, Romania, Russia, Ukraine

When the Soviet Union was dissolved in December 1991, Moldova joined the newly established Commonwealth of Independent States.

In late 1991, Moldova became a battleground for violent ethnic conflict when ethnic Russians and Ukrainians in the Trans-Dniester region declared their independence from Moldova. The separatists feared reunification of Moldova with Romania. By mid-1992, a peacekeeping force entered the region, and fighting ceased. In 1994, Moldova held its first parliamentary elections since declaring independence from the Soviet Union.

In the 1998 parliamentary elections, Communists won more seats than any other party. But several non-Communist parties joined together in a coalition to form the new government. The Communists gained control of Parliament in elections in 2001 and remained in power in elections in 2005. In 2009, the Communists lost control of Parliament to a coalition of four pro-Western parties.

Land and people

Moldova's gently rolling lowlands, fertile black soil, and mild climate make the region ideal for agriculture. Extensive irrigation systems supplement the moderate rainfall. Farmers grow barley, corn, grapes, sugar beets, sunflowers, and wheat. Moldova also raises beef and dairy cattle, chickens, and hogs.

Moldova processes food and other agricultural products and manufactures agricultural machinery, construction materials, refrigerators, television sets, and washing machines. The region's important woodworking industry uses timber from the wooded steppe of the northern region.

About two-thirds of the country's people are ethnic Moldovans. Most of the rest of the population is made up of Russians; Ukrainians; Gagauz, a Turkic people; and Bulgarians. The official language is Moldovan, which differs little from Romanian. More than 90 percent of Moldovans are Eastern Orthodox Christians.

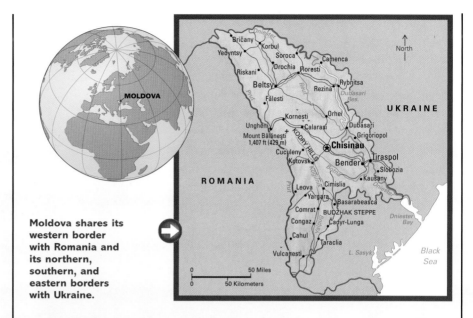

Moldova shares its western border with Romania and its northern, southern, and eastern borders with Ukraine.

Spring blossoms forth in the Moldovan village of Tsbulyovka. The fertile black soil of the lowlands and the mild climate create excellent growing conditions for a variety of crops.

MONACO

Playground of the rich, jewel of the Riviera, Monaco is one of the wealthiest countries in Europe. It is also one of the smallest countries in the world, with a total area of only about 3/4 square mile (1.95 square kilometers). Nevertheless, Monaco enjoys a worldwide reputation for beauty, glamour, and sophistication. High on the cliffs overlooking the harbor, the royal palace stands guard over this independent principality, just as it has for more than 700 years.

Early history

Monaco has a long and colorful history, dating from the arrival of the Phoenicians in about 700 B.C. In the A.D. 1100's, the Genoese of northern Italy gained control of Monaco.

In 1297, the Genoese people granted governing rights over Monaco to the Grimaldi family, who were from the city of Genoa. At first, the Grimaldis allied themselves with France. Later, during the early 1500's to mid-1600's, they sought protection from Spain. During the French Revolution, France seized Monaco, but control was later returned to the Grimaldi family.

Before Prince Albert I approved a constitution in 1911, the princes of Monaco were absolute rulers. Today, a 24-member National Council shares the legislative powers with the prince. In 1997, the country celebrated 700 years of rule by the Grimaldi family. Prince Rainier II died in 2005 and was succeeded by his son, who took the title Prince Albert II.

Land and economy

This small country lies at the foot of Mount Agel on the French Riviera, which borders the Mediterranean Sea. France borders Monaco on the other three sides.

Monaco includes three towns and an industrial area. The town of Monaco, which stands on a rocky point high above the sea, is the site of the royal palace. Monte Carlo features a famous gam-

FACTS

Official name:	Principauté de Monaco (Principality of Monaco)
Capital:	Monaco
Terrain:	Hilly, rugged, rocky
Area:	0.75 mi^2 (1.95 km^2)
Climate:	Mediterranean with mild, wet winters and hot, dry summers
Main rivers:	N/A
Highest elevation:	Mount Agel, 459 ft (140 m)
Lowest elevation:	Mediterranean Sea, sea level
Form of government:	Constitutional monarchy
Head of state:	Monarch
Head of government:	Minister of state
Administrative areas:	None
Legislature:	Conseil National (National Council) with 24 members serving five-year terms
Court system:	Tribunal Supreme (Supreme Court)
Armed forces:	France is responsible for Monaco's defense
National holiday:	National Day (St. Rainier's Day) - November 19 (1857)
Estimated 2010 population:	33,000
Population density:	44,000 persons per mi^2 (16,923 per km^2)
Population distribution:	100% urban
Life expectancy in years:	Male, 76; female, 84
Doctors per 1,000 people:	5.8
Birth rate per 1,000:	17
Death rate per 1,000:	14
Infant mortality:	5 deaths per 1,000 live births
Age structure:	0-14: 14%; 15-64: 64%; 65 and over: 22%
Internet users per 100 people:	61
Internet code:	.mc
Languages spoken:	French (official), English, Italian, Monégasque
Religions:	Roman Catholic 90%, other 10%
Currency:	Euro
Gross domestic product (GDP) in 2008:	N/A
Real annual growth rate (2008):	N/A
GDP per capita (2008):	N/A
Goods exported:	N/A
Goods imported:	N/A
Trading partners:	China, European Union countries, United States

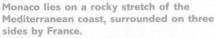

Monaco lies on a rocky stretch of the Mediterranean coast, surrounded on three sides by France.

The Palace of the Prince, in the old town, is the residence of the Grimaldi family, rulers of Monaco since 1297. Part of the fortress was built in the 1200's.

bling casino, an opera house, hotels, and beaches. La Condamine, a port area, lies between the town of Monaco and Monte Carlo, while Fontvieille, the industrial zone, is west of the town of Monaco.

With its sunny beaches, glamorous casinos, and exciting night life, Monaco is best known as a popular tourist resort. But Monaco is also a major industrial and administrative center, producing chemicals, cosmetics, electronics, pharmaceuticals, plastics, and processed foods. Many foreign companies have headquarters in Monaco because of the low taxation there. Monaco's colorful postage stamps are prized by collectors and represent an important source of income.

Many wealthy people from other countries make Monaco their home because the principality has no income tax. But since 1963, most French people living in Monaco have had to pay income tax at French rates.

Monaco is a center of learning and culture. The Grand Theater of Monte Carlo presents performances by some of the world's greatest singers and ballet dancers, and the Monaco government awards the Rainier III prize for literature each year to a writer in the French language. In addition, the study of marine life is the focus of Monaco's Oceanographic Museum and its world-famous aquarium.

Across the entrance to the port of Monaco lies the town of Monte Carlo. The green-roofed gambling casino is one of Monaco's chief attractions.

Mongolia lies north of China in east-central Asia. Mongolia is a rugged country covered mostly by plateaus and towering mountain ranges. The vast, bleak Gobi Desert blankets much of southeastern Mongolia. Temperatures in the country range from very hot to very cold, and rainfall is usually very light. Violent earthquakes sometimes rock the country.

Mongolia is the home of an Asian people called Mongols. Traditionally, the Mongols were nomadic herders who traveled from place to place with their animals. Today, some Mongols still follow their ancestors' nomadic lifestyle, roaming the plains and living in collapsible felt tents called *ger* or *yurts*. Today, however, most Mongol people live on cooperative livestock farms set up by the government.

During the 1200's, the Mongols built the largest land empire in history. Led by Genghis Khan—the "lord of all the peoples dwelling in felt tents"—the Mongols conquered most of Asia and parts of eastern Europe.

The rise of the Mongol Empire

In the late 1100's, Temüjin, a Mongol chieftain who later became known as Genghis Khan, rose to power. He began to organize the Mongols and other scattered nomadic tribes and trained them to be a superior fighting force.

Determined to build a Mongol empire, Genghis Khan invaded China. First, he attacked and conquered the state of Xi Xia in northwestern China, and then he led his warriors across the Gobi Desert and seized North China in 1215. Before completing the conquest of China, Genghis Khan's armies turned westward and attacked Russia and Persia, almost reaching Constantinople (now Istanbul). The Mongols killed many people during their campaign and destroyed much of Islamic-Arabic civilization.

After Genghis Khan died in 1227, the Mongols pushed into Europe under Ogotai, a son of Genghis Khan. However, Ogotai died during this campaign, forcing the Mongols to return to Mongolia to elect a new khan. Kublai Khan, a grandson of Genghis Khan, was elected. He completed the conquest of China and founded the Yuan dynasty, which lasted from 1279 until 1368.

MONGOLIA

Decline of the empire

The Mongol Empire began to disintegrate shortly after it reached its peak. In some areas, the Mongols had not firmly established their rule, and corrupt government and incompetent administration resulted in revolts in different parts of the empire. The Mongols lost control of many of their conquered lands.

When Kublai Khan died in 1294, his empire broke up. The Yuan dynasty in China ended in the 1300's. In the late 1500's, Mongol princes reunited Mongolia and converted the people to Lamaism, a form of Buddhism. In the early 1600's, the Manchu rulers of Manchuria divided Mongolia into Inner and Outer Mongolia and gained control of Inner Mongolia. The Manchus then conquered China in 1644 and seized Outer Mongolia in 1691. Mongolia, like China, had little contact with other nations during the 1700's and 1800's.

By 1911, the Manchu rulers had weakened, and the Mongolians drove the Chinese forces out of Outer Mongolia. They appointed a priest, called the *Living Buddha,* as king and appealed to Russia for support. However, in 1913, Outer Mongolia came under the control of Russia. In 1920, during Russia's civil war, anti-Communist Russian troops occupied Outer Mongolia and ruled it through the Living Buddha. Mongolian and Russian Communists gained control of Outer Mongolia in 1921, but though his authority was very limited, the Living Buddha retained his throne until his death in 1924. The Mongolian People's Republic was then established.

The new state supported the Soviet Union in the Soviet-Chinese dispute for leadership of the Communist world in the 1960's and 1970's. In 1990, people in Mongolia held demonstrations for more freedom. As a result, the country's ruling Communist party gave up its monopoly on power. The country adopted a multiparty system of government and began a shift toward a free-enterprise economy.

MONGOLIA TODAY

After the Communists gained control of Mongolia in 1921, a Communist party called the Mongolian People's Revolutionary Party (MPRP) became Mongolia's only political party and had complete control of the government. In order to modernize the country's economy, the MPRP gradually replaced the Mongols' traditional nomadic way of life with a more settled lifestyle. The government set up hundreds of livestock farms. Today, many of the Mongolian people live on these farms.

The farms are like huge ranches with small towns in the center. The central buildings include houses, offices, shops, and medical clinics for the people and animals. The state has also settled nomadic farmers on agricultural cooperatives. As a result, agriculture is an important economic activity in Mongolia.

Advances in industry, which is also controlled by the state, have brought many people from the rural areas to Mongolia's cities. About one-third of the Mongolian people live in Ulaanbaatar, the country's capital and industrial center. Many of these people work in factories or government offices.

The Mongolian people's traditional way of life has changed over the years. Modern farming methods and livestock-breeding techniques have been adopted, and schools and medical care units have been established. The Mongols traditionally ate a great deal of meat, but today, they eat more grains, fruits, and vegetables. Many Mongols, particularly those in the cities, now wear Western-style clothing.

In the late 1980's, reforms that brought more freedom to the Soviet Union and eastern Europe influenced the Mongolian people. They held demonstrations in early 1990 to demand similar changes in their country. As a result, Mongolia's Communist party gave up its monopoly on power, a multiparty system was adopted, and free elections were held in 1990. Although Communists won a majority of the government positions, the opposition parties gained a large percentage of seats.

FACTS

Official name:	Mongol Uls (Mongolia)
Capital:	Ulaanbaatar
Terrain:	Vast semidesert and desert plains; mountains in west and northwest; Gobi Desert in southeast
Area:	603,909 mi² (1,564,116 km²)
Climate:	Desert; continental (large daily and seasonal temperature ranges)
Main river:	Selenge
Highest elevation:	Nayramdal Uur, 14,350 ft (4,374 m)
Lowest elevation:	Hoh Nuur, 1,699 ft (518 m)
Form of government:	Mixed parliamentary/presidential
Head of state:	President
Head of government:	Prime minister
Administrative areas:	21 aimags (provinces), 1 independent city
Legislature:	State Great Hural with 76 members serving four-year terms
Court system:	Supreme Court
Armed forces:	10,000 troops
National holiday:	Independence Day (Revolution Day) - July 21 (1921)
Estimated 2010 population:	2,748,000
Population density:	5 persons per mi² (2 per km²)
Population distribution:	58% urban, 42% rural
Life expectancy in years:	Male, 63; female, 69
Doctors per 1,000 people:	2.6
Birth rate per 1,000:	21
Death rate per 1,000:	6
Infant mortality:	40 deaths per 1,000 live births
Age structure:	0-14: 28%; 15-64: 68%; 65 and over: 4%
Internet users per 100 people:	12
Internet code:	.mn
Languages spoken:	Mongolian (official), Turkic, Russian
Religions:	Buddhist Lamaist 50%, Shamanist and Christian 6%, Muslim 4%, other 40%
Currency:	Tugrik
Gross domestic product (GDP) in 2008:	$5.26 billion U.S.
Real annual growth rate (2008):	8.9%
GDP per capita (2008):	$1,969 U.S.
Goods exported:	Clothing, coal, copper, fluorspar, gold, hides, meat, wool
Goods imported:	Food, machinery, motor vehicles, petroleum products, sugar
Trading partners:	Canada, China, Japan, Russia, United States

The legislature elected Punsalmaagiyn Ochirbat as Mongolia's first president. Ochirbat was elected as an MPRP candidate, but he criticized the party's refusal to make economic reforms.

In 1992, a new democratic constitution went into effect. In 1993, for the first time, voters directly elected the president. Ochirbat ran as the candidate of the National Democratic and Social Democratic parties and won the election. In 1996, a coalition of democratic parties won the largest number of legislative seats, but the MPRP returned to power after legislative elections in 2000. The MPRP held or shared power through most of the first decade of the 2000's.

Mongolia's president is elected by voters to a four-year term. The president is the head of the armed forces and nominates the prime minister, who carries out the day-to-day operations of government. The prime minister is usually the leader of the party or coalition with the most seats in the legislature. The prime minister nominates the ministers who make up the Cabinet.

Mongolians wait in line to vote at a polling place in Ulaanbaatar. They are electing members of a national legislature called the State Great Hural. The legislature makes decisions regarding domestic and foreign affairs and appoints the prime minister and Cabinet.

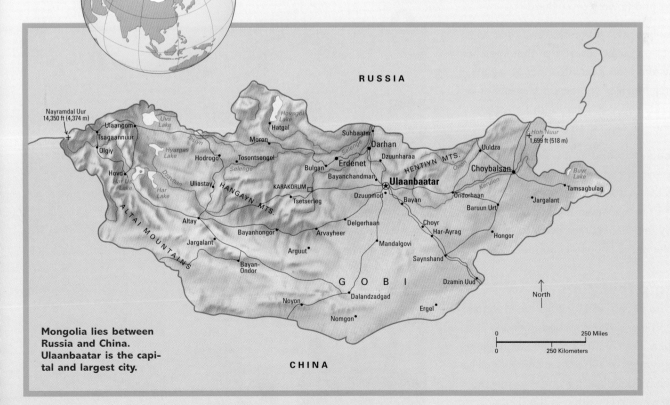

Mongolia lies between Russia and China. Ulaanbaatar is the capital and largest city.

LAND AND PEOPLE

Mongolia is a land of high mountains, plateaus, and barren desert. The Altai Mountains in western Mongolia, the highest mountains in the country, rise more than 14,000 feet (4,270 meters), and snow covers their peaks throughout the year. Farther east lie the Hangayn Mountains. North of these mountains lies a volcanic region, dotted with crater lakes and extinct volcanoes.

A high plateau lying between the Altai Mountains and the Hangayn Mountains in central Mongolia contains a number of large lakes. Uvs Lake, the largest, covers an area of about 1,300 square miles (3,370 square kilometers). Dense forests of spruce, pine, and fir trees cover the Hentiyn Mountains northeast of Ulaanbaatar.

Most of the country's people live in eastern Mongolia, a lower plateau of grassland that includes Ulaanbaatar and other major population centers. The plateau is fed by numerous rivers, and many kinds of grass and flowers grow there.

The plateau becomes less fertile and drier as it nears the Gobi—a bleak desert area that stretches from southeastern Mongolia into Inner Mongolia in northern China. Much of the desert consists of dry, rocklike or sandy soil, but *steppes* (dry grassland areas) surround the central area of the Gobi.

The Gobi often has long heat waves in summer and cold waves in winter. In Ulaanbaatar, average temperatures range from a winter low of about −14° F (−26° C) to a summer high of about 75° F (24° C). Heavy rains sometimes occur in July and August, but the entire country is normally very dry.

A growing population

Nearly all of the people of Mongolia are Mongols, though some Chinese, Kazakhs, and Russians also live in Mongolia. The country's official language is Mongolian, and most of the people speak Khalkha Mongolian, the official dialect. Mongolian may be written in two ways. It is written in the Uyghur script,

Nomadic herdsmen in the Gobi Desert stand guard while their camels drink at an oasis. Although camel caravans still cross the desert, their number continues to decline as the nomads give up their traditional way of life to settle on farms.

A camel and a pickup truck are both "parked" on the high plateau in central Mongolia in the shadow of the Altai Mountains. Today, the Mongolian people often use trucks rather than camels or horses for cross-country transportation.

A Mongol family living on a state-run livestock farm enjoys a meal of fried mutton.

a traditional Mongolian alphabet, and also in a special form of the Cyrillic alphabet.

Mongolia is very thinly populated, with an average density of only 5 people per square mile (2 per square kilometer). In the 1980's, the government introduced a program designed to encourage population growth by rewarding families with many children. Mongolia's population has grown as a result of this program, and today, much of the population is under the age of 25.

A changing way of life

For centuries, nomads have roamed the Mongolian plains with herds of sheep, cattle, and goats. They lived in tents made of layers of felt covered with canvas or hide, and they traveled from place to place on horseback. Today, the government is gradually settling the nomads on farms, and few Mongolians follow the traditional nomadic way of life

Increasingly, the Mongolian people are moving to the cities. Over half of the total population lives in Mongolia's towns and cities. Many other Mongolians live on livestock and agricultural farms set up by the state. Modern conveniences such as radios, stoves, and televisions have become popular as the nomads give up their tents and settle in new apartments and houses.

Modernization has also changed some aspects of traditional family life in Mongolia. For example, parents have much less influence today in arranging their children's marriages, and elaborate marriage rituals have been replaced by more simple ceremonies.

During the years of strict rule by the Mongolian People's Revolutionary Party, traditional religious festivals were replaced by festivals celebrating the state, and the practice of Lamaism, Mongolia's chief religion, was discouraged. Today, however, Mongolia's democratic government permits greater religious expression.

MONTENEGRO

Montenegro is a country in southeastern Europe. It is bordered on the west by the Adriatic Sea, on the northwest by Bosnia-Herzegovina, on the east by Serbia, and on the south by Albania.

A republic of Yugoslavia for more than 50 years, Montenegro became part of the country of Serbia and Montenegro in 2003. In 2006, Montenegro separated from Serbia and became an independent country.

Montenegro is a mountainous land whose ranges stretch down to the Adriatic coast. Dense beech and pine forests blanket the northern region, where the winters are harsh and snowy. The southernmost area along the Adriatic enjoys a mild Mediterranean climate. The rivers flowing through Montenegro are clear, fast-moving streams that wind their way though deep canyons.

Podgorica is the capital and largest city in Montenegro. It lies in a fertile plain near the junction of the Morača and Zeta rivers. The city's cultural institutions include a university, a theater, a museum of art, and a sports center.

A president is Montenegro's chief of state, and a prime minister heads the government. An 81-member National Assembly, led by the prime minister, makes the republic's laws. The prime minister is usually the leader of the party that controls the Assembly. The voters elect the president to a five-year term and the Assembly members to four-year terms.

Most of the people in Montenegro are Montenegrins. The official language of the country is Montenegrin, a language related to Serbian. Minority groups in Montenegro include Albanians, Muslim Slavs, and Serbs.

For much of the 1900's, a poor network of roads and railroads held back the country's economic development. New roads eventually improved the transportation system and the economy. In addition, a railway line opened in 1976 between Bar, Montenegro's major seaport, and Belgrade, then the capital of Yugoslavia.

FACTS

Official name:	Republic of Montenegro
Capital:	Podgorica
Terrain:	Mountains and thick forests over most of the country; narrow plain along the Adriatic coast
Area:	5,333 mi² (13,812 km²)
Climate:	Cold, snowy winters in most of the country; summers cool in the mountains and warm in the valleys; mild climate along the coast
Main rivers:	Bunë, Lim, Morača, Piva, Tara, Zeta
Highest elevation:	Mount Durmitor, 8,274 ft (2,522 m)
Lowest elevation:	Adriatic Sea, sea level
Form of government:	Republic
Head of state:	President
Head of government:	Prime minister
Administrative areas:	21 municipalities
Legislature:	National Assembly with 81 members elected to four-year terms
Court system:	Constitutional Court, Supreme Court
Armed forces:	4,500 troops
National holiday:	National Day - July 13 (1878)
Estimated 2010 population:	612,000
Population density:	115 persons per mi² (44 per km²)
Population distribution:	62% urban, 38% rural
Life expectancy in years:	Male, 71; female, 75
Doctors per 1,000 people:	N/A
Birth rate per 1,000:	11
Death rate per 1,000:	9
Infant mortality:	11 deaths per 1,000 live births
Age structure:	0-14: 18%; 15-64: 69%; 65 and over: 13%
Internet users per 100 people:	45
Internet code:	.me
Languages spoken:	Montenegrin (official), Serbian, Albanian
Religions:	Orthodox 74.2%, Muslim 17.7%, Catholic 3.5%, other 4.6%
Currency:	Euro
Gross domestic product (GDP) in 2008:	$4.52 billion U.S.
Real annual growth rate (2008):	6.5%
GDP per capita (2008):	$7,188 U.S.
Goods exported:	Aluminum, electrical energy, food, iron and steel
Goods imported:	Food, machinery, motor vehicles, petroleum products
Trading partners:	Greece, Italy, Serbia

Montenegro mines bauxite and coal. Factories manufacture aluminum, food products, iron and steel, and paper. The most important crops are corn, olives, potatoes, tobacco, and wheat. Farmers also grow cherries, figs, grapes, peaches, pears, and plums. They raise cattle, hogs, and sheep.

Tourism is a major source of income for Montenegro. Vacationers come to Montenegro's coast to enjoy the warm climate and scenic beaches. People who fish, hike, hunt, and ski visit the mountains.

Present-day Montenegro became part of the Roman Empire in about 11 B.C. Slavs settled in the region in the A.D. 600's. The region became part of Serbia in the late 1100's. The Ottoman Empire, based in modern-day Turkey, defeated the Serbs at the Battle of Kosovo Polje in 1389. Local nobles ruled Montenegro on behalf of the Ottomans until 1516, when Serbian Orthodox bishops began to rule part of it. By the late 1700's, the bishops' rule extended to all of Montenegro. In 1852, Montenegro's ruler took the title of prince, and the position of bishop became a separate office.

In 1878, the Congress of Berlin, a meeting of European leaders, formally recognized Montenegro as independent. The congress granted new lands to Montenegro, about doubling its size. Prince Nicholas, who had taken the throne in 1860, declared himself king in 1910.

In the early 1900's, a movement to unite Serbs and other Slavic peoples gathered strength in the region. Montenegro helped drive the Ottomans out of the Balkan Peninsula in the First Balkan War (1912-1913) and aided Serbia in World War I (1914-1918). In 1918, city residents in Montenegro deposed the king, and the country became part of the new Kingdom of the Serbs, Croats, and Slovenes. Rural villagers resisted incorporation into the kingdom until the mid-1920's, however.

In 1946, Montenegro became one of six republics in Yugoslavia. After four of the republics declared their independence in 1991 and 1992, Montenegro joined Serbia in forming a new Yugoslavia. In 2000, many people in Montenegro began pressing for independence from Serbia, which held most of the power in Yugoslavia. In 2003, the two republics adopted a new constitution and renamed the country Serbia and Montenegro.

Still, the demands for Montenegrin independence from Serbia continued. On May 21, 2006, a majority of Montenegrins voted for separation from Serbia. Shortly afterward, Montenegro declared its independence. A new constitution was adopted in 2007. Since independence, the Democratic Party of Socialists, which has governed Montenegro since 1991, has remained in power.

Red-roofed buildings in the Montenegrin town of Perast nestle between mountains and the Gulf of Kotor, a bay of the Adriatic Sea. Spectacular scenery, an abundance of beaches, and a mild Mediterranean climate draw many tourists to Montenegro.

Montenegro is a country on the Balkan Peninsula of southeastern Europe. It borders the Adriatic Sea.

The Kingdom of Morocco lies in the northwest corner of Africa. Because of its strategic location, many powers throughout history have tried to rule this region.

As early as 6000 B.C., farming people lived in what is now Morocco. By 1000 B.C., Berbers, who may have come from Europe, southwestern Asia, or northeastern Africa, migrated to the region. About A.D. 40, the area fell under the control of the Roman Empire. Then the Vandals, a barbarian tribe from northern Europe, took control, and later the region was conquered by the Byzantines of Constantinople.

During the 680's, Arab Muslims invaded Morocco, and the land became part of the Muslim empire. Many Berbers adopted Islam, the religion of the Muslims, but they resented Arab control.

In the late 700's, an Arab leader named Idris ibn Abdallah created the first Moroccan state by uniting the region's Arabs and Berbers. The Idrisid *dynasty* (series of rulers from the same family) ruled Morocco for almost 200 years. Moroccan rulers came to be called *sultans*.

From about 1050 through the mid-1400's, three Islamic Berber dynasties governed Morocco. These sultans built empires that covered much of northern Africa as well as Spain and Portugal. But in the 1200's, European Christians began to drive the Muslims out of Spain and Portugal, and by 1500, when the last Muslims were forced to leave Spain, Spanish and Portuguese invaders had begun to seize land on Morocco's coast.

Muslims and Christians also fought naval battles on the Mediterranean Sea. Private warships commanded by Muslim *corsairs* (pirates) attacked the ships and coastal towns of Christian nations, and Christian corsairs attacked Muslim ships and bases.

In the mid-1500's, a family named the Saadians gained control of Morocco and ruled for about 100 years. The Saadians were *sharifs,* said to be descendants of Muhammad, the founder of the Islamic religion. They were followed by the Alawis, a sharifian dynasty that has governed Morocco ever since.

By the early 1900's, though Moroccan sultans sat on the throne, Moroccans had actually lost control of their economy and politics to France and Spain. Through battles and treaties, the two European powers had established separate zones of in-

MOROCCO

fluence within Morocco. Spain controlled the north and a strip of land in the south, while France claimed the rest of the country.

Moroccans grew increasingly hostile toward the Europeans, and France sent troops into the country in 1907. In 1912, Sultan Abd al-Hafidh signed the Treaty of Fez, which officially gave control of Morocco to France. France in turn acknowledged Spain's control of its zones of influence.

In the 1920's, a rebel named Abd al-Krim led other Moroccans in a fight for independence. The French defeated the rebels in 1926, but the movement for independence continued until 1937, when its leaders were arrested or exiled.

An independence political party called the Istiqlal Party rose up in 1943. In 1953, Sultan Mohammed V was exiled for supporting the party. Moroccans reacted violently to their sultan's exile and formed a National Liberation Army to fight French troops. Two years later, France brought Sultan Mohammed V back and promised Moroccans their freedom. On March 2, 1956, Morocco became independent of France. In April, Spain gave up nearly all its claims in northern Morocco.

Mohammed's great popularity with the Moroccan people allowed him to organize the government as he wished. In 1957, he changed his title from sultan to king as part of his plan to make Morocco a constitutional monarchy. When Mohammed died suddenly in 1961, his son, Hassan II, became king and prime minister. In 1965 and again in 1972, Hassan took control of the entire government.

In the 1970's, Hassan began to press Morocco's claim to the Spanish Sahara—the southern area still controlled by Spain. In 1976, Spain gave up the region, and its name was changed to Western Sahara. But an independence movement in Western Sahara called the Polisario Front challenged Morocco's claim. In 1991, the United Nations arranged a cease-fire between Morocco and the Polisario Front.

King Hassan died in 1999. His son Sidi Mohammed succeeded him as King Mohammed VI.

MOROCCO TODAY

Morocco is a kingdom that lies in the northwest corner of Africa. The Strait of Gibraltar, which connects the Atlantic Ocean to the Mediterranean Sea, separates Morocco from Spain.

Government

Morocco is a constitutional monarchy. Its original Constitution gave the king broad powers. However, in 2011, voters approved changes that strengthened the role of the elected government.

The king is the head of state, the commander of the armed forces, and the highest religious authority in the country. The prime minister is the head of government. The king chooses the prime minister from the largest party elected to the legislature. The prime minister appoints a Cabinet, and a national legislature makes the country's laws.

At the local level, Morocco is divided into 16 regions, including 3 regions either wholly or partially in the disputed area of Western Sahara. Morocco's capital is Rabat. Casablanca is the largest city

Islam is the nation's official religion. About 99 percent of its people are Muslims. The Istiqlal (Independence) Party promotes Arab culture and reforms based on Islamic teachings. The conservative Mouvement Populaire (Popular Movement) generally supports the king.

King Hassan II ruled Morocco from 1961, when his father died, until his own death in 1999. When economic problems plagued Morocco in the 1960's, Hassan presented reforms to help the economy. When the legislature refused to accept the reforms, Hassan took control of the government until 1970. He took control of the government again in 1972, after an attempt on his life.

Hassan's claim to Western Sahara, the area south of Morocco, created problems for the country. From the 1970's until 1991, Moroccan troops fought an independence movement in Western Sahara called the Polisario Front. Most of Morocco's political par-

FACTS

Official name:	Al Mamlakah al Maghribiyah (Kingdom of Morocco)
Capital:	Rabat
Terrain:	Northern coast and interior are mountainous with large areas of bordering plateaus, intermontane valleys, and rich coastal plains
Area:	172,414 mi² (446,550 km²)
Climate:	Mediterranean, becoming more extreme in the interior
Main rivers:	Tensift, Oum er Rbia, Moulouya, Sous
Highest elevation:	Jebel Toubkal, 13,665 ft (4,165 m)
Lowest elevation:	180 ft (55 m) below sea level
Form of government:	Constitutional monarchy
Head of state:	Monarch
Head of government:	Prime minister
Administrative areas:	16 regions (including 1 region within the disputed Western Sahara and 2 regions partially within Western Sahara)
Legislature:	Parliament consisting of an upper house or Chamber of Counselors with 270 members serving nine-year terms and a lower house or Chamber of Representatives with 325 members serving five-year terms
Court system:	Supreme Court
Armed forces:	195,800 troops
National holiday:	Throne Day - July 30 (1999)
Estimated 2010 population:	32,554,000
Population density:	189 persons per mi² (73 per km²)
Population distribution:	57% urban, 43% rural
Life expectancy in years:	Male, 69; female, 73
Doctors per 1,000 people:	0.5
Birth rate per 1,000:	21
Death rate per 1,000:	6
Infant mortality:	37 deaths per 1,000 live births
Age structure:	0-14: 30%; 15-64: 65%; 65 and over: 5%
Internet users per 100 people:	33
Internet code:	.ma
Languages spoken:	Arabic (official); Tamazight (official [a Berber language]; French
Religions:	Muslim 99%, Christian, Jewish, and others 1%
Currency:	Moroccan dirham
Gross domestic product (GDP) in 2008:	$86.39 billion U.S.
Real annual growth rate (2008):	5.9%
GDP per capita (2008):	$2,712 U.S.
Goods exported:	Clothing, electric wire, fertilizers, fish products, food, phosphates
Goods imported:	Cotton, machinery, motor vehicles, petroleum and petroleum products, plastics, wheat
Trading partners:	France, Italy, Spain, United Kingdom, United States

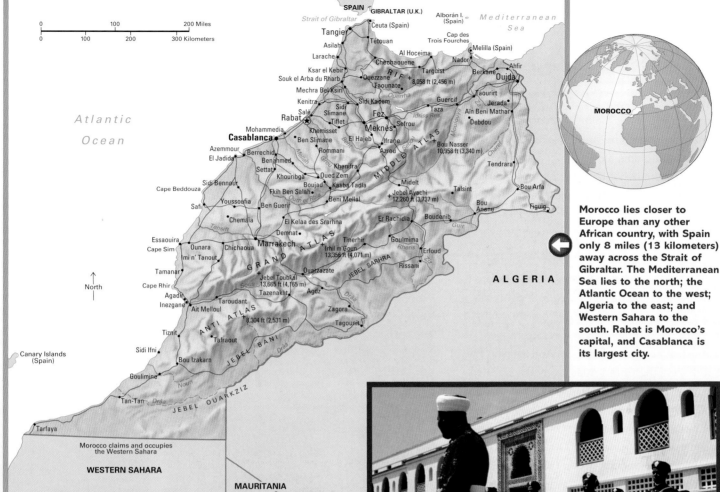

SPAIN   GIBRALTAR (U.K.)

Strait of Gibraltar   Ceuta (Spain)   Alborán I. (Spain)   *Mediterranean Sea*

Tangier

Asilah   Tétouan   Cap des Trois Fourches   Melilla (Spain)

Larache   Al Hoceima   Nador

Chechaouene   Targuist   Berkane   Ahfir

Ksar el Kebir   Quezzane   8,058 ft (2,456 m)   Oujda

Souk el Arba du Rharb   Taounate   R I F

Mechra Bel Ksiri   Ouerra   Guercif   Taourirt

Kenitra   Sidi   Sidi Kacem   Taza   Jerada

Salé   Slimane   Idriss Res.   Ain Beni Mathar

Atlantic Ocean

Rabat ★   Tiflet   Fez   Sefrou   Debdou

Mohammedia   Khemisset   Meknes

Casablanca   Ben Slimane   El Hajeb   Ifrane

Azemmour   Berrechid   Rommani   Azrou   Bou Nasser 10,958 ft (3,340 m)

El Jadida   Benahmed   M I D D L E   A T L A S   Tendrara

Settat   Khenifra

Cape Beddouza   Khouribga   Oued Zem   Bou Arfa

Sidi Bennour   Boujad   Kasba Tadla   Midelt   Talsint

Youssoufia   Fkih Ben Salah   Beni Mellal   Jebel Ayachi 12,260 ft (3,737 m)   Bou Anane   Figuig

Safi   Ben Guerir   Er Rachidia   Boudenib

Chemaia   El Kelaa des Srarhna   Goulmima

Essaouira   Demnat   Tinerhir   Erfoud

Cape Sim   Ounara   Marrakech   G R A N D   A T L A S   Irhil m'Goun 13,356 ft (4,071 m)   Rissani

Tamanar   mi n' Tanout   Chichaoua   Ouarzazate

Cape Rhir   Jebel Toubkal 13,665 ft (4,165 m)   JEBEL SARHRA

Agadir   Tazenakht   Agdz   Zagora

Inezgane   Taroudant   Tagounit

Ait Melloul   A N T I   A T L A S   8,304 ft (2,531 m)

Tiznit   Tafraout

Sidi Ifni   JEBEL BANI

Bou Izakarn

Canary Islands (Spain)

North

Goulimine   Noun

Tan-Tan   Drâa   JEBEL OUARKZIZ

ALGERIA

Tarfaya

Morocco claims and occupies the Western Sahara

WESTERN SAHARA

MAURITANIA

MOROCCO

Morocco lies closer to Europe than any other African country, with Spain only 8 miles (13 kilometers) away across the Strait of Gibraltar. The Mediterranean Sea lies to the north; the Atlantic Ocean to the west; Algeria to the east; and Western Sahara to the south. Rabat is Morocco's capital, and Casablanca is its largest city.

Morocco's Royal Palace, which stands in the modern section of Rabat, was begun in 1774 by Mohammed III and expanded by Sultan Mohammed V and his son, King Hassan II. Hassan wrote Morocco's first constitution, adopted in 1962. However, he twice took control of the government: in 1965, when the legislature blocked his economic program; and in 1972, when army officers tried to assassinate him.

ties supported the king's policy in Western Sahara. However, the high cost of the war hurt Morocco's economy. The people of Western Sahara were to vote on independence in 1994. Disagreements about voter eligibility have repeatedly delayed the referendum. Hassan's son Sidi Mohammed succeeded him as King Mohammed VI in 1999.

In 2011, antigovernment protesters in several Moroccan cities called for democratic reform. The protests followed similar, but more violent, events in other Arab nations. King Mohammed VI offered changes to the Constitution, which voters overwhelmingly approved in July.

Transportation, communication, and education

Highways and government-owned railroads link the major cities as well as important mining and farm areas. Most of Morocco's trade is handled at Casablanca. Daily newspa-

pers, printed in both Arabic and French, are published in Rabat and Casablanca. The government controls radio and television broadcasts.

Elementary and secondary education is free in Morocco. Classes are taught in Arabic and French, and children from 7 to 13 are required to attend school. However, many children do not go to school, particularly in rural areas, due to a lack of schools and teachers.

About half of Moroccans above the age of 15 can read and write. The nation has a number of universities, colleges, and technical schools.

LAND AND ECONOMY

Morocco has three major land forms—lowlands, mountains, and desert. The fertile lowland plains along the coast have a mild and somewhat dry climate, but the rich farmland is irrigated by many shallow rivers. Most of Morocco's crops are grown in these lowlands.

Moving east from the Atlantic coast, the land gradually rises to form a plateau before it reaches the mountains. The Atlas Mountains cross the middle of Morocco from southwest to northeast. Three heavily forested ranges form this mountain chain: the Anti Atlas in the southwest; the Grand Atlas (sometimes called Haut Atlas or High Atlas) in the center of the chain; and the Middle Atlas (or Moyen Atlas) in the northwest. Peaks in the Grand Atlas rise more than 13,000 feet (4,000 meters). The Rif, a fourth mountain group that is sometimes included in the Atlas chain, rises in the far north.

The inland regions of Morocco are generally drier and warmer than the coast, but rainfall and temperatures vary greatly. Fertile valleys in the mountains provide farmland.

East and south of the mountains lies the Sahara, a vast and desolate desert region of sand dunes, rocks, and stones. Scattered throughout the desert are green oases.

Morocco is a developing country with an economy based on agriculture and mining. The government controls the mining industry and some manufacturing, but most farms and businesses are privately owned. King Hassan II called the nation's economy a good blend of capitalism and socialism.

About 45 percent of Morocco's workers farm or fish for a living. Most farmers own a small parcel of land, but more than a third of the nation's farmland is owned by only a small percentage of the farmers. These large farms produce the vast majority of all crops.

A carpet woven in striking geometrical patterns forms a colorful backdrop for a Moroccan woman. Moroccans have long been known for producing fine rugs, and their beautiful carpets—along with other handicrafts—are valuable export items.

Spices and vegetables are on display at an outdoor market in Tangier, an ancient port at the northwest tip of Morocco. Agriculture is extremely important to the Moroccan economy. When rainfall is adequate, Moroccan farmers can produce almost all the nation's food.

Carefully cultivated fields lie at the foot of sparsely forested hills in central Morocco, near the towering peaks of the Grand Atlas Mountains. The highest peak in Morocco, Jebel Toubkal, rises in this mountain chain.

Moroccan farmers grow such cereals as barley, corn, and wheat, as well as beans, citrus fruits, olives, potatoes, sugar beets, and tomatoes. Most cereal farmers use old-fashioned methods and grow their crops for their own use, while the large farms use modern methods to produce fruits and vegetables for export. Moroccan farmers also raise beef and dairy cattle, chickens, goats, and sheep.

Fishing crews catch anchovies, mackerel, tuna, and sardines off the Moroccan coast. Much of their catch is canned for export or processed as fertilizers or animal feed.

About 35 percent of the nation's workers are employed in service industries. Some work for the government or perform community service, and others have jobs in the tourist industry. Millions of tourists come each year to enjoy Morocco's pleasant climate, white sandy beaches, and scenic mountains, and to visit the country's historic sites. Today, many Moroccans work in the hotels and restaurants that accommodate tourists.

Although mining does not create many jobs for Moroccans, it is extremely important to the nation's economy, as it brings in much foreign money. Morocco is the world's leading exporter of phosphate rock, which is used to produce fertilizers and other chemicals. Other minerals include coal, copper, iron ore, lead, natural gas, and zinc. However, Morocco imports oil to meet most of its energy needs.

Manufacturing provides jobs for less than 20 percent of the work force. Small firms produce consumer goods, and most larger firms manufacture products for local use, including cement; chemicals; leather goods; metal, rubber, and plastic products; paper; processed foods; and textiles. Some large firms produce goods for export, especially fertilizers and petroleum products.

Many people are employed in small workshops, making handicrafts and other goods. Leather goods, rugs, and other handicrafts are valuable Moroccan exports.

Fishing trawlers lie at anchor in the port of Essaouira on the Atlantic coast. The Portuguese built forts along the coast in the 1400's and 1500's. Today, Essaouira is a center for Morocco's fishing industry.

PEOPLE

Most of the people who live in Morocco reflect the history of the country in their mixed Berber and Arab ancestry. Berbers lived in the region as far back as 1000 B.C., and Arabs began to move into the area in the A.D. 600's.

Moroccans today are identified as Arabs or Berbers chiefly by their native language. Most Moroccans speak Arabic, but many speak Berber languages too. A large number of Moroccans also speak French or Spanish—a reminder of the days when France and Spain controlled parts of Morocco.

Over 32 million people live in Morocco. According to Morocco's government, Arabs make up about 65 percent of the population, and the rest are Berbers. Most Arabs live in the cities or on the Atlantic coast, and most Berbers live in rural mountain areas.

Almost all Moroccans—99 percent—are followers of Islam, the nation's official religion. Islamic teachings govern family and community life.

The traditional Moroccan household consists of a mother and father, their unmarried children, their married sons, and the wives and children of those sons. When the father dies, each married son establishes his

Berber warriors launch a thundering charge. In the past, such riders attacked communities, shooting from the backs of horses or camels. Today, they perform for visitors in a popular tourist attraction called the *fantasia*.

own household. But in the cities, where there is not enough room for the whole family to live together, many households split up before the father's death.

Many urban Moroccans live in small houses that are attached to one another. Wealthier people live in modern apartments or large homes, while poor people live in slum shacks made of flattened tin cans. In rural areas, many people live in primitive houses made of dried mud bricks, wood, or stone. Many such homes have only one room, which serves as living room, kitchen, bedroom, and barn. In the desert, nomads live in tents.

The busy market place is the heart of a Moroccan city. In rural communities, people gather at a weekly outdoor market called a *suq* to buy and sell goods and chat with one another. Many people also enjoy meeting friends at neighborhood cafes.

Berber shepherds watch their flocks in a remote mountain valley. Each is wrapped in the traditional hooded burnoose.

The tent is the home of nomadic Berbers in the Sahara, who move frequently in search of water and grazing land. Most Berbers live in the mountains and other rural areas of Morocco, where their homes are made of mud bricks, wood, or stone.

Berber women wearing traditional dress add a drumbeat to the rejoicing at a feast. Moroccans enjoy many local and religious festivals throughout the year.

Moroccans wear traditional clothing, but many city people wear Western-style clothes as well. Outside, men wear a loose-fitting hooded robe with long, full sleeves called a *jellaba*. Rural men wear a similar but heavier robe called a *burnoose*. Most men also wear a turban or a brimless cap. The *fez*, a red, flat-topped hat that many people identify with Morocco, was named for the Moroccan city of Fez, but nowadays it is usually worn only on formal occasions.

Moroccan women also wear jellabas outdoors. Indoors, they wear a long, beautiful robe called a *caftan*. Some older women and women in rural areas still follow Islamic tradition and cover their faces with veils in public.

In traditional Moroccan society, men and women live largely separate lives. Men dominate women in most areas of life, and fewer females attend school because parents place less value on education for girls than for boys. While many such practices continue, society is beginning to change. More girls now attend school, and more women work outside the home.

Following Islamic custom, many Moroccans stop to pray five times a day. However, some Moroccans, especially city office workers, no longer follow this practice. Moroccan Muslims fast during the month of Ramadan, eating nothing from sunrise to sunset.

Foods made of barley and wheat are the basis of the Moroccan diet. The national dish is *couscous*, steamed wheat served with vegetables, fish or meat, and a souplike sauce. The national drink is mint tea.

ROYAL CITIES

Today, over half of all Moroccans live in cities. Many city residents are wealthy and middle-class people, but sprawling slums called *bidonvilles* (tin-can towns) border the large cities. The bidonvilles got their name from the flattened *bidons* (tin cans) used to build these shacks. Severe overcrowding is also a problem in the *medinas,* or old sections, of the cities. Large urban areas grew around the medinas, which were the original city settlements.

The cities of Morocco were founded long ago, some as royal capitals. Morocco is part of an area once called the Maghreb. The Maghreb also included what are now Algeria, Tunisia, and part of Libya. The name *Maghreb* came from an Arabic word meaning *the place of the sunset—the west.* When Morocco was the heart of powerful empires that ruled the Maghreb as well as much of Spain, rulers called *sultans* established the cities as their royal capitals.

Fez

The Moroccan ruler Sultan Idris II founded the city of Fez as the capital of his kingdom in A.D. 808. Fez was actually made up of two cities built near the site of the ancient Roman town of Volubilis—one Arab, the other Berber—and later enclosed within one wall. Fez became a major religious and cultural center of the Islamic world. The Mosque of Mulai Idris, a noted Muslim shrine, was built there, as was Karaouiyine University. Founded in A.D. 859, Karaouiyine is one of the oldest universities in the world.

Marrakech

In 1062, the city of Marrakech was founded as the capital of a Berber dynasty, which, along with a second Berber dynasty, ruled a vast empire that included Spain. This empire produced the Moorish culture, renowned for its elegant and unique forms of art and architecture. Marrakech is now noted for its *mosques* (Muslim houses of worship) as well as its lovely parks, gardens, and pink clay buildings.

The simple but elegant interior of a mosque in Meknès features the graceful columns and geometric tilework found in many Muslim places of worship. Worshipers use the fountain for ceremonial washing before prayer.

Rabat and Meknès

A third Berber dynasty founded a new capital at Rabat. Rabat was the site of an old settlement of the Roman Empire as well as a fort called Ribat al Fath (Camp of Victory). A huge wall was built along the coast to protect the city from enemy attack by sea.

Rabat is Morocco's capital today. The royal palace stands in the city with the Hassan Tower—the *minaret* (prayer tower) of an incomplete mosque—rising above it on a bluff. Nearby is the tomb of Mohammed V, the first ruler of independent Morocco.

In the 1600's, an Arab sharifian tribe took control of Morocco. The sharifs were said to be descended from Muhammad, founder of Islam. One of the sharifian rulers, Ismail, made Meknès his capital. There, he built palaces similar to the Palace of Versailles in France. Ismail also had mosques erected, and he ordered the construction of forts called *casbahs* (also spelled *kasbahs)* and deep dungeons for his prisoners.

Tourists crowd the central square of the medina (old section) of Marrakech. Founded in 1062, the city was the capital of a Berber empire until the 1400's, when Arab rulers replaced the Berbers.

A gateway to the old quarter of the city of Fez is constructed in traditional Islamic style. The city was founded as a royal capital in 808. It declined during the 1600's, when a new capital was built at Meknès, but Fez became the capital again from 1728 until 1912.

Casablanca and Tangier

Casablanca was never a royal capital, but it is an important city and the largest in Morocco. Founded in 1575 by the Portuguese on the site of a small fishing village, Casablanca today is a dynamic industrial and business center as well as a major port. Casablanca was also the site of a historic meeting in January 1943, when U.S. President Franklin D. Roosevelt and British Prime Minister Winston Churchill met in the city to plan the next phase of World War II (1939-1945).

Like Casablanca, Tangier was never a royal capital, but the city ranks second only to Casablanca among Moroccan seaports. Located near the northern tip of Morocco, Tangier came under Arab control in the 700's. Portugal, Spain, and England also held the city at various times. From 1923 to 1956, major European powers placed the city under international control. Today, Tangier is a center of shipping and tourism. From the sea, the city looks like an amphitheater, with rows of white houses lining its hills.

At a sidewalk cafe in the historic city of Fez, Moroccans in Western-style clothing enjoy refreshments. Fez remains the center of Islamic religion and culture in Morocco.

TOURISM

Tourism is an important source of income for Morocco. Every year, millions of tourists come to visit the nation's historic cities and enjoy its beach resorts, scenic mountains, and desert vistas.

The cities

Fez, Meknès, and Marrakech were once the capital cities of empires. Today, their royal palaces, graceful mosques, and colorful markets attract many tourists. In Marrakech, for example, a large square is the setting for busy *suqs* (markets) that have taken place there every day for centuries. Water merchants pose for the tourists and sell a drink of water to the thirsty. Jugglers and storytellers entertain the crowds.

Some towns and cities draw tourists to their beautiful beach resorts. The southwest coastal town of Agadir, which was largely destroyed by an earthquake in 1960, was rebuilt and is now a popular seaside resort.

In addition to their many tourist attractions, the cities serve as starting points to the interior of Morocco. Roads link all major Moroccan cities, and bus lines reach almost every part of the country.

The mountains

The little town of Azrou, named for the huge rock bluff on which it stands, lies near the edge of Morocco's Middle Atlas Mountains. The town is surrounded by pine forests where monkeys leap from tree to tree, and some of the Middle Atlas range's most beautiful landscapes lie to the south of Azrou.

Pine and cedar forests line these mountain valleys, and tumbling cascades of water mark the source of the Oum er Rbia River. Nearby is a Berber village with ruins of a casbah built by Sultan Mulay Ismail. On the road from Azrou to Marrakech, a dramatic waterfall named Cascades d'Ouzoud plunges against a backdrop of dark red rocks. The Middle Atlas town of Midelt is famed for its carpet suq.

The Grand Atlas is Morocco's highest mountain range. These mountains act as a natural barrier between the coastal plains and towns to the northwest and the Sahara to the southeast. The main pass through the mountains is the Tichka Pass. The area was remote until the 20th century, and even now few tourists visit this area.

A river valley sprawls beneath the lofty Atlas Mountains, which guard the Sahara's northern approaches with their snow-capped peaks. For centuries, caravans passed this way on their long journeys across the region.

Hiking in the Atlas is popular among foreign tourists. The highest peaks in the Atlas include Jebel Toubkal, which soars 13,665 feet (4,165 meters) above sea level, and Irhil m'Goun, which rises 13,356 feet (4,071 meters). Hundreds of casbahs lie in the Grand Atlas valleys in the south near Ouarzazate.

The Atlas Mountains, which were a barrier to travel for centuries, are also a climate barrier, preventing ocean moisture from reaching the southeast. The western slopes receive rain and even snow in winter, but in the east and south, the mountain slopes descend gradually into the great Sahara.

The desert

From the eastern Grand Atlas slopes, the Sahara comes into view. River valleys lie green against the sand, and palm oases and mud villages are scattered throughout the desert.

Great Moorish caravans of traders and camels once crossed this region. South-bound caravans carried cloth, glass beads, salt, and other products, returning north with gold, slaves, leather, pepper, and kola nuts. Zagora was a stopping place for caravans en route to or from Timbuktu, a great trading center to the south in what is now Mali. Zagora has beautiful palm groves and several well-preserved *ksour* (fortified villages). From Zagora, travelers may journey out to Figuig near the Algerian border, one of the largest oases in North Africa.

Among the residents of the southern oases are the Harratines, a black people. Most Harratines work as farm laborers, and after choosing the Berber farmer they wish to work for, they sacrifice an animal at the Berber's door. This sacrifice involves a curse because any Berber who refuses to hire the Harratine is shamed in the eyes of God.

A shepherd tends his flock in the Middle Atlas Mountains. The Atlas Mountains of northern Morocco resemble the grassy mountains of Mediterranean Europe and have some heavily forested sections. But only scrubby vegetation grows on the Atlas slopes in the south.

A casbah guards the road to the Middle Atlas city of Skoura. Great Moorish caravans, laden with gold, needed such protection on their dangerous journey to Moroccan cities through the Atlas Mountains.

MOZAMBIQUE

The nation of Mozambique lies along the southeastern coast of Africa. People have lived in this region since the 4000's B.C. Bantu-speaking people arrived and settled in the area before A.D. 100, and by the 800's Arabs were living in the region.

The first Europeans to visit what is now Mozambique were Portuguese explorers in 1497. They established a trading post in 1505 and eventually turned the region into a center for slave trading. Through the years, Portuguese control was threatened. However by 1885, much of Africa had come under the control of various European powers, and Mozambique was recognized as a Portuguese colony.

The Portuguese did little to develop Mozambique until the late 1800's, when towns and railroads were built and the colony's Portuguese population grew.

In the 1950's, many black Africans in Mozambique became increasingly discontented with Portuguese rule. A guerrilla group known as the Front for the Liberation of Mozambique, or Frelimo, was established in 1961. Frelimo began attacking the Portuguese in 1964 and eventually gained control of northern Mozambique. Fighting between Frelimo and Portuguese forces continued for 10 years, until Portugal finally agreed to give Mozambique its independence.

On June 25, 1975, the nation of Mozambique was born. Frelimo took control and created a government based on the Communist philosophies of Karl Marx and V. I. Lenin. The highest governmental power lay with the Frelimo party's Central Committee. The Frelimo government controlled education, health and legal services, housing, farmland, and major industries. Most of the Portuguese left Mozambique at that time.

In 1976, Mozambique closed its border with Rhodesia (now Zimbabwe) to protest that country's white minority government. Fighting broke out, but the problem was resolved when blacks gained control in Rhodesia in 1980.

Mozambique also aided guerrilla forces that were fighting the white minority government in South

FACTS

● Official name:	República de Moçambique (Republic of Mozambique)
● Capital:	Maputo
● Terrain:	Mostly coastal lowlands, uplands in center, high plateaus in northwest, mountains in west
● Area:	308,642 mi² (799,380 km²)
● Climate:	Tropical to subtropical
● Main rivers:	Zambezi, Limpopo, Lugenda
● Highest elevation:	Mount Binga, 7,992 ft (2,436 m)
● Lowest elevation:	Indian Ocean, sea level
● Form of government:	Republic
● Head of state:	President
● Head of government:	President
● Administrative areas:	10 provincias (provinces), 1 cidade (city)
● Legislature:	Assembleia da República (Assembly of the Republic) with 250 members serving five-year terms
● Court system:	Supreme Court
● Armed forces:	11,200 troops
● National holiday:	Independence Day - June 25 (1975)
● Estimated 2010 population:	22,351,000
● Population density:	72 persons per mi² (28 per km²)
● Population distribution:	65% rural, 35% urban
● Life expectancy in years:	Male, 42; female, 42
● Doctors per 1,000 people:	Less than 0.05
● Birth rate per 1,000:	39
● Death rate per 1,000:	20
● Infant mortality:	108 deaths per 1,000 live births
● Age structure:	0-14: 44%; 15-64: 53%; 65 and over: 3%
● Internet users per 100 people:	1.6
● Internet code:	.mz
● Languages spoken:	Portuguese (official), indigenous dialects
● Religions:	Christian 40%, Muslim 20%, indigenous African and other beliefs 40%
● Currency:	Metical
● Gross domestic product (GDP) in 2008:	$9.73 billion U.S.
● Real annual growth rate (2008):	6.5%
● GDP per capita (2008):	$466 U.S.
● Goods exported:	Aluminum, cashew nuts, cotton, electrical energy, prawns, sugar, tobacco
● Goods imported:	Chemicals, machinery, motor vehicles, petroleum products, rice, wheat
● Trading partners:	Australia, China, Netherlands, South Africa

Africa. In turn, South Africa aided the Mozambique National Resistance, or Renamo, a guerrilla group that was fighting the Frelimo government. In 1984, Mozambique and South Africa signed a treaty pledging to stop aiding the guerrillas.

But Renamo continued to fight in Mozambique, and the war became widespread and more vicious. Renamo attacked civilians, including women and children. Bridges and railroads were destroyed, and farming was disrupted. The violence caused some 1.5 million people to flee the country. At the same time, droughts led to malnutrition and starvation for millions.

In 1989, the government ended its Marxist economic policies. A new constitution was adopted in 1990. In 1992, President Joaquim Chissano and the head of Renamo signed a peace treaty. Multiparty elections were held in 1994. Chissano won the presidential election and was reelected in 1999. In 2004, Armando Guebuza of the Frelimo party was elected president of Mozambique. He was reelected in 2009.

In February 2000, Cyclone Eline and heavy rains struck Mozambique, causing widespread flooding. About 700 people were killed, and more than 500,000 were left homeless. Severe floods caused additional damage the following year.

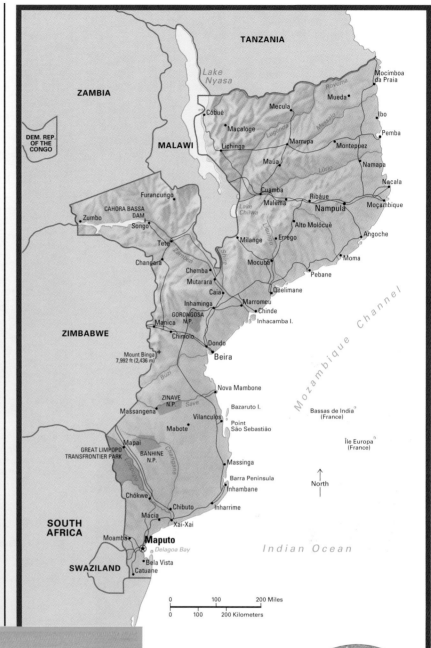

Maputo, capital of Mozambique, lies on the shore of the Indian Ocean. Founded by the Portuguese in 1780, the town was called Lourenço Marques until 1976.

Mozambique, once known as Portuguese East Africa, became independent in 1975. Civil war and droughts have badly hurt the country since that time.

MOZAMBIQUE **171**

ECONOMY AND PEOPLE

Mozambique stretches for about 1,500 miles (2,500 kilometers) along Africa's southeastern coast, and its shoreline has many fine harbors. The country's port facilities are used by neighboring countries, and payments by South Africa, Zimbabwe, Swaziland, and Malawi for the use of its railroads and ports are important to Mozambique's economy.

Behind the sand dunes and swamps that lie along the coastal region, a flat plain extends inland from the coast and covers almost half of Mozambique. Beyond the plain, the land rises steadily, and high plateaus and mountains run along much of the western border. The plain and highlands are covered mainly by grasslands and tropical forests. Crocodiles, elephants, lions, zebras, and other wildlife roam through Mozambique.

Freight trains carry the products of neighboring southeast African countries to Mozambique's ports. The trains are subject to fees for the use of Mozambique's facilities. This money is important to Mozambique's economy.

Rural villagers, like these women with their children, make up about two-thirds of Mozambique's population. Most speak Bantu languages.

Mozambique has a basically tropical climate, but temperatures and rainfall vary considerably in different areas. Most of the annual rainfall occurs from November to March.

Many sizable rivers flow east through Mozambique into the Indian Ocean, creating river basins with extremely fertile soil. Agriculture is the people's leading economic activity. Cashew trees and coconut palms grow throughout the country, and both cashews and coconuts are important farm products. Other crops include cassava, corn, cotton, and sugar cane. Mozambique's farmers also raise beef and dairy cattle, chickens, and goats.

While some Mozambicans use fairly modern techniques, most farming methods are extremely simple. Some farmers use the ancient *slash-and-burn* method of farming, which involves cutting and burning forest trees to clear the land for planting. Ashes from the burned vegetation fertilize the soil, and the farmers can grow crops there for a year or two. When the soil

Simple hand tools are used by farmers to prepare the ground for planting. The Marxist government's policy of setting up large collective farms was a failure. Today, small farms are encouraged in Mozambique.

loses its fertility, the farmers move on to a new plot of ground, where they repeat the process.

The Marxist government tried to create Communist-style cooperative farms after Mozambique became independent, but these were not successful. In the early 1980's, the government shifted to family-run farms.

The government also decided to allow private business to increase, and began helping some Mozambicans to start their own businesses. Industrial development has been slow, however, and limited mainly to food processing and oil refining. The nation's mining industry consists mainly of coal mining in central Mozambique.

While most Mozambicans are farmers, some people catch fish or shrimp in the Indian Ocean for a living. Many also go to South Africa in search of work.

Farmers carry sacks of produce to riverboats that will transport them down the Zambezi River.

About two-thirds of Mozambique's people live in rural areas. The rest live in urban centers, mainly along the coast.

Most Mozambicans belong to groups of Bantu-speaking peoples. The largest of these ethnic groups is the Makua-Lomwe. Small groups of Arabs, Europeans, and Pakistanis also live in Mozambique. Portuguese is the country's official language, but few black Mozambicans speak it. Some speak English when conducting business.

About 40 percent of the people practice traditional African religions. Many of these people are *animists,* who believe that everything in nature has a soul, while others worship the spirits of their ancestors. Another 40 percent of the people are Christians, mostly Roman Catholics. About 20 percent of the people are Muslims.

Most adult Mozambicans cannot read and write, but the government has started programs to educate the people. A university was established in Maputo in 1962.

For many years, the people of Mozambique did not vote for their government officials. Frelimo was the country's only political party, and it controlled the government. But under a 1992 peace pact between Frelimo and the Mozambique National Resistance (Renamo), other political parties were legalized.

Myanmar, also called Burma, is the largest nation on the Southeast Asian Peninsula. The country is bordered by Bangladesh, China, India, Laos, Thailand, and the Bay of Bengal. The Irrawaddy River flows down the middle of the country and is enclosed by mountains in the west, north, and east of Myanmar. The river empties into the Bay of Bengal through many mouths, forming a delta. Myanmar's largest city, Yangon, lies on the Irrawaddy Delta. Yangon, also called Rangoon, is also the country's chief port and industrial center. It is the site of the golden-domed Shwe Dagon pagoda, the most famous Buddhist temple in Myanmar.

Most of Myanmar's people live in villages on the Irrawaddy Delta and in the Irrawaddy Valley. The land in these areas is farmed by Burmans, an ethnic group that makes up about two-thirds of the population.

Smaller ethnic groups in Myanmar include the Karen, Shan, Arakanese, Chin, Kachin, Mon, Naga, and Wa. Most of these groups live in the hills and mountains that separate Myanmar from India, China, Laos, and Thailand. Each of these so-called *hill peoples* preserves its own culture, and some have fought to obtain more rights or to gain independence from the government of Myanmar.

The first known settlers in what is now Myanmar were Mon people who moved into the region as early as 3000 B.C. Many other ethnic groups, including the Burmans, came during the A.D. 800's.

Nearly all of Myanmar's people speak Burmese, the country's official language. About 90 percent of the population is Buddhist. The majority of Myanmar's people live in farm villages. Most villages consist of about 50 to 100 bamboo houses with thatch roofs. The houses are built on poles above the ground for protection against floods and wild animals.

Land and climate

Myanmar has three main land regions: the Eastern Mountain System, the Western Mountain Belt, and the Central Belt. The Eastern Mountain System separates Myanmar from Thailand, Laos, and China. Some of the world's finest jade and rubies come from the region.

174

MYANMAR

The Western Mountain Belt is a region of thick forests along the border between Myanmar and India. A group of low mountains called the Arakan Yoma forms the southern part of the region and extends to the Bay of Bengal. A narrow plain of rich farmland borders the bay.

The Central Belt lies between the eastern and western mountain regions. It includes Myanmar's highest mountains in the far north. The Central Belt consists chiefly of the Irrawaddy and Sittang river valleys.

Most of Myanmar has a tropical climate. From late May to October, Myanmar receives nearly all of its rain. The heavy rainfall is brought by seasonal winds called *monsoons*, which sweep northeastward from the Indian Ocean. From late October to mid-February, temperatures are at their lowest, though the climate remains tropical throughout most of the country. From late February to about mid-May, the temperatures often top 100° F (38° C) in many parts of Myanmar.

Natural resources

Myanmar's potential for economic growth is strong because of the country's wealth of natural resources. Rice, Myanmar's chief crop, is grown in the fertile Irrawaddy River Valley, where there is plenty of water and rainfall. The people of Myanmar eat rice with almost every meal. Farmers in Myanmar also grow beans, sesame seeds, sugar cane, and vegetables. They raise cattle, chickens, and hogs.

The forests that cover about half of Myanmar's land area have most of the world's teakwood. Unfortunately, much of this valuable forestland has been cut down for export to Thailand.

Myanmar also has a wealth of minerals, including copper, lead, tin, tungsten, and silver. It is also rich in jade and such precious stones as rubies and sapphires. However, the nation's mineral wealth remains undeveloped.

MYANMAR TODAY

Myanmar, also called Burma, won independence from the United Kingdom on Jan. 4, 1948. However, the new government's conflict with Communist rebels and various ethnic groups led to civil war. In 1962, General Ne Win seized control, and his Revolutionary Council set up a Socialist government that remained in power until 1988.

The government was organized under the banner of the Burma Socialist Programme Party (BSPP), the only political party allowed in Burma at that time. Military officers held all the key posts. The BSPP cut Burma's ties with other countries and restricted visits by foreign reporters and tourists. The government closed schools, took over newspapers, and established strict control over the nation's industry and agriculture. This rigid system had disastrous economic consequences. Farmers were paid so little for their crops that they grew no more than was necessary. Agricultural and industrial production fell. Student protests against the government were put down violently, and revolts by some of the hill peoples flared.

On March 2, 1974, a new constitution officially created the Socialist Republic of the Union of Burma, with Ne Win as president. Although the new constitution reestablished elections, the BSPP still held all power.

In 1988, Burmese students rose up against the government, calling for an end to one-party rule. As a result, Ne Win resigned as head of the BSPP in July. A military coup in September overthrew the unstable government, replacing it with the newly established State Law and Order Restoration Council (SLORC). The new regime, led by General Saw Maung, killed thousands of protesters. In 1989, the SLORC announced that it had changed the country's official name to the Union of Myanmar.

The SLORC allowed multiparty elections in 1990. The main opposition party, the National League for Democracy (NLD), won a landslide victory, but the party's leader, Aung San Suu Kyi, was placed under house arrest. The SLORC would not allow a transfer of

FACTS

Official name:	Pyidaungsu Thammada Myanmar Naingngandaw (Republic of the Union of Myanmar)
Capital:	Naypyidaw
Terrain:	Central lowlands ringed by steep, rugged highlands
Area:	261,228 mi² (676,578 km²)
Climate:	Tropical monsoon; cloudy, rainy, hot, humid summers (southwest monsoon, June to September); less cloudy, scant rainfall, mild temperatures, lower humidity during winter (northeast monsoon, December to April)
Main rivers:	Irrawaddy, Sittang, Salween
Highest elevation:	Hkakabo Razi, 19,296 ft (5,881 m)
Lowest elevation:	Andaman Sea, sea level
Form of government:	Military regime
Head of state:	Chairman of the State Peace and Development Council
Head of government:	Prime minister
Administrative areas:	7 yin-mya (divisions), 7 pyine-mya (states)
Legislature:	Pyidaungsu Hluttaw consisting of upper house with up to 224 members and lower house with up to 440 members, established by 2008 constitution
Court system:	Limited
Armed forces:	406,000 troops
National holidays:	Independence Day - January 4 (1948) Union Day - February 12 (1947)
Estimated 2010 population:	50,053,000
Population density:	192 persons per mi² (74 per km²)
Population distribution:	69% rural, 31% urban
Life expectancy in years:	Male, 60; female, 65
Doctors per 1,000 people:	0.4
Birth rate per 1,000:	18
Death rate per 1,000:	10
Infant mortality:	70 deaths per 1,000 live births
Age structure:	0-14: 26%; 15-64: 68%; 65 and over: 6%
Internet users per 100 people:	0.1
Internet code:	.mm
Languages spoken:	Burmese, local languages
Religions:	Buddhist 89%, Christian 4%, Muslim 4%, animist 1%, other 2%
Currency:	Kyat
Gross domestic product (GDP) in 2008:	$27.18 billion U.S.
Real annual growth rate (2008):	0.9%
GDP per capita (2008):	$523 U.S.
Goods exported:	Clothing, fish products, natural gas, teak, vegetables
Goods imported:	Edible oil, machinery, petroleum products, plastics, transportation equipment
Trading partners:	China, India, Japan, Singapore, Thailand

power. Aung San Suu Kyi—whose father, Aung San, was a leader of Burma's independence movement—was awarded the 1991 Nobel Peace Prize for her nonviolent struggle for democracy and human rights.

The SLORC changed its name to the State Peace and Development Council (SPDC) in 1997. Major nations withheld economic aid because of the SPDC's human rights violations and its failure to open talks with the NLD. During much of the late 1900's, rebel groups fought the government and each other. Myanmar's military rulers reached cease-fire agreements with most rebels in the 1990's, but fighting continued with other groups.

In 2005, Myanmar began moving government offices to Naypyidaw, the new capital. In 2008, Cyclone Nargis hit Myanmar, leaving nearly 140,000 people dead or missing.

Also in 2008, Myanmar adopted a new constitution that guaranteed the military a leading role in government. In 2010, the Union Solidarity and Development Party (USDP), a civilian party backed by the military, won the most seats in a legislative election and began political reforms. The party freed Suu Kyi and relaxed media restrictions, among other reforms. The new government was sworn in in 2011, and the SPDC was dissolved.

In 2012, Suu Kyi and other members of her NLD opposition party were elected to seats in parliament. That same year, the United States began restoring diplomatic relations with Myanmar.

Myanmar is bordered by Bangladesh, China, India, Laos, Thailand, and the Bay of Bengal. Mountains in the west, north, and east of Myanmar enclose the Irrawaddy River Valley.

Visitors to Yangon's Shwe Dagon pagoda, Myanmar's most famous Buddhist temple, find shelter from the rain beneath their umbrellas. About 90 percent of the people of Myanmar are followers of Buddhism.

HISTORY

The earliest inhabitants of what is now Myanmar were the Mon people, who moved into the region around 3000 B.C. They came from what is now southwestern China and settled near the mouths of the Salween and Sittang rivers, where they grew rice. In time, the Mon came to be greatly influenced by nearby India. Around 200 B.C., some members of the Mon group began to adopt Theravada Buddhism, which was founded in India.

The Pyu arrived in the A.D. 600's, followed, during the 800's, by the Burmans, Chin, Kachin, Karen, and Shan. Like the Mon, these later arrivals migrated from an area in central Asia that is now southwestern China. In general, these peoples lived apart from one another and kept their own cultures. The largest group—the Burmans—obtained the most fertile lands in the region.

In 1044, the Burman ruler Anawrahta united the region under one kingdom. In order to keep peace with the Mon people, the Burmans adopted some features of the Mon and Pyu cultures, including Theravada Buddhism. Art and architecture flourished in the kingdom, and hundreds of beautiful Buddhist shrines and pagodas were built in the capital city of Pagan.

Foreign invaders

The rich kingdom was shattered by Mongol invaders led by Kublai Khan, who captured Pagan in 1287. The once-unified ethnic groups split apart and formed separate states.

Another Burman kingdom was established at Toungoo during the 1500's and lasted until 1752, when it was brought down by a Mon rebellion. By this time, European traders had become well established in Burma, and the Dutch and British East India companies aided the Mon rebellion.

The last Burman kingdom was founded by Alaungpaya, a Burman leader, after the Mon rebellion. However, three wars with the British—triggered by resistance to the United Kingdom's commercial and territorial ambitions—led to the collapse of the last kingdom. By 1885, British forces had conquered all of the country then known as Burma.

The Shwe Dagon pagoda in Yangon is the most sacred Buddhist pagoda for the Burmese. It contains relics of the past four Buddhas. The shrine dates back to the 500's.

Statues of Buddha are found all over Myanmar. Buddhism, adopted by the Mon around the 200's B.C., was founded in India about 500 B.C. by a teacher called Buddha. Buddhism has been a dominant force in most of Asia for many centuries and has hundreds of millions of followers today.

British rule

Burma became a province of India, which was also under British rule, and its population and economy grew. However, many Burmese demanded separation from India and full independence. Although the United Kingdom allowed the Burmese to set up a legislature in the 1920's, unrest continued.

In the early 1930's, university students called the Thakins worked for independence. In 1936, led by Aung San and U Nu, the Thakins organized a student strike that forced the United Kingdom to separate Burma from India and grant the Burmese partial self-government. However, the Burmese still were denied full independence.

During World War II (1939-1945), the Thakins helped the Japanese drive the British out of Burma. The Japanese declared Burma's independence in 1943, but the Japanese actually controlled the government. Disliking Japanese rule even more than British rule, the Burmese then fought against Japan and formed the Anti-Fascist People's Freedom League (AFPFL), led by General Aung San, the former Thakin leader. The AFPFL helped the United Kingdom and other Allied powers regain control of Burma in 1945.

In the meantime, the AFPFL had become a powerful political party under the leadership of Aung San, and the party resisted British rule. In the face of this challenge, the United Kingdom named Aung San prime minister of Burma in 1947. However, Aung San was assassinated before independence came, so the British appointed AFPFL Vice President U Nu as prime minister. Burma finally won full independence on Jan. 4, 1948.

A Myanmar activist holds a portrait of opposition leader Aung San Suu Kyi. She had won the 1991 Nobel Peace Prize for her nonviolent struggle for democracy and human rights in her country.

NAMIBIA

Namibia is an area of southwest Africa that became an independent nation in 1990. It was formerly named South West Africa. Much of the country's land is dry and unfertile, and droughts often occur. However, the land is rich in mineral deposits. The Kalahari Desert occupies eastern Namibia. Windhoek is the capital and largest city.

South African rule

Most of Namibia's people are black Africans, but prior to independence, the region had been controlled by Europeans since the 1800's. Beginning in 1868, Germans colonized the Namibian coastal area. From 1904 to 1907, they brutally put down a revolt by killing about 65,000 black Africans. The Germans lost the area to South African troops during World War I (1914-1918).

For many years, the white-minority government of South Africa ruled Namibia as if it were a province of its own country, despite protests from other nations. In 1966, the United Nations (UN) took steps to try to bring Namibia under UN control. In 1971, the International Court of Justice declared South Africa's control of Namibia illegal.

In 1960, black Namibians formed a group called the South West African People's Organization (SWAPO). At first, SWAPO tried to persuade South Africa to grant Namibia independence. But beginning in the mid-1960's, it began a guerrilla war. SWAPO and South African forces fought each other until 1989.

In 1988, South Africa agreed to grant Namibia independence, and on March 21, 1990, Namibia officially became an independent nation. In 1990, Sam Nujoma, the leader of SWAPO, was elected as Namibia's first president. He was reelected in 1994 and 1999. In 2004, Hifikepunye Pohamba, the SWAPO candidate, was elected president. He was reelected in 2009.

The people and their work

Namibians belong to a number of ethnic groups. The Ovambo (also spelled Owambo) form the largest group, making up more than half of the country's population.

FACTS

Official name:	Republic of Namibia
Capital:	Windhoek
Terrain:	Mostly high plateau; Namib Desert along coast; Kalahari Desert in east
Area:	318,261 mi^2 (824,292 km^2)
Climate:	Desert; hot, dry; rainfall sparse and erratic
Main rivers:	Kunene, Okavango, Kwando, Zambezi, Orange
Highest elevation:	Brandberg, 8,465 ft (2,580 m)
Lowest elevation:	Atlantic Ocean, sea level
Form of government:	Republic
Head of state:	President
Head of government:	President
Administrative areas:	13 regions
Legislature:	Legislature consisting of the National Council with 26 members serving six-year terms and the National Assembly with 72 members serving five-year terms
Court system:	Supreme Court
Armed forces:	9,200 troops
National holiday:	Independence Day - March 21 (1990)
Estimated 2010 population:	2,137,000
Population density:	7 persons per mi^2 (3 per km^2)
Population distribution:	64% rural, 36% urban
Life expectancy in years:	Male, 50; female, 49
Doctors per 1,000 people:	0.3
Birth rate per 1,000:	25
Death rate per 1,000:	13
Infant mortality:	47 deaths per 1,000 live births
Age structure:	0-14: 37%; 15-64: 59%; 65 and over: 4%
Internet users per 100 people:	5
Internet code:	.na
Languages spoken:	English (official), Afrikaans (spoken by most of the population), German, indigenous languages
Religions:	Christian 90% (mostly Lutheran), indigenous beliefs 10%
Currency:	Namibian dollar, South African rand
Gross domestic product (GDP) in 2008:	$8.46 billion U.S.
Real annual growth rate (2008):	3.3%
GDP per capita (2008):	$4,044 U.S.
Goods exported:	Beverages, copper, diamonds, fish, gold, meat, uranium, zinc
Goods imported:	Chemicals, food, machinery, motor vehicles, petroleum products
Trading partners:	Angola, Italy, South Africa, Spain, United Kingdom

NAMIBIA

Fortresslike rock formations shaped by thousands of years of wind erosion rise up from the inland plateau near Khorixas, on the edge of the Namib Desert.

They live in the north, near the Angolan border, in a region called Ovamboland or Ovambo. Other northerners include the Kavango and the Caprivians. The Damara and the Herero occupy central Namibia. San and Tswana people live along the country's eastern border. Two groups of people of mixed ancestry live south of Windhoek—the Basters, who live in or near Rehoboth, and the Nama, who inhabit the far south.

Namibia's population also includes people of Dutch, English, and German descent. Most of these people live in urban areas. People of mixed European and African ancestry, called Coloureds, generally live in urban areas.

Most rural people in Namibia fish, grow crops, or raise livestock for a living. Their food crops include corn, grapes, millet, and vegetables. Beef and dairy cattle, goats, and sheep are the most important livestock. Most rural Namibians raise barely enough food for their own use, as drought and other problems have troubled farmers and herders. In addition, overfishing has reduced the catch of anchovies, mackerel, and sardines in the Atlantic Ocean.

Although much of Namibia's land is dry and infertile, the country is rich in minerals, including diamonds and uranium. Many Ovambo and Kavango men work in copper mines at Tsumeb or in southern diamond mines. Lead, tin, and zinc also help make mining one of Namibia's most important economic activities. Little manufacturing takes place in Namibia.

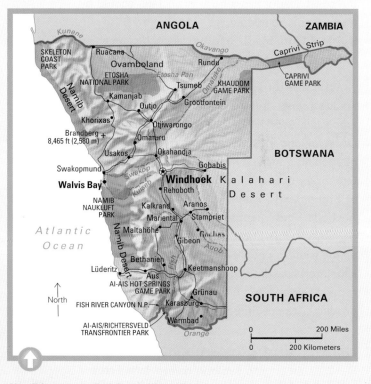

Namibia, once called South West Africa, is situated on Africa's west coast. Major rivers form its northern and southern borders, but inland Namibia is dry.

NAURU

The Republic of Nauru, a small island country in the central Pacific Ocean, is the third smallest country in the world, after Vatican City and Monaco. Nauru is rich in *phosphates*—valuable chemical compounds used in making fertilizers—and phosphate exports are important to Nauru's economy.

Land and people

Nauru is an oval-shaped coral island about 40 miles (65 kilometers) south of the equator, with an area of only 8 square miles (21 square kilometers). Most of the island consists of a plateau, 200 feet (61 meters) high, that contains deposits of phosphates. A small area of fertile land surrounds a lagoon near the center of the plateau, and another belt of fertile land extends around the coast. Nauru has a tropical climate, cooled by trade winds. Temperatures range from 76° to 93° F (24° to 34° C), and the island has an annual rainfall of about 80 inches (200 centimeters).

About half of Nauru's population of 11,000 are Nauruans—people of mixed Polynesian, Micronesian, and Melanesian ancestry. They are Christian, and most speak both the Nauruan language and English. The rest of Nauru's people are temporary residents from the Pacific island groups of Kiribati and Tuvalu, and from Hong Kong and Australia. These people come to Nauru for limited periods to work in the phosphate industry. Most of the island's people live along the 12-mile (19-kilometer) coastline. In the past, the islanders raised their own food, but most food and other products are now imported.

History and government

In 1798, an English explorer named John Fearn became the first European to visit Nauru. Germany took over the island in 1888 and administered it until 1914, when Australia took control. After World War I (1914-1918), Australia began to administer the island under a League of Nations mandate held by the United Kingdom, Australia, and New Zealand.

FACTS

Official name:	Republic of Nauru
Capital:	None
Terrain:	Sandy beach rises to fertile ring around raised coral reefs with phosphate plateau in center
Area:	8 mi² (21 km²)
Climate:	Tropical; monsoonal; rainy season (November to February)
Main rivers:	N/A
Highest elevation:	Unnamed location, 229 ft (70 m)
Lowest elevation:	Pacific Ocean, sea level
Form of government:	Republic
Head of state:	President
Head of government:	President
Administrative areas:	14 districts
Legislature:	Parliament with 18 members serving three-year terms
Court system:	Supreme Court
Armed forces:	Australia is responsible for Nauru's defense
National holiday:	Independence Day - January 31 (1968)
Estimated 2010 population:	11,000
Population density:	1,375 persons per mi² (524 per km²)
Population distribution:	100% urban
Life expectancy in years:	Male, 57; female, 63
Doctors per 1,000 people:	0.8
Birth rate per 1,000:	28
Death rate per 1,000:	8
Infant mortality:	25 deaths per 1,000 live births
Age structure:	0-14: 37%; 15-64: 61%; 65 and over: 2%
Internet users per 100 people:	2.3
Internet code:	.nr
Languages spoken:	Nauruan (official), English
Religions:	Protestant 67%, Roman Catholic 33%
Currency:	Australian dollar
Gross domestic product (GDP) in 2008:	N/A
Real annual growth rate (2008):	N/A
GDP per capita (2008):	N/A
Goods exported:	Chemicals, machinery, manufactured goods, phosphates
Goods imported:	Food, machinery, manufactured goods, petroleum products
Trading partners:	Australia, Germany, South Korea

Japan seized Nauru during World War II (1939-1945). Australia retook the island in 1945, later gaining control of the area under a trusteeship with the United Kingdom and New Zealand. The United Nations granted Nauru independence in 1968. In 1970, the Nauruan government gained control of its phosphate industry.

Nauru is now a republic and a member of the Commonwealth of Nations. An 18-member Parliament makes its laws. The people elect Parliament members who, in turn, elect a president—all to three-year terms. All Nauruans who are 20 years old or older are required to vote. The president selects a Cabinet, and together they carry out the government's operations. Nauru has no capital. The main government offices are on the southwestern part of the island.

The government provides Nauruans with free medical care and modern homes at low rents. Children between the ages of 6 and 17 attend school. The government pays the expenses of students who go to college in other countries.

The government has used revenue from phosphate exports to provide these services, but the phosphate deposits on the island are being used up rapidly. The government has saved revenue from phosphate exports to help the people after all the phosphates have been mined.

Sea birds on Nauru deposit droppings that are rich in phosphates—a valuable fertilizer. The nation's economy depends on phosphate exports.

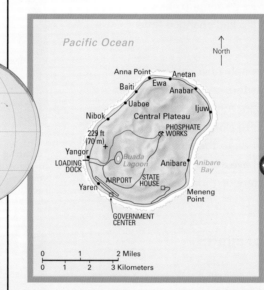

The Republic of Nauru, in the central Pacific, is the third smallest country in the world. Most of the island is a plateau that contains deposits of phosphates.

Ancient and modern vessels reflect the contrasting cultures in Nauru. Outrigger canoes sail near a dock where a freighter loads phosphates.

NEPAL

Nepal is a mountain kingdom located along the southern range of the Himalaya between China and India. Although it is a small country, Nepal has one of the widest variations in altitude on Earth—ranging from the world's highest mountain, Mount Everest, at 29,035 feet (8,850 meters) to 230 feet (70 meters) above sea level.

An exotic land

Until the 1950's, Nepal was isolated from the rest of the world. Largely untouched by new developments and technologies, the Nepalese way of life had changed little through the centuries.

Hundreds of thousands of people now come each year to visit this enchanting land. Visitors are drawn by the extraordinary scenery, mountaineers come to scale the peaks of the Himalaya, and trekkers hike along the trails. From the crowded streets of Kathmandu to the remote mountain villages, Nepal appears to have escaped the passage of time. It is as exotic and mysterious today as it was centuries ago.

Mountains, valleys, farmland, and jungles

Nepal can be divided into three land regions: (1) high mountains made up of the Himalaya, (2) the hills and valleys, and (3) low plains called the Tarai (or Terai). Because these regions are located at different altitudes, their climates, plants, and animals vary greatly.

The Himalaya, in the north, make up much of Nepal. Forests cover the mountains up to the altitude of about 12,000 feet (3,660 meters) above sea level. At higher altitudes, permanent snow and ice cover the peaks, which tower above steep river valleys. Only grasses, moss, and *lichens* (mosslike plants) grow at the higher elevations. Mountaineers in the Himalaya herd sheep and yaks. Birds and mammals are seen occasionally. The snow leopard, for example, may use one of the high mountain passes to get from one valley to another.

South of the Himalaya lie the hills and valleys. Corn, rice, millet, and wheat thrive in the cool, rainy climate on hillside terraces and in the valleys. A wide variety of trees and bamboo grasses are found in the dense forests of this

Terracing allows Nepalese farmers to use steep hillsides for growing crops. Terraces retain rain water and prevent soil from washing down the hillside. However, terracing can also weaken the stability of the slopes if not well designed and maintained.

The magnificent landscape of Nepal attracts thousands of trekkers each year. Travel agencies in Kathmandu provide transportation to mountain sites. The growing tourist industry is important to the country's economy.

region. Timber from the sal, sissoo, pine, oak, poplar, and walnut trees is an important natural resource for the Nepalese.

The valleys of this region are home to Nepal's historic cities—Kathmandu, Patan, Bhaktapur, Gurkha, and Pokhara. Kathmandu, Nepal's capital and largest city, is the center of the country's tourist industry. Kathmandu is known the world over for its many Hindu and Buddhist temples.

The Tarai is a flat, fertile river plain along Nepal's border with India. Its tropical climate and rich farmland make this region ideal for growing corn, jute, millet, mustard, rice, sugar cane, and tobacco. Tarai farmers also raise cattle and water buffalo.

Wildlife in the jungles of the Tarai includes crocodiles, elephants, deer, leopards, rhinoceroses, and tigers. The Tarai's Chitwan National Park is one of the greatest wildlife reserves in Asia.

The Tarai region of Nepal, a fertile river plain that lies along the southern border, provides habitats for a wide range of animals and plants. Some species are not found anywhere else on Earth. Birds of Nepal include the egret (A), whiskered tern (C), grey shrike (E), yellow-billed magpie (M), and pheasant (N). Green bee-eaters (O) are a common sight, often resting on trees between insect-catching expeditions. Leopards (B) and tigers (L) are also found in Nepal. Herds of elephants (D) roam the vast grasslands, along with the extremely rare Indian rhinoceros (K). Nepal's forests provide cover for wild ox (I), buffalo (J), and several species of deer, including the chital (H), sambar (G), and swamp deer (F). Cutting down forests for farmland and timber has destroyed the habitats of several birds and animals. Many species, including the Asian elephant, great Indian rhinoceros, and swamp deer, are now classified as endangered.

NEPAL TODAY

Until the late 1700's, Nepal consisted of many small, independent kingdoms located throughout the central valleys of the present-day country.

In the mid-1700's, Prithwi Narayan Shah, king of the small kingdom of Gorkha, began a series of military campaigns to unite Nepal. By 1775, his army had conquered most of the other kingdoms.

During the early 1800's, the ruling dynasty tried to extend Nepal's territory into Kashmir, Sikkim, Bhutan, and Tibet. When the Nepalese attempted to invade northern India, they were met by British soldiers, who were at that time protecting the East India Company's territory. The United Kingdom declared war on Nepal in 1814 after Nepalese troops attacked a British outpost. Two years later, the British defeated the Nepalese.

Political struggles

In 1846, a political leader named Jung Bahadur seized control of Nepal's government. He took the name of *Rana*. Rana and his descendants ruled Nepal for more than 100 years. The Ranas were harsh leaders. They imprisoned and even murdered their political enemies. The Ranas also kept Nepal isolated from the rest of the world.

During the 1930's and 1940's, many Nepalese began to oppose Rana rule, and in 1950 a revolution overthrew the Rana government. In 1951, Nepal's monarchy was restored under King Tribhuwan Shah.

The modern monarchy

When Tribhuwan died in 1955, his son, Mahendra, became king. King Mahendra was so disturbed by fighting between political groups that in 1960 he banned all political parties and dissolved the elected government. In 1962, he established a *panchayat* (council) system, in which the king holds most of the power. King Mahendra died in 1972, and his son, Birendra, became king.

Many Nepalese objected to the panchayat system. In 1979, they staged violent demonstrations and demanded a more democratic government. In response,

FACTS

Official name:	Kingdom of Nepal
Capital:	Kathmandu
Terrain:	Flat river plain of the Ganges in south, central hill region, rugged Himalaya in north
Area:	56,827 mi² (147,181 km²)
Climate:	Varies from cool summers and severe winters in north to subtropical summers and mild winters in south
Main rivers:	Seti, Karnali, Bheri, Sun Kosi, Arun, Tamur
Highest elevation:	Mount Everest, 29,035 ft (8,850 m)
Lowest elevation:	230 ft (70 m)
Form of government:	Federal republic
Head of state:	President
Head of government:	Prime minister
Administrative areas:	14 anchal (zones)
Legislature:	Constituent Assembly with 601 members
Court system:	Sarbochha Adalat (Supreme Court)
Armed forces:	69,000 troops
National holidays:	Republic Day - May 29 Democracy Day - April 24
Estimated 2010 population:	29,922,000
Population density:	527 persons per mi² (203 per km²)
Population distribution:	83% rural, 17% urban
Life expectancy in years:	Male, 64; female, 65
Doctors per 1,000 people:	0.2
Birth rate per 1,000:	28
Death rate per 1,000:	8
Infant mortality:	48 deaths per 1,000 live births
Age structure:	0-14: 37%; 15-64: 59%; 65 and over: 4%
Internet users per 100 people:	1.4
Internet code:	.np
Languages spoken:	Nepali (official), over 50 other languages and dialects
Religions:	Hindu 80.6%, Buddhist 10.7%, Muslim 4.2%, other 4.5%
Currency:	Nepalese rupee
Gross domestic product (GDP) in 2008:	$12.65 billion U.S.
Real annual growth rate (2008):	5.6%
GDP per capita (2008):	$461 U.S.
Goods exported:	Carpets, clothing, food, textiles, yarn
Goods imported:	Electrical goods, machinery, petroleum products, pharmaceuticals, transportation equipment
Trading partners:	Mostly India, also China, Indonesia, Singapore, United States

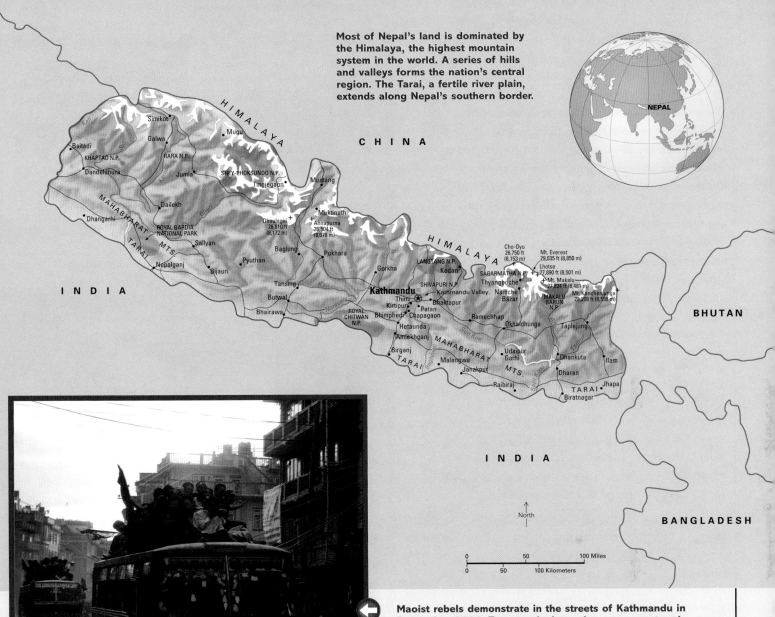

Most of Nepal's land is dominated by the Himalaya, the highest mountain system in the world. A series of hills and valleys forms the nation's central region. The Tarai, a fertile river plain, extends along Nepal's southern border.

Maoist rebels demonstrate in the streets of Kathmandu in September 2006. Two months later, the government and the rebels signed a peace treaty, and in early 2007, the Maoists joined an interim government.

King Birendra allowed a national vote on the issue. By a narrow margin, Nepalese voters chose to continue the panchayat system. But pressure for political change continued. In 1990, a new constitution established a constitutional monarchy, and in 1991, multiparty elections were held. In 1996, Maoist rebels began fighting to replace Nepal's constitutional monarchy with a Communist government.

In June 2001, King Birendra's son Prince Dipendra killed the king and most of the royal family, then killed himself. The king's brother Gyanendra then assumed the throne. In 2002, King Gyanendra dismissed Nepal's elected prime minister, Sher Bahadur Deuba. Two years later, King Gyanendra assumed full executive control of Nepal. After the king's seizure of power, several protests were held demanding a return to democracy. In April 2006, Gyanendra reinstated Nepal's parliament, which later stripped the king of most of his powers.

In November 2006, the government and the Maoist rebels signed a peace deal, and in early 2007, the Maoists joined an interim government. The deal brought an end to about 10 years of fighting, during which more than 16,000 people died. In parliamentary elections held in April 2008, the Maoists won the most seats. The following month, the government officially abolished the monarchy and declared the country a republic.

PEOPLE

The earliest settlers in what is now Nepal were probably Mongoloid peoples from central Asia and Tibet. Later, Aryan immigrants from northern India entered the country. Eventually, the Aryans made up the majority of Nepal's people. By about A.D. 300, Hindu dynasties had established their rule over Nepal. Today, the Nepalese population is made up of a number of ethnic groups, each with its own language and its own cultural and religious practices. Most Nepalese are closely related to the peoples of northern India. Other Nepalese are of Tibetan descent. Still others are of mixed Indian-Tibetan descent.

The Sherpas are a Himalayan people who live in the mountainous northern and eastern regions of Nepal. The Sherpas are known for their mountaineering skills and often serve as guides and porters for mountain-climbing expeditions. In 1953, a Sherpa named Tenzing Norgay and Sir Edmund Hillary of New Zealand became the first people to climb to the top of Mount Everest.

The Gurkhas are Nepalese soldiers serving in the British or Indian army. The salaries and pensions paid to Gurkha soldiers are a significant contribution to Nepal's economy.

Way of life

The Nepalese people live a simple, rural life in small villages. Their homes are usually two-story houses made of stone or mud brick.

About three-fourths of the people earn their living by farming and related work, though most Nepalese farmers can barely grow enough food for their own families. Surplus crops are traded for such items as kerosene and salt.

Some Nepalese make their living as craft workers, including blacksmiths, goldsmiths, shoemakers, and tailors. Others are merchants and government

Brightly colored prayer banners decorate a shrine as Nepalese monks perform a Buddhist ceremony. Nepal is the birthplace of Siddhartha Gautama, the Buddha, who founded the Buddhist religion in about 500 B.C.

The Swayambhunath Temple towers over the rooftops of Kathmandu from a hillside west of the city. The temple houses a long-established monastery as well as a resident troop of monkeys, which is cared for by the monks.

A poultry farmer stands outside his home in Nepal's heartland, the Kathmandu Valley. Modern poultry farms are operated mostly by Newars, the original settlers of the valley. Newar towns include Thimi, Bode, and Chapagaon.

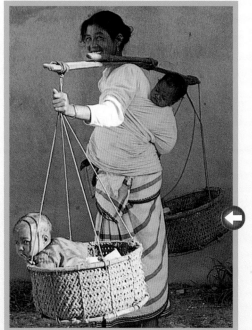

A Nepalese mother carries her babies. The government's development projects have helped many Nepalese villagers raise their standard of living. Improved health care and sanitation have reduced the infant death rate.

workers. Today, many Nepalese work in the country's growing tourism industry.

Nepal's century of isolation under the Rana dynasty held back the nation's social development. In the 1950's, only about 5 percent of the Nepalese people over 15 years old could read and write. With the help of government programs, that percentage is now up to about 50 percent.

Malnutrition, contaminated water, and poor sanitation have caused many health problems for the Nepalese people, and epidemics are a constant threat. However, government programs have helped control malaria, leprosy, and tuberculosis.

Poor communication and transportation systems have slowed further progress in raising educational and health levels. The wide, deep gorges across Nepal's landscape form natural barriers between the villages and settlements. However, foreign aid has helped the Nepalese build roads for year-round traffic.

Language and religion

The official language, Nepali, has its origins in Sanskrit, the classic Hindu language. More than 50 other languages and various dialects are spoken in Nepal.

Hinduism has long been Nepal's official religion, and some Nepalese worship the king as the Hindu god Vishnu reborn on Earth. Nepalese Hinduism has been influenced by Buddhism, and both religious groups live in harmony. Buddhist temples are given as much respect as Hindu temples.

THE HIMALAYA

According to an ancient Hindu proverb, "One hundred lives of the gods would not be long enough to describe all the wonders of the Himalaya." The world's highest mountain system, the Himalaya has some of the most spectacular scenery on Earth.

The Himalaya is not a single mountain chain, but a system of parallel mountain ranges. It extends in a 1,500-mile (2,410-kilometer) curve across southern Asia. Beginning with the Pamirs, west of the great bend of the Indus River, the Himalaya sweeps eastward to the great bend of the Brahmaputra River near the border of Myanmar. The Karakoram range is the northwestern extension of the Himalaya.

Known as "the roof of the world," the Himalaya contains many of the tallest mountains on Earth. These in-clude Mount Everest (29,035 feet or 8,850 meters), K2 (28,250 feet or 8,611 meters), Mount Kanchenjunga (28,208 feet or 8,598 meters), Mount Makalu (27,824 feet or 8,481 meters), and Annapurna (26,504 feet or 8,078 meters).

Myth and legend

The Himalaya has been the subject of myth and legend for centuries. The *Abominable Snowman,* a legendary beast that purportedly has a large apelike body and a face that looks human, is said to live on Mount Everest and other Himalayan peaks. There is no evidence that the Abominable Snowman, or *Yeti,* exists, but sightings of the creature have been reported by travelers since the 1890's, when mountaineering first became popular.

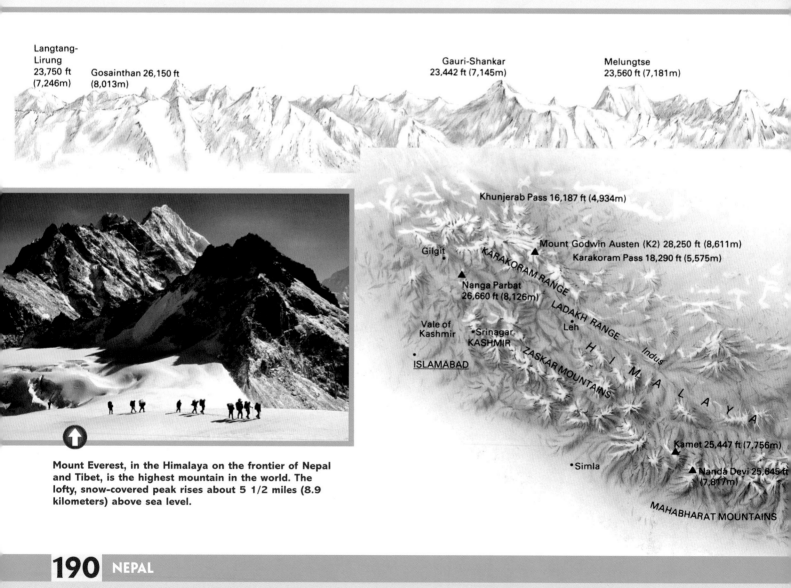

Langtang-Lirung
23,750 ft
(7,246m)

Gosainthan 26,150 ft
(8,013m)

Gauri-Shankar
23,442 ft (7,145m)

Melungtse
23,560 ft (7,181m)

Khunjerab Pass 16,187 ft (4,934m)

Gilgit

KARAKORAM RANGE

Mount Godwin Austen (K2) 28,250 ft (8,611m)
Karakoram Pass 18,290 ft (5,575m)

Nanga Parbat
26,660 ft (8,126m)

LADAKH RANGE

Indus

Vale of
Kashmir

•Srinagar
KASHMIR

Leh

H
I
M
A
L
A
Y
A

•
ISLAMABAD

ZASKAR MOUNTAINS

Kamet 25,447 ft (7,756m)

•Simla

▲ Nanda Devi 25,645 ft
(7,817m)

MAHABHARAT MOUNTAINS

Mount Everest, in the Himalaya on the frontier of Nepal and Tibet, is the highest mountain in the world. The lofty, snow-covered peak rises about 5 1/2 miles (8.9 kilometers) above sea level.

A biological wonderland

The Himalaya came into being less than 25 million years ago, which is fairly recent in geological terms. Its major river systems—the Indus, Sutlej, Kali Gandaki, Tista, and Brahmaputra—were in place before the mountains were pushed upward.

The great difference in altitude in many parts of the Himalaya has resulted in a variety of plant and animal life. Tropical heat and arctic cold can be found in a span only 40 miles (64 kilometers) wide in the Himalaya of Sikkim and Bhutan.

At the 20,000-foot (6,000-meter) *aeolian,* or highest zone, life is limited to bacteria, fungi, insects, and crustaceans that live on airborne food particles blown up by the wind. Moving down in altitude between the snow line and the timber line, the alpine meadows support such plants as stonecrops, rock jasmines, primroses, and edelweiss. Lynxes, wolves, and brown bears are found in this zone.

Below the timber line, about 15,000 feet (4,600 meters), a forest belt abounds in deodar cedar, Himalayan fir, blue pine, cypress, hemlock, and spruce trees. The Himalaya is famous for the variety of rhododendrons that flourish in this zone. Animal life ranges from wild goats—such as the *serow, goral,* and *tahr*—to macaque monkeys and rodents.

Tropical forests blanket the hills bordering the lowlands of the eastern and central Himalaya. Many hardwood trees grow in this zone, including bauhinia, teak, sal, horse chestnut, and walnut. At about 4,500 feet (1,400 meters), the tropical forests give way to the subtropical forest, where chital deer, tigers, water buffaloes, and hog deer roam.

A cross section of Nepal, covering just 100 miles (161 kilometers), includes many of the world's highest peaks. The Himalaya forms a huge arc that separates India from the Tibetan Plateau in China.

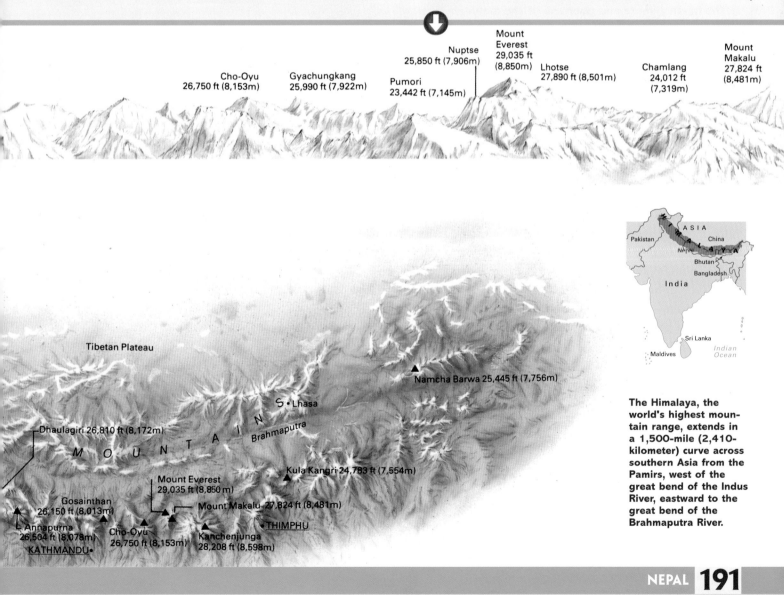

The Himalaya, the world's highest mountain range, extends in a 1,500-mile (2,410-kilometer) curve across southern Asia from the Pamirs, west of the great bend of the Indus River, eastward to the great bend of the Brahmaputra River.

PEOPLE OF THE HIMALAYA

Tucked in the foothills, valleys, and highland basins are settlements of strong, hardy, and religious Himalayan people. For centuries, they have lived and worked in the shadow of the highest mountains in the world. Some live in such fertile, sheltered areas as the Vale of Kashmir, the Kathmandu Valley, and the Tarai plain of southern Nepal. Others spend their lives in the remote highlands, almost completely cut off from the rest of the world.

A challenging way of life

Life in the Himalaya is difficult. The mountain people live mainly in small agricultural communities at altitudes between 3,000 feet (1,000 meters) and 12,000 feet (3,500 meters).

The harsh climate and poor soil of the mountain slopes make farming difficult. Farmers are able to grow only enough food to live on, and little more. A few mountain tribes consist of seminomadic farmers, who move from plot to plot, and herdsmen who lead their flocks through the mountains.

The Himalayan people are made up of many different ethnic and cultural groups, but they all share two important characteristics: physical strength and spiritual faith.

The Sherpas of Nepal, for example, take great pride in being able to carry a load equal to their own body weight up to a height of about 10,000 feet (3,050 meters). Most people could not carry such a load, even at ground level. This ability has allowed some Himalayan people to make their living as guides and porters for mountaineers and trekkers.

A deeply religious people

Religion plays a major part in the lives of the Himalayan people. Most follow one of the region's three great religions—Hinduism, Buddhism, or Islam. A few worship gods connected with plants, animals, or the forces of nature. Their beliefs are often combined with a deep respect for the beauty and mystery of their mountains.

A Nepalese citizen pays his respects at an entrance to the Royal Palace in Kathmandu, Nepal. The entrance to the palace bears the name Hanuman Dhoka in honor of the Hindu monkey god, one of the heroes of the epic *Ramayana*.

The market place in Thimphu, the capital of Bhutan, is a busy trading center. It also serves as a gathering place for social activities. Festivals that include dancing, eating, and entertainment provide welcome relief from the hard life of the Himalayan people.

The charming village of Pangeboche, Nepal, is perched on a mountain slope. The well-constructed houses of the Sherpas are generally built of stone and timber, with a roof made of wooden slats.

To Himalayan people, the mountains are known as "the seat of the gods." Even their local names for various peaks carry religious symbolism. The Tibetans call Mount Everest *Chomolungma,* or *Mother Goddess of the World. Annapurna* means *Goddess of the Harvest,* and *Kanchenjunga* means *Treasure of the Eternal Snows.*

Mount Kailas, which rises 22,028 feet (6,714 meters), is sacred to the Hindus. They believe it is the secret home of their powerful god Shiva, and his wife, Parvati. It is also the source of four important rivers: the Brahmaputra, Indus, Sutlej, and the sacred Ganges.

Today, pilgrims from all parts of central Asia and India come to Nepal to climb the mountain. The journey takes them from tropical jungles to freezing heights. Below the peak, at an elevation of 14,950 feet (4,557 meters), lies the holy Lake Mansarowar. The lake is worshiped by some who believe it is the home of the spirit of the god Brahma, creator of the universe, who was born from a golden egg. Many religious ceremonies are held along the 54-mile (87-kilometer) path that surrounds the sacred lake.

Religion is at the heart of many political conflicts in the Himalaya region. India, a Hindu nation, controls the territory of Jammu and Kashmir, but the mostly Muslim inhabitants would like to be part of Pakistan. The Buddhist majority in Kashmir's eastern province of Ladakh would like to be more independent. At the same time, China claims Ladakh because its people belong to the Tibetan ethnic group and practice Tibetan Buddhism.

NATURE UNDER THREAT

The Himalaya is one of the world's most endangered environments. Although its terrain is mighty and rugged, its ecological balance is quite delicate. Many of the problems in the Himalaya occurred because people ignored this vital balance of nature.

Increasing population density

Many Himalayan areas have seen a rapid growth in population. The population of Nepal in particular has more than doubled in only 30 years. All these people need food and shelter.

Because the steep terrain of the Himalaya makes trade and industry difficult, most Nepalese make their living as farmers. As the population grows, they need more and more land to develop for agriculture. Forests are cleared to make room for farmland, and the trees that are cut down supply wood used in building, cooking, and domestic heating.

But clearing forests upsets the balance of nature. Forests keep water from running off the land by allowing it to filter into the ground. The water then flows through underground channels and refills lakes and streams. But when forests are cleared, Earth's plant cover is removed, and this natural process is interrupted.

Soil erosion is another result of clearing the forests. The topsoil, which contains important nutrients and organic matter, is washed away by the monsoon rains. This leaves poor soil that is unable to absorb water.

Meanwhile, the topsoil washes down to the plains, where the muddy waters silt up the rivers. Even such large rivers as the Ganges, Brahmaputra, and Indus cannot absorb the huge quantity of

The environmental problems of the Himalaya affect huge numbers of people. The delicate balance of nature is disturbed when an increasing population makes greater demands on the environment. The clearing of forests causes soil erosion and destroys the natural habitat of wildlife. Overgrazing also upsets the balance of nature. Among the more serious problems are the ditches created by running water, inset below, and flooding in the lower plains, inset below right.

Soil erosion not only destroys the areas where the soil is washed away but also affects areas all the way down the watercourse.

Erosion robs the land of productive topsoil, which washes down to the plains. There, muddy waters clog the rivers, which may overflow and cause major flooding.

muddy water. As a result, the rivers overflow and cause major flooding in Pakistan, India, and Bangladesh.

Clearing forests also destroys the natural habitat of the animals who live there. There is much less land where wild animals can nest, breed, and feed. Many species are threatened with extinction because they no longer have a place to live.

Another threat to the Himalayan environment is overgrazing of land. At higher altitudes, where rainfall is scarce, the land is not suitable for growing crops. Instead, Himalayan herders tend flocks of sheep and goats. When too many animals graze an area, or when animals stay in one place too long, the land becomes overgrazed. The grasses die and are replaced by weeds and poisonous plants.

The threat of tourism

Tourism is a major source of revenue for Himalayan countries, as mountaineering and trekking have become popular. However, trekkers in particular have become dangerous to the Himalayan environment because they use more firewood than local people do, and more trees are cut down to build roads that make trekking easier.

To prevent further damage to the environment, Nepal has begun to restrict the movements of tourists in certain areas. India has severely restricted the hunting of wild game. The Indian government has also established a number of national parks and game reserves in the southern Himalaya. The Himalayan countries have announced the first steps in a united campaign to protect their mountains.

Many great Himalayan forests fall victim to the woodcutter's ax, leaving the hillsides bare.

Supplies from a mountaineering expedition litter the base camp on Mount Everest in Nepal. Pollution of the natural environment is threatening the future of the Himalaya.

Pakistan's magnificent Karakoram Highway opened in 1978. It runs through the steep Hunza Valley to the Chinese border.

TREKKING

The vast, almost unearthly landscape of the Himalaya has attracted thousands of adventurous tourists. In the past, most of those visitors were hardy mountaineers armed with ice axes, oxygen tanks, and *crampons* (metal spikes on boots that prevent slipping on hard ice or snow). They braved the harsh climate and terrain of the Himalaya's highest altitudes to see the most glorious scenery in the world.

Today, trekking—hiking through the mountain passes—has become one of the Himalaya's most popular attractions.

Trekking at elevations between 1,350 feet (500 meters) and 8,300 feet (2,500 meters) does not require unusual equipment, experience, or physical strength. Trekkers can enjoy all the magic and mystery of the Himalaya without the danger and hardship of climbing at higher altitudes.

Walking the mountain trails

People have traveled through the passes of the Himalaya for hundreds of years. Some were merchants and traders, whose caravans brought salt, tea, textiles, grains, spices, and other goods to Europe from the Far East. Others were political diplomats and pilgrims. Traders can still be seen along the Himalayan trails, carrying goods in homespun woolen bundles on the backs of sheep and goats.

Modern trekkers journey on foot over these same well-used trails, which vary from wide, stone-paved routes to winding paths and narrow ledges. Most trekking is done in the mild Himalayan summer, which lasts from May to October. A trek may range from a few days of backpacking along the trails to a three-week, or longer, expedition from Kathmandu Valley to the base camp of Mount Everest.

Most trekkers travel in small groups with a porter as a guide. Larger groups often include a *sirdar* (foreman) with a crew of porters who make camp for the travelers at night and cook their meals. About five or six hours of hiking a day between 4,900 feet (1,500 meters) and 6,600 feet (2,030

meters) is typical. A long meal stop is usually made in the middle of the day. Meals are eaten either at camp or at a village tea shop.

Trekkers traveling in small groups often sleep in *bhattis* (wayside inns) or in village homes. An evening meal may include such local favorites as *dal bhatu* (rice with lentil paste) or curried potatoes washed down Tibetan-style with buttered and salted tea.

Preparing for a trek

Although trekking does not require unusual skills or equipment, a certain amount of advance preparation is necessary. All would-be trekkers must have the proper visas, immunizations, and trekking permits. Comfortable, durable clothing is a must, along with a sleeping bag, cooking equipment, and a tent.

A trekking party crosses a mountain stream in a Nepalese valley. A vast network of trails through the mountain passes connects remote Himalayan villages. Some of these trails include footbridges.

Because of Nepal's rugged terrain and limited medical facilities, experienced backpackers travel in small groups to assure a safe, enjoyable trek. Most groups hire a porter, who guides the travelers and helps carry food and equipment.

A serious health danger facing the inexperienced trekker is *altitude sickness*. This condition is caused by climbing too fast for the body to adjust to the change in altitude. The result is a decrease In the amount of oxygen in the blood, which causes headaches, weakness, sleeplessness, mild nausea, and loss of appetite. To prevent altitude sickness, careful trekkers sleep at an altitude that is lower than the highest point reached during the day.

Careful planning is important, but nothing can prepare a trekker for the magnificent scenery to be encountered on the Himalayan trails. From a view of snow-capped mountains to a walk through an alpine meadow or a forest of blooming rhododendrons, the Himalaya offers a new and wondrous sight with every footstep.

A simple dwelling home of a Sherpa family. Because of their physical strength and mountaineering skills, Sherpas have been used as guides through the mountains and passes since the 1950's.

THE NETHERLANDS

The Netherlands is a small, densely populated, and highly industrialized country on the North Sea in northwestern Europe. The Netherlands is often called *Holland,* though this name actually refers to only one part of the country. The people of the Netherlands call themselves *Hollanders* or *Nederlanders,* but in English-speaking countries, they are known as the *Dutch.*

The word *Netherlands* means "Low Countries"—an appropriate name for a nation where more than 40 percent of the land was once covered by sea, lakes, or swamps. The Dutch "created" this land by pumping out the water, and today these drained areas, called *polders,* support the country's richest farmlands and largest cities. Amsterdam, the Dutch capital and largest city, is on a polder.

The Dutch have great pride in their long battle against the sea. They take extreme care to protect their hard-won land and to use every acre wisely. Several times during their history, however, the Dutch have opened the dikes and flooded the land to save their country from invaders.

In 1986, the massive Delta Project was completed to help control flooding. A product of nearly 30 years of construction, the Delta Project consists of a series of huge dams with floodgates that can be closed during storms. However, recovering land and protecting it from flooding is a constant battle in the Netherlands. Because most of the polders are below sea level, they have no natural drainage, so water must be continually pumped into a series of canals that flow into the North Sea.

In addition to draining the low-lying Dutch land, the canals also serve as waterways, forming an extensive transportation network with the country's major rivers. When the winters are harsh enough to freeze the canals, they are also used for ice skating, an extremely popular sport. Schools sometimes close to let the children skate. The Dutch also enjoy watching the *Elfstedentocht,* an ice-skating race held on the canals of the northern province of Friesland.

In the Netherlands, where most of the countryside is flat, cycling is a good way to get around. Most Dutch people own a bicycle. There are nearly as many bicycles as there are people in the country.

The Netherlands attracts many tourists throughout the year. In the spring, colorful fields of tulips, daffodils, and hyacinths attract thousands of visitors. In the summer, people flock to seaside resorts on the North Sea coast, especially those at Scheveningen, Noordwijk, Zandvoort, and Egmond aan Zee.

THE NETHERLANDS TODAY

The Netherlands is one of the most densely populated countries in the world, averaging 1,033 people per square mile (399 people per square kilometer). But the Dutch keep their fields, towns, and cities so neat and clean that few areas ever seem crowded. The Netherlanders' particular style of good fellowship, called *gezelligheid,* also helps make life pleasant in their heavily populated country. This combination of order and tolerance is reflected in Dutch society, which blends tradition with modern innovation.

Government

The Netherlands has a democratic government based on its Constitution. However, the nation is officially a constitutional monarchy. The country's Constitution identifies the king or queen as the head of state, but the monarch has little real power. The monarch names all appointed government officials on the advice of various government bodies and signs all laws passed by the parliament.

The capital of the Netherlands is Amsterdam, but the country's national government meets in The Hague, which is 34 miles (55 kilometers) away. Invading French troops captured Amsterdam in 1795 and made it the capital. The Dutch restored their government in The Hague in 1814.

The Netherlands is part of the Kingdom of the Netherlands, which also includes several Caribbean islands. Aruba, Curaçao, and Saint Martin are self-governing territories. Each has an appointed governor and a Council of Ministers led by a prime minister. Bonaire, Saba, and Saint Eustatius are overseas municipalities, with a status similar to that of small towns in the Netherlands.

Town and country

The Netherlands is a highly industrialized and technically advanced nation. The country's key position at the mouth of the Rhine River has made it a gateway between the inland capitals of Europe and the North Sea. Vast urban centers have grown up in the area that includes Amsterdam, Rotterdam, and The Hague. This region of concentrated urban centers is called the *Randstad Holland.*

FACTS

Official name:	Koninkrijk der Nederlanden (Kingdom of the Netherlands)
Capital:	Amsterdam (official capital); The Hague (seat of government)
Terrain:	Mostly coastal lowland and reclaimed land (polders); some hills in southeast
Area:	16,034 mi² (41,528 km²)
Climate:	Temperate; cool summers and mild winters
Main rivers:	Rhine, Maas, Waal, Lek, IJssel
Highest elevation:	Vaalserberg, 1,053 ft (321 m)
Lowest elevation:	Prins Alexander Polder, 22 ft (6.7 m) below sea level
Form of government:	Constitutional monarchy
Head of state:	Monarch
Head of government:	Prime minister
Administrative areas:	12 provincien (provinces)
Legislature:	Staten Generaal (States General) consisting of the Eerste Kamer (First Chamber) with 75 members serving four-year terms and the Tweede Kamer (Second Chamber) with 150 members serving four-year terms
Court system:	Hoge Raad (Supreme Court)
Armed forces:	40,500 troops
National holiday:	Queen's Day - April 30 (1909 and 1980)
Estimated 2010 population:	16,567,000
Population density:	1,033 persons per mi² (399 per km²)
Population distribution:	81% urban, 19% rural
Life expectancy in years:	Male, 77; female, 82
Doctors per 1,000 people:	3.7
Birth rate per 1,000:	11
Death rate per 1,000:	8
Infant mortality:	4 deaths per 1,000 live births
Age structure:	0-14: 18%; 15-64: 67%; 65 and over: 15%
Internet users per 100 people:	89
Internet code:	.nl
Languages spoken:	Dutch (official), Frisian (official in Friesland)
Religions:	Roman Catholic 30%, Protestant 20%, Muslim 5.8%, other 44.2%
Currency:	Euro
Gross domestic product (GDP) in 2008:	$868.94 billion U.S.
Real annual growth rate (2008):	1.8%
GDP per capita (2008):	$52,622 U.S.
Goods exported:	Chemicals, dairy products, electronic equipment, flowers, machinery, meat, motor vehicles, natural gas, petroleum products, vegetables
Goods imported:	Automobiles, chemicals, clothing, electronic equipment, food, iron and steel, machinery, paper and paper products, petroleum and petroleum products, plastics
Trading partners:	Belgium, China, France, Germany, Italy, Spain, United Kingdom, United States

The Dutch balance the spread of urban centers by protecting their countryside and wildlife. In the Hoge Veluwe—a national park in the province of Gelderland—wild pigs and deer roam freely. Many of the country's coastal areas have also been preserved. Some of the people in these areas, particularly in the fishing communities, wear the Dutch national costume. Traditional clothing includes caps and full trousers for the men, lace caps and full skirts for the women, and wooden shoes for everyone.

The former Royal Palace in The Hague was first built in 1533 and rebuilt in 1640. It was the residence of Dutch princes until invading French troops moved the capital to Amsterdam.

NETHERLANDS

The Netherlands is a small country located in northwestern Europe. Its four main land regions include the sandy and infertile Dunes that line the North Sea coast; the flat, fertile recovered land regions of the Polders; the low, sandy ridges of the eastern Sand Plains; and the Southern Uplands, which form the highest land region. A marshy delta area in the southwest, formed by the Maas and Schelde rivers and branches of the Rhine, provides a plentiful catch for local fishermen.

North

North Sea

West Frisian Islands

Rottumeroog
Schiermonnikoog
Ameland
Dollard Bay
Terschelling
Holwerd
Dokkum
Appingedam
Delfzijl
Vlieland
Waddenzee
Buitenpost
GRONINGEN
Lauwerszee
Leeuwarden
Groningen
Hoogezand-Sappemeer
Harlingen
Franeker
FRIESLAND
Roden
Veendam
Winschoten
Texel
Bolsward
BARRIER DAM
Heerenveen
Assen
Stadskanaal
Den Helder
Workum
Sneek
Wolvega
Musselkanaal
Ter Apel
Staveren
Lemmer
DRENTHE
North Holland Canal
Wieringermeer Polder
Den Oever
Northeast Polder
Steenwijk
Beilen
Emmen
Schagen
Medemblik
IJsselmeer
Emmeloord
Hoogeveen
Coevorden
Bergen
Heerhugowaard
Enkhuizen
Urk
Meppel
Bergen aan Zee
Alkmaar
Hoorn
Staphorst
Hardenberg
Egmond aan Zee
Heiloo
Markermeer
FLEVOLAND
Kampen
Ommen
Den Ham
Heemskerk
Edam
Lelystad
Dronten
Elburg
Zwolle
Vecht
OVERIJSSEL
Beverwijk
Purmerend
Flevoland Polder
Raalte
Hellendoorn
Almelo
North Sea Canal
NORTH HOLLAND
Zaanstad
Marken
Nunspeet
Epe
Olst
Nijverdal
Almelo
Oldenzaal
Velsen
Harderwijk
Ermelo
Deventer
Borne
Hengelo
Losser
Haarlem
Amsterdam
Almere
Goor
Zandvoort
Amstelveen
Huizen
Apeldoorn
Haaksbergen
Heemstede
Bussum
Baarn
Nijkerk
Voorst
Enschede
Noordwijk
Lisse
Aalsmeer
Hilversum
Zutphen
Lochem
Katwijk aan Zee
Leiden
UTRECHT
Soest
Amersfoort
HOGE VELUWE NATL. PARK
Wassenaar
Alphen aan den Rijn
Maarssen
De Bilt
Barneveld
Rheden
Groenlo
Scheveningen
SOUTH HOLLAND
Woerden
Zeist
Ede
GELDERLAND
Winterswijk
The Hague
Rijswijk
Gouda
Utrecht
Veenendaal
Renkum
Arnhem
Doetinchem
Delft
Naaldwijk
Zoetermeer
Lek
Rhenen
Wageningen
Zevenaar
Aalten
Hoek van Holland
Rotterdam
Schoonhoven
Culemborg
Oude IJssel
EUROPOORT
Maassluis
Ridderkerk
Tiel
Waal
Nijmegen
Vlaardingen
Sliedrecht
Gorinchem
Rhine
Spijkenisse
Zwijndrecht
Leerdam
Maas
Cuijk
Haringvliet
Dordrecht
Zaltbommel
Oss
Wijchen
Ouddorp
Grave
Middelharnis
Willemstad
Waalwijk
's Hertogenbosch
Vught
Boxmeer
Zierikzee
Oosterhout
NORTH BRABANT
Uden
Venray
Oosterschelde
Stavenisse
Steenbergen
Etten
Breda
Dongen
Tilburg
Veghel
Gemert
Domburg
Goes
Bergen op Zoom
Roosendaal
Gilze
Oirschot
Best
Helmond
GERMANY
Middelburg
Borssele
Zundert
Eindhoven
Geldrop
Deurne
Vlissingen
ZEELAND
Westerschelde
Veldhoven
Asten
Venlo
Oostburg
Terneuzen
Valkenswaard
Tegelen
Sas van Gent
Hulst
Schelde-Rhine Canal
Weert
LIMBURG
LIMBURG
Roermond
Echt
BELGIUM
Juliana Canal
Sittard
Geleen
Brunssum
Meerssen
Heerlen
Maastricht
Kerkrade
Vaalserberg
+1,053 ft (321 m)

0   25   50 Miles
0   25   50   75 Kilometers

PEOPLE

The Dutch people are descended from several different Germanic tribes. The Frisians occupied the northern coastal area about 2,000 years ago, while the Saxons lived in the Rhine Delta. During the A.D. 400's, the Franks drove the Romans out of northern Europe and established their kingdom in the Low Countries, which included what are now the Netherlands, Belgium, and Luxembourg.

The Dutch language was influenced primarily by the many dialects of Old Low German spoken by the Franks. However, the Frisian language has survived and is still spoken in the northern province of Friesland. The Dutch language did not achieve its final written form until the 1600's, the Golden Age of the Netherlands.

In the 1600's, the country became the leading sea power and developed a profitable and far-flung colonial empire. Dutch trade gave the country the world's highest standard of living. Art also flourished during this period, when such artists as Rembrandt, Frans Hals, and Jan Vermeer produced some of the world's greatest paintings.

Religious differences

In the 1500's, a religious movement called the Protestant Reformation had spread through the Low Countries. Protestantism became stronger in the northern provinces (now the Netherlands). During the 1560's, the northern provinces rebelled against rule by predominantly Roman Catholic Spain, and in 1581, they declared their independence. The new Dutch Republic—the Netherlands—finally gained its freedom in 1648. However, the country was still divided by religious differences. The southern provinces of the Netherlands had remained mostly Catholic, while the northern provinces had converted to Protestantism.

Today, although the geographical boundaries are not so clear-cut, these religious divisions still exist. Roman Catholics and Protestants make up about half of the Dutch population. Both religions traditionally remained separate, each with its own

Businessmen enter a Euronext office in Amsterdam. Euronext is a European stock exchange based in Paris, with subsidiaries in the Netherlands and other European countries. Euronext was formed in 2000, following a merger of the Amsterdam Stock Exchange, Brussels Stock Exchange, and Paris Bourse.

schools, newspapers, and political parties. Since the 1950's, however, a trend of tolerance has broken down this voluntary segregation, particularly among young people.

Population changes

During the 1960's and 1970's, the Dutch policy of tolerance extended to the hundreds of thousands of immigrants who swelled the country's population. People from former Dutch colonies, especially Indonesia and Suriname, and from

Rich farmland, much of it reclaimed from the sea, covers over half of the total land area in the Netherlands. Canals both drain the land (with the aid of pumps) and provide transportation.

The Dutch use their canals for ice skating when winter weather causes the water to freeze. Some Dutch people skate to and from work.

Mediterranean countries moved to the Netherlands, attracted by its booming economy.

Today, the Netherlands has a population of more than 16 million. About 35 percent of the people live in two coastal provinces—Noord-Holland (North Holland) and Zuid-Holland (South Holland). The three largest Dutch cities—Amsterdam, Rotterdam, and The Hague—are located in these provinces, along with much of Randstad Holland, a strip of densely populated urban centers.

CITIES OF THE NETHERLANDS

The cities of the Netherlands first began to achieve importance in the 1100's, when trade and industry with France and Germany expanded rapidly. The country's position at the mouth of the Rhine River made it a major trading center, and fishing, ship-building, shipping, and textile manufacturing be-came especially important. Commercial centers developed in the cities of Delft, Leiden, Gouda, and Haarlem, while cities such as Amsterdam, Edam, and Rotterdam, which are located at the mouths of rivers, became international ports.

By the 1600's, Dutch shipbuilders provided about half of Europe's shipping needs. The great Dutch artists of this period glorified the rich trading cities in paintings. Many of the buildings in these paintings are still standing today, in settings that are almost unchanged.

The Hague

The Hague was originally a hunting lodge belonging to the count of Holland. In 1250, it became his resi-dence. The Hague's official name, *'s Gravenhage*, which means *the count's hedge,* is a reference to the city's origins.

Today, though Amsterdam is the capital of the Netherlands, The Hague is the country's seat of gov-ernment and the official residence of the monarch. Also, the city's magnificent Peace Palace, built in the early 1900's, serves as headquarters for the Perma-nent Court of Arbitration and the International Court of Justice. The Peace Palace reflects the idea of The Hague as an international neutral center where disputes among nations can be resolved peacefully.

Scheveningen, a large seaside resort near The Hague, attracts tourists with its fine beaches. Its picturesque pier has shops and restaurants as well as sun terraces and a huge aquarium.

Alkmaar's famous cheese mar-ket is held on Fridays from spring to fall. Porters wearing colorful hats carry hundreds of delicious cheeses to the mar-ket on special racks.

Amsterdam's Leidseplein attracts visitors with its modern nightclubs and cafes, but many local people prefer to get together in the city's little "brown cafes."

The city of Delft is famous for its Delft porcelain, which has been highly prized since the mid-1700's. Crafts-persons continue the tradition today.

The Hague is a handsome city with many stately old buildings and elegant residences that reflect its role as a center of government. In the heart of The Hague's old section stand the parliament buildings, called the Binnenhof. Next to the Binnenhof is the Mauritshuis, a famous art museum that contains the largest collection of Rembrandt paintings in the world. Nearby is the *Huis ten Bosch* (House in the Woods), the residence of the country's monarch.

Utrecht

Utrecht, the capital of Utrecht province, lies along the Rhine River. A fortified Roman city in A.D. 48, Utrecht is one of the oldest cities in the Netherlands. In 696, it became a *bishopric*—a church district. Many medieval churches still stand in Utrecht, among them Saint Martin Cathedral, a beautiful Gothic structure that boasts the tallest church tower in the Netherlands. The tower, called the *Domtoren,* is 367 feet (112 meters) high and offers splendid views across the IJsselmeer. The University of Utrecht, one of the largest universities in the country, stands nearby.

Delft

In the Middle Ages, Delft was a flourishing commercial center. However, it was not until the mid-1700's that the city reached the height of its prosperity with the manufacture of its famous blue porcelain. Craftspeople continue to produce the traditional designs of Dutch delft pottery today.

Its cobbled streets, delicately curved bridges, and picturesque canals make Delft one of the most beautiful cities in the Netherlands. Many of the city's famous buildings have been preserved, including the Nieuwe Kerk (New Church), which was built in the 1400's. The church contains the tomb of William I, prince of Orange, who led a revolt against Spain in 1568. He was assassinated in the Prinsenhof, now a museum, in 1584. Other fine old buildings include the Town Hall, built during the Renaissance, and the Oude Kerk (Old Church), built from the 1200's to the 1500's.

AMSTERDAM

Amsterdam, the capital and largest city of the Netherlands, is situated at the mouth of the Amstel River. The word Amsterdam, which means dam of the Amstel, refers to a dam built there in the 1200's.

The city of Amsterdam lies on marshy land slightly below sea level. Most of its houses are built on wooden piles, or posts, driven into the soggy ground. More than 100 canals crisscross the city and help drain the land.

A lively city of history

The old section of Amsterdam lies at the heart of the city. Damrak, the city's main street, leads to Dam Square—the site of the Royal Palace and the Nieuwe Kerk (New Church). The palace was built in the mid-1600's, and the church, where the nation's monarchs are invested, was built in the 1400's. Nearby stands one of the world's oldest exchanges, the Amsterdam Stock Exchange, built in 1612.

Damrak continues toward Munt Plein, or Mint Square, amid streets lined with shops and restaurants. Nearby Leidseplein, the center of Amsterdam's nightlife, has most of the city's cinemas, its municipal theater, and numerous nightclubs. South of this area lies the Museumplein, which houses many of Amsterdam's art museums, including the Rijksmuseum and the Van Gogh Museum. Down the street from the Rijksmuseum stands the Concertgebouw, home of the world-famous Concertgebouw Orchestra.

Amsterdam's trams crisscross the city, but many of its citizens prefer to travel by bicycle. They wind their way through the traffic, often carrying the day's shopping in their baskets. Many people, however, prefer to explore Amsterdam's narrow streets—many of which are closed to traffic—on foot.

Boating on the canals is yet another popular means of transportation. Three canals—the Herengracht, the Keizersgracht, and the Prinsengracht—border the city's old section on the east, south, and west. A boat ride offers an excellent view of the impressive mansions, dating from the 1600's, that

Bicycle travel is widespread in Amsterdam. The Netherlands has nearly as many bicycles as it has people.

Amsterdam's Montelbaans Tower was built in the early 1500's, and the elegant clock tower was added in the 1600's. The tower was once a lookout for the defense of the city. Today it is the home of the City Water Office.

line the canals. Many of these mansions are now banks or office buildings.

The buildings that line Amsterdam's streets may appear narrow on the outside, but some are actually quite roomy. Many merchants in the 1600's built secret rooms in their homes and offices to avoid paying extra taxes on their property.

One particularly noteworthy Amsterdam building is the house where Anne Frank and her family were concealed from the Nazis during World War II (1939-1945). The family, who were German Jews, hid in a secret annex behind the office of Anne's father's business. They hid for two years before they were betrayed, arrested, and sent to concentration camps, where the 16-year-old Anne died. Her diary, which her father published after the war, gives a vivid account of a life of hiding in the annex.

The central railroad station, shown in the background, lies in the center of Amsterdam. The station opened in 1889 and is one of the country's major railroad hubs.

Everyday life

Most of Amsterdam's people live in tall, narrow apartment buildings set very close together. The city has had a housing shortage since the end of World War II.

Many inhabitants enjoy getting together in Amsterdam's bars and cafes. When the weather is pleasant, a table at an outdoor cafe is a good spot from which to view the city—or listen to its sounds. Bells pealing from the many churches blend with the clanging of the trams and the music of street organs.

Amsterdam's many street markets include the Albert Cuypmarkt, where vendors sell a variety of food and clothing. Specialties from Suriname and Indonesia recall the country's days as a colonial empire, and Turkish and Moroccan goods draw Amsterdam's many *gastarbeideren,* or guest workers.

Waterlooplein, in Amsterdam's old Jewish quarter, was once the largest market in Europe. Jews made up about 10 percent of Amsterdam's population before World War II, but the city's Jewish community was almost entirely wiped out in Nazi concentration camps during the war.

BATTLE WITH THE SEA

According to an old Dutch saying, "God created the world, but the Dutch created Holland." More than 40 percent of the Netherlands has been "created" by pumping the water out of areas that were once swamps, marshes, and shallow river estuaries. Generations of Dutch farmers and engineers have turned these areas—called *polders*—into rich farmland.

The Polders region was drained by a network of canals, ditches, and dikes. However, pumping must be continued after the polders are built, because most of them are below sea level and have no natural drainage.

To make a polder, the Dutch build a dike around the area that is to be drained of water. The water is then pumped into a series of canals that flow into the North Sea. Windmills were originally used to power the pumps, but electric pumping stations now handle the job.

The sandy Dunes region, which lies along much of the coastline, does not provide adequate protection against the powerful storms, tides, and currents of the

North Sea. Therefore, all along the coast, the Dutch have strengthened these natural defenses with barricades and piers.

Battles won

The Dutch began their battle with the sea many centuries ago. In the 1300's, the sea level rose dramatically, and the Zuider Zee, which had been a river estuary, widened into a huge bay. To preserve their fragile coastline from further destruction, the people built dams to control the rivers, and barricades to protect the land from the tides. The dam on the Amstel River, for which the city of Amsterdam is named, was built in the 1200's.

By the 1200's, people in the Netherlands were using windmills to pump water from submerged areas and to keep land dry. In the 1500's and 1600's, a new type of windmill that could pump more water made the construction of stronger defenses against the sea possible.

BUILDING A SEA DIKE

The modern method of constructing a sea dike begins with digging a trench in the seabed parallel with the shore (1). Clay, which does not allow the seawater to seep through, is dumped into the trench (2) and built up to form a low mound (3). Gravel is then piled on top of the clay—a large mound on the seaward side (4), and a smaller mound on the landward side (5). The hollow center is filled with clay (6). On the seaward side, synthetic matting is used to cover the gravel mound (7), and is held in place with large boulders (8). Then the whole seaward side of the dike is topped with a layer of brick (9), the outermost defense against the sea. The top of the structure is covered with topsoil and planted with grass seed (10). Roads on the landward side of the dike (11) are protected by the seaward mound of gravel.

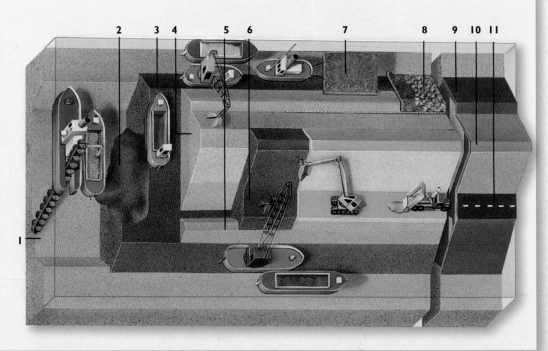

A diagram of a windmill shows how the Dutch used windmills to pump water out of the land and into ditches and canals. The huge sails of the mill rotate the headwheel, which turns the main shaft by means of the gearwheel. Another gearwheel at the base of the shaft is connected to a large screw—the Archimedes screw. As the screw turns, a steady stream of water is drawn inside the windmill and released into a nearby canal. The energy harnessed by the windmills was used to grind the grain grown on the reclaimed land.

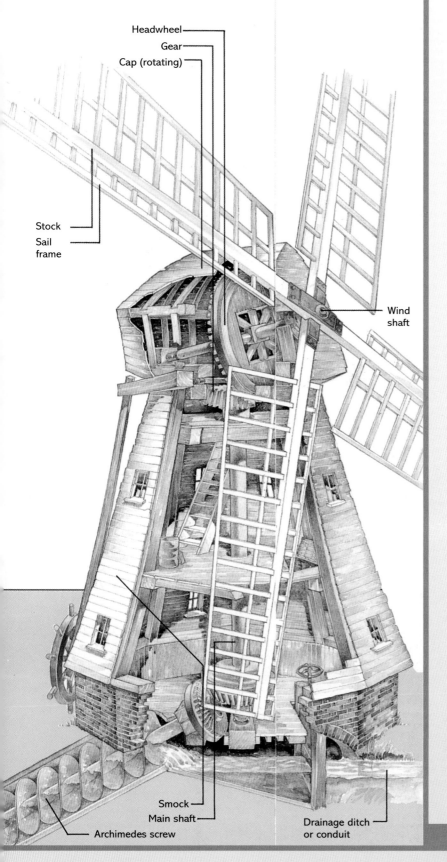

Headwheel
Gear
Cap (rotating)

Stock
Sail frame

Wind shaft

Smock
Main shaft
Archimedes screw
Drainage ditch or conduit

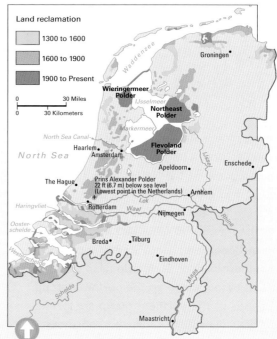

Land reclamation

1300 to 1600
1600 to 1900
1900 to Present

0   30 Miles
0   30 Kilometers

Groningen

Waddenzee

Wieringermeer Polder

IJsselmeer

Northeast Polder

Markermeer

North Sea Canal

Flevoland Polder

Haarlem

North Sea

Amsterdam

Apeldoorn

Enschede

The Hague

Prins Alexander Polder
22 ft (6.7 m) below sea level
(Lowest point in the Netherlands)

Arnhem

Haringvliet

Lek

Oosterschelde

Rotterdam

Waal

Nijmegen

Rhine

Westerschelde

Breda

Tilburg

Eindhoven

Schelde

Maas

Maastricht

Battles against the sea have won much rich farmland for the Dutch.

Over the next 300 years, the Dutch continued to "create" land from the sea. In 1932, the Zuider Zee was cut off from the North Sea by a dike 20 miles (32 kilometers) long. This project changed the Zuider Zee into a vast freshwater lake called the IJsselmeer. Since then, much of the lake has been drained, adding hundreds of square miles of new land.

Battles lost

In spite of their skill at holding back the sea, the Netherlands suffered terrible floods in 1953. Storms broke the dikes in the southwestern delta area, and the sea flooded the land. More than 1,800 people drowned, and some 375,000 acres (151,800 hectares) of land were submerged.

In 1958, work began on the Delta Project to prevent a similar disaster. The project, completed in 1986, includes a series of massive dams and floodgates that have greatly reduced the risk of flooding. In February 1995, however, the country was hit by the worst floods since 1953. More than 250,000 people were evacuated from their homes, and several died.

THE NETHERLANDS ANTILLES AND ARUBA

The Netherlands Antilles, also called the Dutch West Indies, was a largely self-governing part of the Kingdom of the Netherlands. It consisted of two groups of islands. Bonaire and Curaçao, which made up the southern group, are located about 50 miles (80 kilometers) north of Venezuela. Saba, St. Eustatius, and the southern part of St. Martin (also called Sint Maarten) Island, made up the northern group. The islands of the northern group are located about 500 miles (800 kilometers) northeast of Bonaire and Curaçao. The islands that made up the southern group are larger than those of the northern group and have more people.

The southern group once included Aruba, but that island separated from the Netherlands Antilles. Aruba became self-governing in 1986.

In 2005, the Dutch government and the leaders of Bonaire, Curaçao, Saba, Saint Eustatius, and the southern part of Saint Martin agreed to dissolve the Netherlands Antilles. In 2010, Curaçao and Saint Martin became self-governing countries within the Kingdom of the Netherlands, like Aruba. The Netherlands is responsible for their defense and foreign affairs. Bonaire, Saba, and Saint Eustatius became overseas municipalities, with a political status resembling that of towns in the Netherlands.

History

Europeans first sighted the islands in 1499. Spaniards who arrived in Curaçao in 1527 killed the Indians who lived there and used the islands as a base from which to conquer South America. The Dutch, however, were interested in the large salt deposits on the islands and captured the Antilles area in 1634.

The economy of the islands is based on oil refining and tourism. Crude oil is shipped from

Imported fruits are displayed at a dockside market in Willemstad, Curaçao. The city, originally founded as a Dutch trading center in the 1600's, is built around the entrance to St. Anna's Bay. Its fine harbor makes Willemstad an important center for shipping and trading.

The delicate pastel colors and red tile roofs of the Dutch colonial buildings in Willemstad, Curaçao, add an Old World charm to the city. Islanders speak Dutch, English, Spanish, and a mixture of all three called Papiamento.

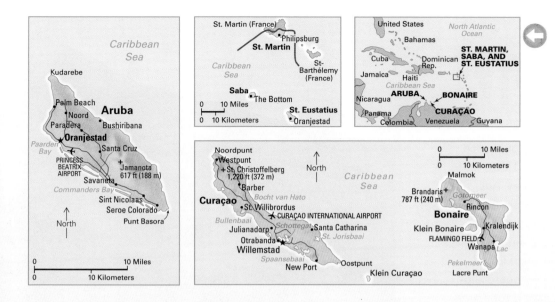

The Caribbean islands that once formed part of the Netherlands Antilles include Aruba, Bonaire, Curaçao, Saba, St. Eustatius, and St. Martin. Aruba, Bonaire, and Curaçao lie slightly north of Venezuela. The other three islands lie to the east of the Virgin Islands. Curaçao, the largest island, covers 171 square miles (444 square kilometers). Willemstad, the capital of Curaçao, once was the capital of the Netherlands Antilles.

Venezuela to refineries on Curaçao. The islands' warm weather, lovely beaches, and picturesque cities and towns draw thousands of tourists every year.

The islands

Curaçao and Bonaire are low-lying, rocky islands surrounded by coral reefs. Curaçao, the largest of the islands that formerly made up the Netherlands Antilles, is generally flat, with some low hills in the northwest. The island is so rocky that little farming is possible, and most food must be imported.

Willemstad, the former capital of the Netherlands Antilles and a major oil-refining center, lies on the southwest coast of Curaçao. It has one of the Caribbean's finest harbors. The city also contains two of the oldest Jewish landmarks in the Western Hemisphere—a cemetery established in 1659 and a temple built in 1732. Jews had fled to Curaçao during colonial times to escape religious persecution.

Bonaire is less developed than Curaçao. Plant life is scarce on this arid island. The soil, like that of Curaçao, has been damaged by overgrazing, but many species of birds thrive. Bonaire also has some of the world's finest coral reefs.

Saba is an extinct volcano and is primarily a tourist center. Tourism is also increasing on Saint Eustatius, which is too dry to support agriculture. The people who live on the southern part of Saint Martin also make their living from tourism.

Palm trees shade the entrance to a colonial-style building on Bonaire. The island's abundant bird life includes its famous flamingo colonies. The fascinating marine life of the island's coastal waters attracts divers from all over the world.

NEW CALEDONIA

New Caledonia, an overseas territory of France, lies in the South Pacific Ocean about 1,200 miles (1,930 kilometers) northeast of Sydney, Australia. The territory consists of one main island called New Caledonia, the Loyalty Islands, the Bélep Islands, the Isle of Pines, and a few uninhabited islands. The mountainous main island covers 6,321 square miles (16,372 square kilometers). The rest of the islands have a total area of only 851 square miles (2,203 square kilometers).

The main island is geologically similar to larger land masses, while some of the other islands are coral formations. New Caledonia's climate is subtropical, with higher temperatures in the rainy season, which lasts from December to March. Annual rainfall in the wettest region averages around 80 inches (205 centimeters). Such conditions encourage vegetation, and the islands have both tropical rain forests and grasslands.

History

Melanesians, probably from New Guinea, reached New Caledonia at least 4,000 years ago. In 1774, James Cook, a British navigator, became the first European to land on the main island. He called it New Caledonia because it resembled Scotland (*Caledonia* in Latin). France took possession of New Caledonia in 1853 in order to set up coconut palm, cocoa, and coffee plantations. The United States had a large military base on the main island from 1942 to 1945.

In 1946, New Caledonia was incorporated into the French republic as an overseas territory, and certain categories of its people became French citizens. The people gained civil rights in stages.

In the 1980's, some Melanesians demanded independence for New Caledonia, but most other New Caledonians favored continued French control. Riots between the opposing groups broke out on a number of occasions. But in a referendum held in 1987, New Caledonians voted to continue French control.

The result of the referendum was controversial, however, because voters who favored independence had boycotted the voting. This group continued to demand independence, and violence erupted in 1988 between some Melanesians and French officials. Later that year, voters approved a peace agreement. In a referendum held in 1998, New Caledonians voted in favor of greater self-government for the territory.

Way of life

New Caledonia has a population of about 252,000. Melanesians, the largest group of people, make up about two-fifths of the population. Europeans form the second largest population group. Other groups include Indonesians, Polynesians, and Vietnamese. Nouméa, on the main island, is the capital and New Caledonia's only city.

Largely cleared of vegetation, a mountain on New Caledonia shows the effects of mining activity. The territory is a major mineral producer, with large deposits of nickel, chromite, and cobalt.

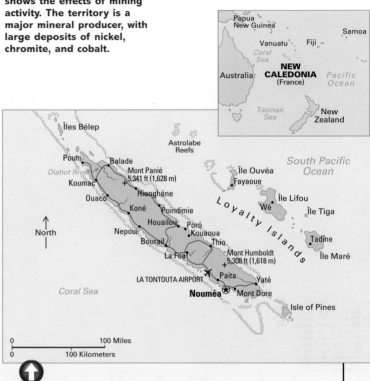

A New Caledonian fisherman removes a nautilus from a trap. The nautilus, a type of shellfish related to the squid and octopus, lives at depths of 20 to 1,000 feet (6 to 300 meters) in the South Pacific and Indian oceans.

New Caledonia consists of one large island and a number of smaller ones in southern Melanesia. It is an overseas territory of France, which took possession of the islands in 1853. Nouméa is New Caledonia's capital and only city.

Nickel mining and smelting are the leading industries of the territory, and New Caledonia ranks among the world's leading producers of nickel. The territory's economy boomed in the 1940's and 1950's due to the growth of its nickel industry, and Nouméa's standard of living increased, along with the population. However, mining has scarred vast areas of the countryside with ugly, open mines, and interest in farming and other traditional occupations has declined. Today, farmers raise their own food and sell small amounts of coffee and copra for export.

A French official appointed by the French government heads New Caledonia's government, presiding over a locally elected congress of New Caledonians who share in the government. New Caledonia is considered part of France. The people vote for the president of France and send representatives to both houses of the French Parliament.

NEW ZEALAND

The lovely island country of New Zealand lies about 1,000 miles (1,600 kilometers) southeast of Australia in the South Pacific Ocean. New Zealand belongs to a large island group called Polynesia. It is the country farthest south of all the Pacific nations. New Zealand is a highly developed nation with a modern economy.

The country consists of two main islands—the North Island and the South Island—and several dozen much smaller islands. The North and South islands extend in a curve more than 1,000 miles long. Most of the smaller islands are hundreds of miles from the main ones. Once part of the British Empire, New Zealand is now an independent member of the Commonwealth of Nations, an association of countries that once lived under British law and government.

New Zealand has a mild, moist climate like that of the Pacific Northwest Coast of the United States. But since New Zealand lies south of the equator, its seasons are opposite those of the Northern Hemisphere. Snow-capped mountains, green lowlands, sandy beaches, and many lakes and waterfalls grace the landscape throughout New Zealand. The Aoraki/Mount Cook region, on the South Island, has some of the country's most spectacular scenery. Glaciers cover the mountain slopes above the dense, green forests, and sparkling lakes nestle in the valleys.

The first people to live in New Zealand were a people who became known as Maori. They came from Polynesian islands northeast of New Zealand. Today, only about 15 percent of New Zealand's people are Maori. Most New Zealanders are descendants of Europeans who began to settle there in the 1800's.

New Zealand's standard of living ranks among the highest in the world. The country's economy, which depended largely on agriculture for many years, now also includes a number of important manufacturing and service industries.

The New Zealand way of life combines an easy informality with a British and Polynesian sense of politeness. Since the arrival of British settlers around 1800, many New Zealanders have kept close cultural and emotional ties to the United Kingdom, and many New Zealand customs resemble British customs. But New Zealand has developed a feeling of national identity as a Pacific nation of both British and Polynesian heritage.

NEW ZEALAND TODAY

About 70 percent of New Zealand's more than 4 million people are descendants of European settlers who came to the country during the 1800's. Nearly 75 percent of all New Zealanders live on the North Island, and more than 85 percent of the country's people live in urban areas.

Children must attend school from the age of 6 to 16, but most youngsters start school at the age of 5. Education is free to all students in primary and secondary school. New Zealand has several universities, and the government pays about one-third of the universities' operating expenses.

New Zealand is a constitutional monarchy. It recognizes the British monarch as its head of state, but the monarch has little real power. The British monarch appoints a governor general to represent the Crown in New Zealand. The legislature is a 120-member House of Representatives, also called the Parliament. The legislature, prime minister, and Cabinet run the national government.

The United Kingdom gave New Zealand a constitution in 1852, when it was a British colony, but the New Zealand legislature has changed almost all its provisions through the years. For all practical purposes, the nation today has no written constitution.

New Zealand has managed to limit or reduce many of the problems that face other countries, such as environmental pollution, poverty, racial conflict, and urban overcrowding. Today, New Zealand's top goals include managing the environment, advancing health care, and helping more Maori obtain positions of leadership in industry and the professions.

Today, New Zealand is finding new overseas markets for its dairy and meat products. The United Kingdom was the country's chief trading partner until 1973, when the United Kingdom joined the European Economic Community (now the European Union). This organization has no tariffs on trade among its members, but there is a common tariff on goods imported from other countries. Because goods from New Zealand carry this tariff, the country is now at a disadvantage in trading with the

FACTS

Official name:	New Zealand
Capital:	Wellington
Terrain:	Predominantly mountainous with some large coastal plains
Area:	104,454 mi² (270,534 km²)
Climate:	Temperate with sharp regional contrasts
Main rivers:	Waikato, Clutha
Highest elevation:	Aoraki/Mount Cook, 12,316 ft (3,754 m)
Lowest elevation:	Pacific Ocean, sea level
Form of government:	Constitutional monarchy
Head of state:	British monarch, represented by governor general
Head of government:	Prime minister
Administrative areas:	16 regions and 1 territory
Legislature:	House of Representatives, commonly called Parliament, with 120 members serving three-year terms
Court system:	Supreme Court, Court of Appeal
Armed forces:	9,300 troops
National holiday:	Waitangi Day - February 6 (1840) ANZAC Day - April 25 (1915)
Estimated 2010 population:	4,293,000
Population density:	41 persons per mi² (16 per km²)
Population distribution:	86% urban, 14% rural
Life expectancy in years:	Male, 78; female, 82
Doctors per 1,000 people:	2.1
Birth rate per 1,000:	15
Death rate per 1,000:	7
Infant mortality:	5 deaths per 1,000 live births
Age structure:	0-14: 21%; 15-64: 67%; 65 and over: 13%
Internet users per 100 people:	75
Internet code:	.nz
Languages spoken:	English, Maori, New Zealand Sign Language (all official)
Religions:	Anglican 14%, Catholic 13%, Presbyterian 10%, other Christian 19%, other 44%
Currency:	New Zealand dollar
Gross domestic product (GDP) in 2008:	$131.63 billion U.S.
Real annual growth rate (2008):	0.2%
GDP per capita (2008):	$31,430 U.S.
Goods exported:	Aluminum, dairy products, fish, fruit, machinery, meat, wood and wood products, wool
Goods imported:	Aircraft, machinery, motor vehicles, petroleum and petroleum products, plastics
Trading partners:	Australia, China, Germany, Japan, Singapore, United Kingdom, United States

The "Beehive," in Wellington, is the circular building in which New Zealand's government ministers have their offices. It stands next to the building in which the legislature meets.

New Zealand is made up of two large islands—the North Island and the South Island—plus a number of smaller islands. The South Island boasts the country's highest peak and some of its most spectacular scenery.

United Kingdom. New Zealand has since increased the variety of its exports and found some new markets for its products.

The 1990's brought major political changes to New Zealand. Until the early 1990's, New Zealand had a *first-past-the-post* electoral system, in which each parliamentary representative was the person who had received the most votes in an electoral district. In 1993, New Zealand adopted a *mixed member proportional* (MMP) system of electing members of Parliament. In this system, some seats are reserved for elected legislators, while others are divided among political parties according to their share of the total votes cast. In the 1996 election, the first held under the new MMP system, the number of seats held by third parties and Maori increased dramatically.

In 1997, Jenny Shipley replaced Jim Bolger as National Party leader and prime minister. Shipley was New Zealand's first woman prime minister. In the general election of 1999, Helen Clark, of the Labour Party, became the first elected woman prime minister in New Zealand. Clark served as prime minister until 2008, when John Key of the National Party replaced her.

In 2010, a 7.1-magnitude earthquake struck Christchurch, causing widespread damage but no direct fatalities. In 2011, a 6.3-magnitude quake caused extensive damage and left 181 people dead.

ECONOMY

New Zealand has lots of sheep and cattle. In fact, the country has many times as many farm animals as it has people. Sheep are so numerous that a distant hillside may resemble a field of cotton because so many fluffy white sheep are grazing there.

The economy of New Zealand has long depended on farming and foreign trade. Exports of dairy products, meat, and wool still provide much of the nation's income. But manufacturing has been increasing, and about twice as many New Zealanders now work in factories as on farms. Tourism has also become an important source of income.

New Zealand's economy depends heavily on trade. The country's chief trading partners are Australia, China, Japan, and the United States. New Zealand's leading exports include aluminum, dairy products, fish, fruits, machinery, meat, wood and wood products, and wool. The country's chief imports include aircraft, machinery, petroleum and petroleum products, and plastics.

Agriculture and mining

New Zealand's greatest natural resource is its land. About 50 percent of the land consists of cropland and pastureland, and about 25 percent is covered with forests that provide valuable timber as well as protection from land erosion. Much of the rest of the country is made up of lakes, rivers, and mountain areas.

Sheep raising is New Zealand's most important agricultural activity. Traveling down a rural highway often means giving the right of way to a passing flock.

The country has a wide variety of minerals. The most important include clay, coal, *dimension stone* (stone cut to specific sizes and shapes), gold, iron ore, lime, limestone, marble, natural gas, oil, salt, and silver. Water power provides more than half of the nation's electricity. Underground steam in the volcanic area of the North Island has become an increasingly important source of power.

GEOTHERMAL ENERGY

Geothermal energy, which supplies some of New Zealand's electricity, is generated when water comes into contact with heated underground rocks and turns into steam. The layer of solid bedrock overlying Earth's mantle (1) conducts heat to porous rock layers (2), where water is heated to temperatures of 482° to 662° F (250° to 350° C). Forced upward, the steam is trapped under layers of solid cap rock (3), where its pressure increases. The steam escapes to the surface through cracks and fissures (4), forming geysers or hot springs. Power companies drill into areas where underground steam is trapped and direct it into the blades of steam turbines. Geothermal power plants do not burn anything, so there is no smoke to pollute the air.

Earth's mantle

New Zealand produces enough meat and dairy products to feed millions of people in other countries as well as its own people, thanks to the country's mild climate, modern machinery, and scientific farming methods. Cattle are raised throughout the North Island, and many sheep are raised in the Eastern Hills. On the South Island, cattle and sheep are both primarily raised in the Canterbury Plains and at the southern end of the island. New Zealand farmers also raise beef and dairy cattle, chickens, and hogs. Chickens provide eggs and meat. New Zealand is one of the world's leading producers of milk and wool.

The chief crops include apples, barley, grapes, kiwi fruit, onions, potatoes, and wheat. New Zealand is one of the world's largest producers of kiwi fruit.

Forestry and fishing

A small amount of New Zealand's total forest production comes from native forests on the South Island. But most timber comes from planted forests, primariliy fast-growing Monterey pine forests. The logs are processed into plywood, wood pulp, and other products.

New Zealand's exclusive economic fishing zone is one of the largest in the world—an area about 15 times larger than the country's land mass. Valuable commercial fish include blue grenadier, jack mackerels, orange roughy, snoek, southern blue whiting, squid, and tuna. Mussels, oysters, and salmon are important aquaculture products.

A ferry sails past the city of Wellington in the Hurt Valley. The snow-capped Taraua mountain range rises in the background. The Taraua is one of several mountain ranges on the North Island of New Zealand

The Wairakei power plant on the North Island is situated above a large geo-thermal system containing water at temperatures up to 464 °F (240 °C). Steam is directed toward the turbines through a network of pipes. Underground steam in the North Island has become an increasingly important source of power.

Manufacturing

Processed foods rank as New Zealand's most valuable manufactured goods. Milk is made into butter, cheese, and milk powder, while lamb and beef are frozen for export. Factories also process wool and weave woolen carpets. Other manufactured items include machinery, paper, textiles, and wood products. Large-scale projects in the 1980's developed wider uses for local resources, including the use of *ironsand* (sand containing iron ore) in steel manufacture and the use of wood from plantation forests in pulp, paper, and packaging enterprises.

Auckland, New Zealand's most populous city, is its largest manufacturing center. Wellington, the country's capital and second largest city, is also an important manufacturing center. Nearly 15 percent of New Zealand's labor force is employed in factories.

PEOPLE

Most of New Zealand's more than 4 million people are descendants of European settlers. Immigrants still come to New Zealand, chiefly from Asia, Africa, and eastern Europe.

Maori make up about 15 percent of New Zealand's population—the country's largest minority group. The Maori are a Polynesian people whose ancestors came to New Zealand nearly 1,000 years ago. Through the years, many Maori have intermarried with people of European ancestry. As a result, large numbers of New Zealanders of mixed parentage share the physical characteristics of both Europeans and Maori.

English, one of the official languages of New Zealand, is spoken throughout the country. Many Maori also speak their own language, Maori, another official language.

The people of New Zealand have a high standard of living—they have long been among the best-fed people in the world. The nation also has a tradition of equal rights and benefits for all its citizens. In 1893, New Zealand became the first nation in the world to give women the right to vote. Today, the nation has one of the world's finest social security, pension, and public health programs.

Of the 120 seats in the New Zealand House of Representatives, 5 are reserved for Maori, who are voted for by Maori only. Maori who prefer to vote in the 115 general *electorates* (voting districts) may do so.

To protect the rights of citizens, the House of Representatives selects an official called an *ombudsman*. The ombudsman investigates complaints by citizens against government departments and sends an opinion to the department involved. If the department does not take the action that the ombudsman believes is needed, the findings may be reported to the House of Representatives.

The law requires children from 6 to 16 to attend school. New Zealand offers a free education to all students in primary and secondary schools. The government provides school bus service for children in rural areas who live beyond walking distance from school.

↑ The All Blacks, New Zealand's famous national Rugby Union team, play in black jerseys, shorts, and socks. British settlers introduced the game to New Zealand about 1870, but some of the greatest players in the game's history have been Maori.

Uniformed students gather outside their school in Christchurch. The city, founded by the British in the 1850's, is the largest on the South Island.

Most of New Zealand's families own their own homes, usually a single-family house. Almost every New Zealand family has a car. Almost all New Zealanders have refrigerators, washing machines, and other modern electrical appliances.

Although most people live in urban areas, New Zealand's cities are relatively uncrowded, with few traffic problems even in downtown areas. The cities have theaters, concert halls, and other entertainment. In rural New Zealand, good roads link some settlements, but some ranchers in rugged country may live in near isolation.

New Zealanders enjoy outdoor activities and sports, and the country's mild climate allows for camping, hiking, hunting, and mountain climbing during much of the year. Ski areas attract large numbers of people. Many New Zealanders enjoy swimming and tennis, as well as such team sports as *cricket,* which somewhat resembles baseball, and *rugby,* a form of football.

Cathedral Square in the city of Christchurch.

A crowd gathers on the shore of the Bay of Islands during the Waitangi Day celebrations in Paihia. Waitangi Day is the national day of New Zealand, celebrating the signing of the Treaty of Waitangi. The treaty is New Zealand's founding document, signed on Feb. 6, 1840.

THE MAORI

The first people to live in New Zealand were Polynesians who probably came to the country by canoe around A.D. 1200 from islands northeast of New Zealand. Historians have disagreed about whether these people, who later came to be called Maori, arrived by accident or by planned migration. However, recent successful voyages between other Polynesian islands and New Zealand —using replicas of the old Maori dugout canoes and following only the stars and other natural guides—tend to suggest that the voyages were planned.

Most Maori are tall people with broad faces, brown eyes, and wavy black hair. Through the years, many Maori have intermarried with people of European ancestry.

Traditional Maori culture

The first Maori lived in isolated villages, mainly by fishing and hunting. They have been called the *moa hunters* because their chief prey was the now-extinct *moas,* a group of large, wingless birds. Later, the Maori also became farmers. The Maori were skilled woodcarvers, and they decorated war canoes and communal houses with complicated designs. Their religion was based on *taboos* (prohibitions on certain objects, people, and places).

All the inhabitants of a village were related to one another and bore the name of their common ancestor. Villages were made up of tribes and subtribes. Each subtribe had a number of family groups, and each group had a leader who reached decisions by discussions with other leaders and with the people.

The people moved with the seasons to various parts of the tribal lands to hunt specific animals. In late summer, for example, they might travel to the sea to catch and dry sharks for winter food supplies.

A Maori meeting house, now the setting for ceremonial events, formed the center of tribal life during the 1800's. Parts of the building often symbolized the parts of an ancestor's body, with the face at the peak.

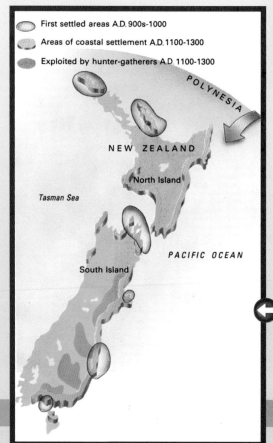

First settled areas A.D. 900s-1000

Areas of coastal settlement A.D. 1100-1300

Exploited by hunter-gatherers A.D. 1100-1300

POLYNESIA

NEW ZEALAND

North Island

Tasman Sea

PACIFIC OCEAN

South Island

Kiri Te Kanawa, descended from Maori chiefs, achieved international fame as an opera singer.

Maori migration from other parts of Polynesia occurred nearly 1,000 years ago. Most Maori settled around the northern coast of the North Island where the soil was good and the climate was warm.

Maori woodcarving developed into a major art form in New Zealand, where soft-wood timber and tough rock for chisels called greenstone were plentiful. With these materials, Maori developed carving skills superior to any found elsewhere in Polynesia.

Maori and Pakeha

Today, most New Zealanders are descendants of early European settlers. Maori used the term *Pakeha* ("pale-faced strangers") for the European settlers. Today, the term refers to any non-Maori New Zealander.

The arrival of the Europeans brought great suffering to the Maori. The Pakeha brought firearms, which intensified warfare among the Maori tribes. The newcomers also brought diseases against which the Maori had no resistance. By 1840, warfare and disease had reduced the Maori population from about 100,000 to about 70,000. Disputes over land ownership led to the New Zealand Wars, which lasted off and on from 1845 to 1872. In the 1890's, the Maori population dropped to only about 20,000.

Until World War II (1939-1945), the great majority of Maori lived in rural districts. During the war, however, educational and job opportunities drew many Maori into the cities. Today, the nation's Maori and Pakeha live in an atmosphere of common trust, and Maori political leaders and professional people play important roles. However, many Maori see a need for better housing, employment opportunities, and education, and they believe that Maori should play a greater role in the government of New Zealand.

Maori point out that subjects taught in New Zealand schools are mainly related to Pakeha culture, and most television and radio stations broadcast in the English language. Many Maori feel that they have lost their cultural heritage, and they are working to revive the Maori language, customs, and traditions. Above all, Maori are working to regain ownership of their lands.

Maori "warriors" open the Commonwealth Games in Auckland. The Maori tribal history is a tale of conflict and warfare, but Maori today live much like other New Zealanders.

WILDLIFE

Most of New Zealand's land animals were introduced from other countries. European settlers brought deer and rabbits, as well as cattle, pigs, and sheep. *Wallabies* (small kangaroos) and brush-tailed possums were brought from Australia. Two species of bats are the only native land mammals. The lizard-like *tuatara,* a native reptile unchanged since prehistoric times, still lives in New Zealand. The lakes and rivers are stocked with salmon and trout brought from other countries.

Most of New Zealand's trees are evergreens and tree ferns. In the country's luxuriant rain forests, the trees, standing close together, grow very tall and straight. Moss, lichens, and ferns cover their trunks. The country's pulp and paper industry depends mainly on the fast-growing Monterey pine imported from California, one of the many foreign trees introduced since 1900.

Animals

New Zealand has no snakes. Scientists believe that this may be due to the fact that New Zealand broke away from the large combined southern continent of Australia and Antarctica millions of years ago.

The kiwi is a New Zealand bird that cannot fly. It has short legs and a long bill, and its body is covered with shaggy feathers. People use the term kiwi as a nickname for a New Zealander.

Birds are New Zealand's dominant *vertebrates* (animals with backbones). Native birds include such flightless species as the kakapo parrot, kiwi, takahe, and weka. The kiwi may be the best known, though it is a shy, nocturnal bird and usually runs away and hides when anyone comes near. The kiwi is the only bird that has nostrils at the tip of its bill.

Unlike the rest of the world, where land birds dominate, only about one-third of New Zealand's birds are land birds. Some, such as the kiwi, probably lived in New Zealand before it broke away from Australia. Others, including the takahe and weka, arrived after the break, probably mainly from Australia.

New Zealand once had many ostrichlike moas, but they have become extinct. Moas could not fly, and some grew to be 13 feet (4 meters) tall. These birds lived in New Zealand when the Maori arrived there about 800 years ago. Hunting and the destruction of their lowland forest habitat probably led to the birds' extinction several hundred years later.

Plants

Volcanic eruptions in prehistoric times destroyed large areas of forest in the central plateau of the North Island. As a result, small shrubs, such as the manuka, now cover much of the region. Manukas, the most common shrub in New Zealand, have papery bark and masses of pink or white flowers.

The yellow-eyed penguin is one of six species of penguins that make their home among the islands near New Zealand. The species breeds around the South Island of New Zealand, as well as on Stewart Island and Auckland Island. They build their nests in burrows under large rocks or bushes.

The green, rolling pastureland of the Wairarapa region makes it an important cattle- and sheep-raising area. The Wairarapa lies in the southeastern part of New Zealand's North Island, at the southern edge of a belt of ranch land running from East Cape to Cook Strait. Farmers there also raise fruits and vegetables along the coast. Masterton is the chief town of the region.

Aoraki/Mount Cook, the highest peak in New Zealand, towers over the Southern Alps of the South Island, attracting many mountain climbers. The Maori name for the mountain is Aorangi, which means cloud piercer.

Forests of pinelike kauri trees once thrived on the northern peninsulas, but the early European settlers almost destroyed the kauri forests. However, kauris still flourish on both the large islands. These huge trees, which live to a great age, are the most impressive of the many types of pine trees in New Zealand, growing up to 100 feet (30 meters) tall and towering above other trees in the forests. Great stands of kauris form a vaulted roof of branches.

The beech is one of the loveliest of New Zealand's trees. These trees belong to the oak family and grow to 100 feet (30 meters) or more high on the plains, on alpine slopes, and even near the seacoast. Beech forests grow on the cooler uplands of both islands.

Since 1900, many foreign trees have been introduced into New Zealand. The fast-growing Monterey pine, an import from California, now supports the country's pulp and paper industry.

Cropland and pastureland occupy about 50 percent of New Zealand's land.

NICARAGUA

Nicaragua, the largest Central American country in size, was named for an Indian chief and his people—both named Nicarao—who lived in the area when the Spaniards arrived in the 1500's. Today, Nicaragua is troubled by severe economic problems and other effects of the civil war that raged from the late 1970's through the 1980's.

Economy

Farming is the leading economic activity in Nicaragua, and farm products provide much of the country's export income. Valuable agricultural exports include beef, coffee, and sugar cane. Beans, corn, and rice are the main food crops raised for domestic use.

Nicaragua's leading service industry is wholesale and retail trade. The marketing of farm products is the most important sector of that industry. The manufacturing industry produces mainly processed foods and beverages, clothing, and textiles. Other products are cement, cigarettes, leather goods, petroleum, and wood.

History

In 1502, Christopher Columbus landed in what is now Nicaragua and claimed the land for Spain. Settlements were built near the Indians so that they could work on the Spaniards' farms and in their mines.

The area along the Caribbean coast, however, went largely unsettled and became a hideout for English, French, and Dutch pirates. In the 1700's, the English gained control over the Miskito, or Mosquito, Indians who lived there. However, the United Kingdom gave up its claim to the region in the mid-1800's.

On Sept. 15, 1821, Nicaragua and other Central American states declared their independence from Spain. They became part of Mexico, but in 1823 they formed the United Provinces of Central America—a union with liberal political and economic policies. The union established civil rights and tried to curb the power of the rich landowners and the Roman Catholic Church.

However, Nicaragua left the union in 1838. By then, a dispute had started between liberal people in the city of León and conservative people in the city of Granada. The two cities fought for control of the country.

The liberals of León asked an American soldier and adventurer, William Walker, to help them. In 1855, Walker and his followers captured Granada in a surprise attack, and Walker seized control of the government. In 1857, the liberals and conservatives joined forces and drove Walker out of the country.

In the late 1800's, the United States was planning to build a canal in Nicaragua that would link the Atlantic and Pacific oceans. In 1901, however, Nicaraguan President José Santos Zelaya began to argue with the United States over the agreement. When a revolt broke out against Zelaya's harsh rule in 1909, the United States sided with the rebels, and Zelaya was driven out.

In 1911, U.S. banks began to lend money to Nicaragua under agreements that gave them control over the country's finances until the debts were paid. Some Nicaraguans objected to this control. In 1912, U.S. Marines landed in Nicaragua to put down the protests and remained in the country.

When rebels led by General Augusto César Sandino tried to make the U.S. forces leave, the United States trained a new Nicaraguan army, called the National Guard, to help the U.S. Marines. Anastasio Somoza Garcia headed the National Guard. When the U.S. Marines left in 1933, the National Guard, under orders from Somoza, killed Sandino.

Somoza then took control of the government and ruled as dictator. He established great political and economic power for himself and his family. Somoza was assassinated in 1956, and first one son and then another succeeded him. From 1937 to 1979, a Somoza was either the president of Nicaragua or the real power behind the president.

Widespread protests against Anastasio Somoza Debayle began in the mid-1970's. By 1978, the conflict had become a civil war. Many of the rebels were Sandinistas, members of a group named for the slain rebel leader Sandino.

In 1979, the Sandinistas drove Somoza from Nicaragua and took control of the country. The Sandinistas were *leftists* who favored increased governmental control over the economy. The Sandinistas took over key parts of the economy and adopted policies designed to help the poor. However, economic recovery was slow. War with antigovernment forces called *contras* and a United States trade embargo hurt Nicaragua's economy. Daniel Ortega became head of the Sandinista government. In 1984, he was elected president of Nicaragua.

In 1990, the people voted the Sandinistas out of office, electing Violeta Barrios de Chamorro to the presidency. But after being defeated in the 1996 and 2001 presidential elections, Daniel Ortega was reelected president in 2006. Ortega won the election again in 2011, despite the fact that the Constitution forbids consecutive terms. In 2009, the Sandinista-controlled Supreme Court had ruled that the Constitution violated the president's rights.

The colorful Granada Cathedral is a prominent landmark in the city of Granada. The city is a center of commerce, including timber, gold, and silver. Its beautifully preserved colonial architecture makes Granada a popular tourist destination.

Shoppers wander through an open-air market in Granada. The city, founded in the mid-1520's by Spanish conquistadors, ranks among the oldest in Central America.

NICARAGUA TODAY

Nicaragua stretches from the Pacific Ocean to the Caribbean Sea on the Central American land bridge. About three-fifths of the people live on the Pacific side, in one of the country's three main land regions.

The land and climate

The Pacific Region lies from north to south along the western coast. Lake Managua is in the center of this hot, humid region, and Lake Nicaragua takes up much of its southern portion. Volcanoes—both active and inactive—rise up out of this low area, while mountains up to 3,000 feet (910 meters) high rim the Pacific coast.

The Central Highlands are Nicaragua's highest and coolest region. Pico Mogotón, the country's highest point, rises 6,913 feet (2,107 meters) lies in this region. Forests cover most of the region's slopes, and deep valleys nestle between their peaks.

The Caribbean Region is mainly a long, flat plain stretching down the Caribbean coast. In the west, the land slopes up toward the highlands, and many rivers that rise in the Central Highlands flow through the plain. The region's only areas of fertile farmland line the riverbanks. Some grasslands and palm and pine forests lie in the north, but rain forests cover most of the Caribbean Region. Temperatures average 80° F (27° C), and easterly trade winds drench the region with about 165 inches (419 centimeters) of rain each year. This hot, wet area is known as the Mosquito Coast.

In 1998, a hurricane struck Nicaragua, producing floods and landslides. The storm killed about 3,000 people and caused more than $1 billion in damage.

The people and their government

Nicaragua has about 6 million people. The great majority of them are *mestizos,* people with both Indian and European ancestors. They follow a Spanish American way of life, much as other Central

FACTS

Official name:	República de Nicaragua (Republic of Nicaragua)
Capital:	Managua
Terrain:	Extensive Atlantic coastal plains rising to central interior mountains; narrow Pacific coastal plain interrupted by volcanoes
Area:	50,193 mi² (130,000 km²)
Climate:	Tropical in lowlands, cooler in highlands
Main rivers:	Tuma, Rio Grande de Matagalpa, Escondido, San Juan, Coco
Highest elevation:	Pico Mogotón, 6,913 ft (2,107 m)
Lowest elevation:	Pacific Ocean, sea level
Form of government:	Republic
Head of state:	President
Head of government:	President
Administrative areas:	15 departamentos (departments), 2 regiones autonomistas (autonomous regions)
Legislature:	Asamblea Nacional (National Assembly) with at least 90 members serving five-year terms
Court system:	Corte Suprema de Justicia (Supreme Court of Justice)
Armed forces:	12,000 troops
National holiday:	Independence Day - September 15 (1821)
Estimated 2010 population:	5,916,000
Population density:	118 persons per mi² (46 per km²)
Population distribution:	59% urban, 41% rural
Life expectancy in years:	Male, 69; female, 74
Doctors per 1,000 people:	0.4
Birth rate per 1,000:	25
Death rate per 1,000:	5
Infant mortality:	28 deaths per 1,000 live births
Age structure:	0-14: 37%; 15-64: 59%; 65 and over: 4%
Internet users per 100 people:	3
Internet code:	.ni
Languages spoken:	Spanish (official), English, indigenous languages
Religions:	Roman Catholic 58.5%, Evangelical 21.6%, Moravian 1.6%, Jehovah's Witness 0.9%, other 17.4%
Currency:	Gold cordoba
Gross domestic product (GDP) in 2008:	$6.50 billion U.S.
Real annual growth rate (2008):	2.0%
GDP per capita (2008):	$1,191 U.S.
Goods exported:	Beef, coffee, gold, lobster and shrimp, sugar
Goods imported:	Electronics, machinery, motor vehicles, petroleum and petroleum products, pharmaceuticals
Trading partners:	Costa Rica, El Salvador, Guatemala, Honduras, Mexico, United States, Venezuela

American mestizos do. They speak Spanish and belong to the Roman Catholic Church.

The only Indian groups who still follow traditional Indian ways of life live in the Caribbean Region. This region also has several communities of black people or people with both black and Indian ancestors who speak Indian languages and generally follow Indian customs and traditions.

About two-fifths of Nicaraguans are farmers. The majority live in the Pacific Region. Some peasants in this region work on their own farms, some work on cooperatives or state farms, and some have jobs on large private farms. In the warmer areas, farm-workers live in houses with palm-leaf or metal roofs. In the colder areas of the Central Highlands, farmers live in adobe houses with tile roofs. Most of the Indians and blacks in the thinly populated Caribbean Region live by farming small plots or by fishing, lumbering, or mining.

Nicaragua's largest cities and many large farms are in the Pacific Region. Managua is the capital and largest city.

Nicaraguans elect a president and a legislature called the National Assembly. The president appoints a cabinet to help run the government. However, the country has a history of political unrest and dictatorship. The Supreme Court of Justice, whose judges are elected by the National Assembly to five-year terms, is Nicaragua's highest court.

Lake Nicaragua lies in southwestern Nicaragua. Several large islands rise from the lake's waters, including Ometepe, the biggest, which has several small communities and two volcanoes.

COPING WITH CRISIS

The history of Nicaragua is marked by natural, social, and political crises. In 1972, for example, an earthquake killed about 5,000 people and destroyed so much of Managua that the city had to be rebuilt. Poverty and lack of education affect much of the population. Political revolts have shaken the country.

From 1979 to 1984, the revolutionary Sandinista group controlled Nicaragua, largely through a three-member *junta,* or ruling council. In 1984, the Sandinista candidate Daniel Ortega was elected president.

During the 1980's, the Sandinista government tried to correct some of the country's economic and social problems. The Sandinistas took over key parts of the economy, including agricultural exports, banking, insurance, and mining. The government adopted programs to help the poor and tried to improve the economy, which had been damaged during the civil war of the 1970's.

The Sandinistas also spent a great deal of money on health and education. Before 1980, only about half the country's children went to school, and many rural areas had no schools at all. The Sandinista government built hundreds of rural schools and also established a successful literacy program, headed mainly by young volunteer teachers.

Under Ortega, however, the government also restricted civil rights, especially those of its political opponents. Press censorship increased. Partially as a result of these measures, opposition to the Sandinistas developed in the early 1980's. In 1981, the United States charged that the Sandinistas were providing weapons to rebels in other countries and cut off all aid to Nicaragua. That same year, contras stepped up their attacks on Nicaragua from bases over the border in Hon-

Sandinista soldiers were everpresent in Nicaragua in the 1980's, even in the market places. The government built up its military forces to fight the contras.

A shantytown shows the poverty of Nicaragua. The Sandinistas tried to mix socialism with private business, but economic problems plagued the nation during their rule.

duras. Many contras were soldiers who had belonged to the National Guard under Anastasio Somoza Debayle, the president who was overthrown by the Sandinistas.

In response to contra attacks, the Nicaraguan government built up its military forces. In 1983, several thousand contras invaded northeastern Nicaragua, and fighting between government troops and contras began to take many lives.

The Soviet Union, Cuba, and Western European nations aided the Nicaraguan government during the fight. The U.S. government under President Ronald Reagan gave financial aid to the contras. In 1983 and 1984, the United States also helped the contras place mines in Nicaraguan harbors. In 1985, Reagan ordered an embargo on trade with Nicaragua on the grounds that the government was a Communist dictatorship.

Some of the Indians in the Caribbean Region also helped the contras. The government moved these Indians from their homes near the border to the interior of the country.

The fighting continued until March 1988, when a cease-fire was negotiated. No peace agreement was ever reached, however, and a low level of fighting resumed. In February 1990, Daniel Ortega was defeated in a presidential election by Violeta Chamorro, and the Sandinistas lost control of the Nicaraguan government. Ortega would later be reelected president in 2006.

Economic recovery from the civil war in the 1970's was never completely achieved. The cost of war against the contras, the U.S. trade embargo, and the high government spending on health and education added to the country's economic problems. Life continues to be very difficult for many Nicaraguans.

NIGER

Niger is a large, landlocked country in western Africa. It is an extremely poor country with few natural resources. More than 15 million people live in Niger, and most of them cannot read and write. "Tent schools" serve some of the nomad groups in the north—when a group moves, the school moves with it. Some areas have Qur'ānic schools, which concentrate on the teachings of Islam. The government of Niger offers free public education, but many areas have no schools.

Only a small portion of Niger's land is used to grow crops. Years of drought have destroyed crops and livestock, forcing many of Niger's nomads into urban areas.

Government

The president is the most powerful official in Niger's government. The president appoints a prime minister and other members of the Cabinet. The president is elected by the people to a five-year term. The National Assembly, which is made up of more than 100 members who are also elected to five-year terms, is responsible for making Niger's laws.

History

During its history, Niger has been part of two great African empires. About A.D. 1000, Berber nomads called the Tuareg began moving south from the middle of the Sahara into what is now Niger. They eventually controlled the wealthy caravan routes that crossed the desert. By the 1400's, the Tuareg had created an empire around the city of Agadez.

The powerful Songhai Empire, based in neighboring Mali, conquered the Tuareg during the 1500's. Central and western Niger fell under Songhai control, but the empire collapsed under Moroccan invaders in 1591.

European explorers arrived in the Niger region in the early 1800's. France, which had gained control of most of Niger by 1900, overcame the fierce resistance of the Tuareg in 1906. Niger became part of French West Africa in 1922.

FACTS

Official name:	République du Niger (Republic of Niger)
Capital:	Niamey
Terrain:	Predominantly desert plains and sand dunes; flat to rolling plains in south; hills in north
Area:	489,191 mi² (1,267,000 km²)
Climate:	Desert; mostly hot, dry, dusty; tropical in extreme south
Main river:	Niger
Highest elevation:	Mount Bagzane, 6,634 ft (2,022 m)
Lowest elevation:	Niger River, 656 ft (200 m)
Form of government:	Republic
Head of state:	President
Head of government:	President
Administrative areas:	8 regions, 1 capital district
Legislature:	National Assembly with 113 members serving five-year terms
Court system:	Cour d'État (State Court), Cour d'Appel (Court of Appeal)
Armed forces:	5,300 troops
National holiday:	Republic Day - December 18 (1958)
Estimated 2010 population:	15,768,000
Population density:	32 persons per mi² (12 per km²)
Population distribution:	83% rural, 17% urban
Life expectancy in years:	Male, 55; female, 55
Doctors per 1,000 people:	Less than 0.05
Birth rate per 1,000:	49
Death rate per 1,000:	15
Infant mortality:	83 deaths per 1,000 live births
Age structure:	0-14: 49%; 15-64: 48%; 65 and over: 3%
Internet users per 100 people:	0.5
Internet code:	.ne
Languages spoken:	French (official), Hausa, Djerma
Religions:	Muslim (predominant), indigenous beliefs, Christian
Currency:	Communauté Financière Africaine franc
Gross domestic product (GDP) in 2008:	$5.35 billion U.S.
Real annual growth rate (2008):	5.9%
GDP per capita (2008):	$348 U.S.
Goods exported:	Mostly uranium, also livestock
Goods imported:	Food, machinery, motor vehicles, petroleum products
Trading partners:	Côte d'Ivoire, France, Japan, Nigeria, United States

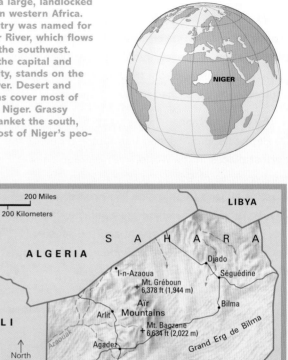

A camel caravan crosses the bleak Saharan landscape in northern Niger. Such caravans once carried precious salt southward through the desert, where temperatures reach 122° F (50° C).

Niger is a large, landlocked country in western Africa. The country was named for the Niger River, which flows through the southwest. Niamey, the capital and largest city, stands on the Niger River. Desert and mountains cover most of northern Niger. Grassy plains blanket the south, where most of Niger's people live.

Niger won independence from France in 1960, and Hamani Diori—the leader of the Niger Progressive Party (*Parti Progressiste Nigérien,* or PPN) was elected as the country's first president. During his term, a severe drought struck the country, causing food shortages and other problems.

In 1974, Diori was overthrown by army officers led by Seyni Kountché. Kountché outlawed the PPN, suspended the Constitution, and dissolved the national legislature. He then became president of the Supreme Council, which held all the power in the country. Kountché died in 1987, and the council chose Colonel Ali Saibou as president. However, the price of uranium, Niger's most important export, dropped, and Niger's economy continued to suffer. In September 1989, Niger adopted a new constitution. In a presidential election held in December, Saibou ran unopposed.

In 1992, Niger adopted a multiparty system. Mahamane

Ousmane was elected president in 1993. He was ousted in a coup d'état in January 1996 and replaced by army officer Ibrahim Baré Maïnassara. Maïnassara was assassinated in 1999, and military leaders took control of the government. In November elections to restore civilian rule, Mamadou Tandja was elected president. He was reelected in 2004. When Tandja tried to change the Constitution to allow him a third term, he was overthrown in a military coup in 2010. A junta (group that sets up a dictatorship) called the Supreme Council for the Restoration of Democracy took over the government. A new constitution was approved in a referendum in October. In 2011, voters elected former opposition leader Mahamadou Issoufou as president.

Since 2007, unrest with the Tuareg in the north has resulted in violence and the displacement of thousands of people.

LAND AND PEOPLE

Niger is a large country. But the Sahara, with its sandy plateaus and central highland region called the Aïr Mountains, covers the northern two-thirds of the nation. A grassy, thinly wooded plain called a *savanna* stretches from the Niger River in the southwest to Lake Chad in the southeast.

The Niger savanna—home to such large animals as elephants, giraffes, and baboons—is one of the hottest places in the world, with average daily temperatures of 95° to 100° F (35° to 38° C). Most of Niger's people also live on the savanna, where water and farmland are available. The area receives most of Niger's rain, and the seasonal floods of the Niger River provide water for irrigating crops.

Citizens of Niger are called *Nigeriens*. The major ethnic groups in Niger include the Hausa, Djerma-Songhai, Tuareg, Fulani, and Kanuri.

The Hausa make up more than half of the population of Niger. They live mainly in the south and work as farmers. About one-fourth of the people are members of the Djerma-Songhai ethnic group. The Djerma-Songhai are farmers and live in the southwestern corner of the country, along the Niger River. Many of the Tuareg and the Fulani are nomadic people who raise livestock for food. The Tuareg and the Fulani each make up about 10 percent of the population. The Kanuri make up about 5 percent of the population. They farm the rich land in southeast Niger.

An open-air market attracts crowds of shoppers in Lagos, Nigeria's chief port and commercial center. The Lagos metropolitan area is one of the largest in the world, with more than 14 million people.

The Niger River gives Niger its name. It also provides valuable water to irrigate farmland. Some Nigeriens make a living by fishing in its waters. The Niger is the third longest river in Africa. Only the Nile and the Congo are longer, and only the Congo carries more water. The Niger River flows through Guinea, Mali, Benin, and Nigeria, in addition to Niger, before it empties into the Atlantic Ocean.

Niger's farmers grow cotton, cowpeas, millet, peanuts, rice, and sorghum. They also raise beef and dairy cattle, camels, goats, and sheep. The basic foods of Nigeriens are grains and dairy products, and they enjoy dishes made with millet and sorghum, which are often cooked in a porridge and served with sauce.

Many nomadic Nigeriens move across the desert with their herds of camels, cattle, goats, and sheep, searching for water and pasture. The nomads live mainly on milk products from their herds and trade these products with farmers for grains and vegetables. During the rainy season, the nomads travel through the northern desert, and during the dry season they move south. The Tuareg live in tents made of mats or animal skins. The Fulani have houses of straw and branches, so they must build new homes every time they move.

The savanna in Niger is part of a larger region called the Sahel. Since the late 1960's, severe droughts in the Sahel region have killed millions of livestock. As a result, many nomads have been forced to become farmers or move to urban areas.

Less than one-fifth of all Nigeriens live in cities or towns. Most urban workers have jobs with the government or other service industries, or in businesses. The government has built low-cost single-family homes for urban dwellers in the largest city, Niamey.

Niger's ethnic groups have long produced distinctive crafts, music, dance, and art. Craft workers make gold and silver jewelry, pottery, cloth, leatherwork, and wood-carvings.

Most Nigerien women wear long wraparound skirts topped with short blouses. The men wear pants or knee-length shorts with loose shirts or robes. The Fulani and Tuareg, however, wear long, loose robes to protect them from the desert sun. Tuareg men also wear turbans with veils over their faces as a shield against the blowing sand.

Because of Niger's colonial history, French is the official language of the country. But most Nigeriens speak the language of their ethnic group. Hausa is the language generally used in trade, and the Djerma-Songhai language is the second most widely spoken tongue. Most Nigeriens are Muslims. A small percentage are Christians or practice traditional African religions.

The west African nation of Nigeria is a land of great variety in both its scenery and its people. Nigeria's landscape ranges from hot, rainy swamps and forests to dry, sandy beaches, grassy plains, and rocky mountains. More than 155 million people live in Nigeria, more than in any other African country. They belong to more than 250 different ethnic groups.

Early history

Beginning about A.D. 1000, various kingdoms ruled different parts of what is now Nigeria, and the northern and southern regions developed independently of each other. The Kanem-Bornu kingdom, an Islamic trading kingdom, was centered in the northeast. The Hausa people developed a number of city-states in the region west of Bornu (now called Borno) that became important trade centers.

Throughout much of the 1500's, the Hausa city-states were under the control of the Songhai Empire, a powerful west African realm. The states later regained their independence and prospered during the 1600's and 1700's in the gold and slave trades.

Then in the early 1800's, local Fulani Muslims led by Usuman dan Fodio joined forces with Muslim Hausa rebels and overthrew the traditional leaders of the city-states. They formed a Hausa-Fulani empire that remained largely self-governing until the early 1900's.

Meanwhile in the south, the Yoruba people had established an important cultural center at Ife as early as the mid-900's. Yorubas from Ife later moved into surrounding territories and founded other states. The kingdom of Benin developed in the area between Lagos and the Niger Delta and flourished as a prosperous trade center from the 1400's to the 1800's.

The Portuguese were the first Europeans to reach Nigeria. As early as the 1400's, they had established a trading post near Benin and developed a slave trade with African chiefs. The British, the Dutch, and other Europeans soon followed to compete with the Portuguese for

NIGERIA

control of the slave trade, and by the 1700's the British were the leading slave traders on the Nigerian coast.

Then in 1807, the United Kingdom not only outlawed the slave trade but began warring against slave ships of other nations and freeing their slaves. British traders then turned to dealing in palm oil and other Nigerian agricultural products. In 1851, the British seized the port of Lagos to increase their influence over the area, and in 1861 Lagos was named a British colony.

Parts of southern Nigeria became British protectorates late in the 1800's, and in 1900 most of northern Nigeria was also made into a protectorate. In 1906, these regions were combined into one large colony and protectorate. Nigerians resisted British rule, especially in the north, but they were unsuccessful. In 1914, the United Kingdom joined the northern and southern regions into one political unit called the Colony and Protectorate of Nigeria.

Ethnic conflict

Nigerians began demanding a say in their government during the 1920's, but the various ethnic groups also fought among themselves. In 1946, the United Kingdom divided Nigeria into three regions—each with an assembly made up of both Nigerian and British members that advised the central government in Lagos. In 1954, Nigeria became a federation of these three regions. Sir Abubakar Tafawa Balewa, a northerner, became the federation's first prime minister in 1957 and remained in that position when Nigeria gained full independence on Oct. 1, 1960.

Ethnic groups within the regions of the Nigerian federation continued to compete for power, while at the same time different groups fought for control of the federal government. Southern Nigerians, especially the Igbo people, resented the power of the Hausa in the north. Such ethnic rivalries would lead to assassinations, military revolts, and civil war in the years following independence.

NIGERIA TODAY

Today, Nigeria has a civilian government. But many times in its history, Nigeria has had military rule. The current civilian government came into being when a new constitution was adopted in 1999.

The National Assembly is Nigeria's legislature. The Assembly consists of the 360-member House of Representatives and the 109-member Senate. Nigeria's people elect the representatives and senators to four-year terms. All Nigerian citizens who are 18 years of age or older may vote.

The previous military government was the result of one of the many military revolts that have taken place since Nigeria became independent. Much of the political turmoil in the country is due to differences between ethnic groups, especially between those in the south and those in the north.

Northerners controlled the new nation's federal government just after independence in 1960 because the north had more people than other regions. However, when censuses taken in 1962 and 1963 showed that the north had even more people than expected, people in the south protested that the censuses were not accurate. Some Nigerians also charged that a federal election in 1964 and a regional election in 1965 were dishonest. Violent riots followed.

In January 1966, a group of army officers—mainly Igbo people from the south—overthrew the federal and regional governments, and murdered Prime Minister Balewa and two regional officials. General Johnson Aguiyi-Ironsi, an Igbo army commander, then took control.

Aguiyi-Ironsi set up a strong central government and appointed many Igbo people as advisers, but riots broke out in the north, and thousands of Igbo were killed. Aguiyi-Ironsi's rule lasted only until July 1966, when he was assassinated by northern army officers.

Yakubu Gowon, the army chief of staff, then became head of the new military government. But the governor of Nigeria's Eastern Region, Colonel Odumegwu

FACTS

Official name:	Federal Republic of Nigeria
Capital:	Abuja
Terrain:	Southern lowlands merge into central hills and plateaus; mountains in southeast, plains in north
Area:	356,669 mi² (923,768 km²)
Climate:	Varies; equatorial in south, tropical in center, arid in north
Main rivers:	Niger, Benue
Highest elevation:	Dimlang Peak, 6,699 ft (2,042 m)
Lowest elevation:	Atlantic Ocean, sea level
Form of government:	Federal republic
Head of state:	President
Head of government:	President
Administrative areas:	36 states, 1 territory
Legislature:	National Assembly consisting of Senate with 109 members serving four-year terms and House of Representatives with 360 members serving four-year terms
Court system:	Supreme Court, Federal Court of Appeal
Armed forces:	80,000 troops
National holiday:	Independence Day (National Day) - October 1 (1960)
Estimated 2010 population:	155,142,000
Population density:	435 persons per mi² (168 per km²)
Population distribution:	51% rural, 49% urban
Life expectancy in years:	Male, 46; female, 47
Doctors per 1,000 people:	0.3
Birth rate per 1,000:	40
Death rate per 1,000:	17
Infant mortality:	97 deaths per 1,000 live births
Age structure:	0-14: 44%; 15-64: 53%; 65 and over: 3%
Internet users per 100 people:	7
Internet code:	.ng
Languages spoken:	English (official), Hausa, Yoruba, Igbo, Fulani
Religions:	Muslim 50%, Christian 40%, indigenous beliefs 10%
Currency:	Naira
Gross domestic product (GDP) in 2008:	$215.59 billion U.S.
Real annual growth rate (2008):	6.1%
GDP per capita (2008):	$1,530 U.S.
Goods exported:	Mostly crude oil, also cocoa, natural gas, rubber
Goods imported:	Chemicals, electronics, food, machinery, petroleum products, transportation equipment
Trading partners:	Brazil, China, France, India, South Korea, United Kingdom, United States

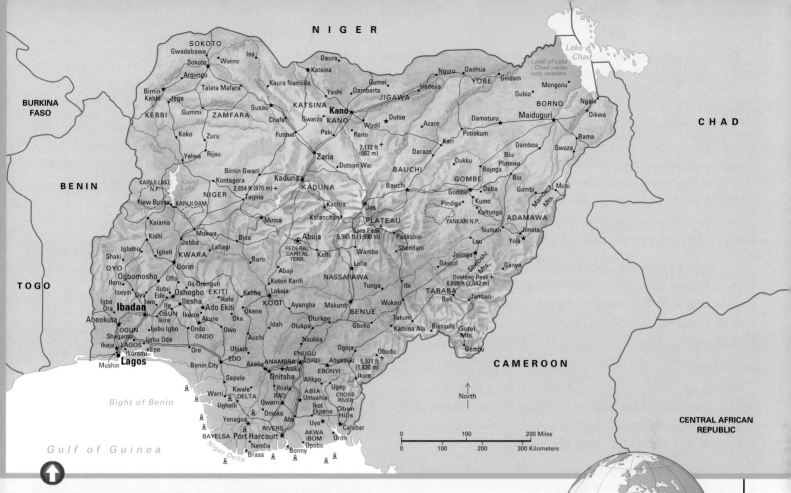

Nigeria, with its population of about 155 million, has more people than any other African nation. Abuja has served as the capital since 1991. Lagos, Nigeria's largest city, was formerly the capital.

Ojukwu, refused to recognize Gowon as head of state. In 1967, when Gowon tried to divide the Eastern Region into three smaller states, Ojukwu declared the Eastern Region an independent republic named *Biafra*. A bloody civil war broke out and lasted for 2 ½ years. In January 1970, Biafra surrendered. The war caused widespread death and destruction in southeastern Nigeria. Gowon's government established relief programs to help the people.

A civilian government replaced military rule in 1979. But in 1983, military officers overthrew the civilian government and placed Major General Mohammed Buhari in power. In 1985, Buhari in turn was overthrown by Major General Ibrahim Badamosi Babangida.

In 1992 elections for a new National Assembly, the Social Democrats won a majority in both legislative chambers. However, Babangida announced that the change in government was being postponed to August 1993. In August, Babangida resigned. His successor, Ernest Shonekan, was ousted in November by Defense Minister Sani Abacha, who proclaimed himself ruler. Abacha dissolved the National Assembly, outlawed political parties, and dismissed all elected officials of Nigeria's local governments. In June 1998, Abacha died and was succeeded as president by General Abdulsalami Abubakar.

In 1999, civilian rule was restored, and a new constitution was adopted. Olusegun Obasanjo was elected president in 1999 and reelected in 2003. In April 2007, Umaru Yar'Adua, governor of the northern state of Katsina, was elected president. He died in 2010 and was succeeded by Vice President Goodluck Jonathan. Jonathan then won the 2011 election. Muslims in northern Nigeria protested the results, and riots broke out.

Since 1999, ethnic, religious, and political tensions in Nigeria have sparked several outbreaks of violence in which tens of thousands of people have died. Many conflicts have been over access to land or other resources. Muslims and Christians have clashed over the adoption of the *Sharī`ah* (Islamic law) in many northern Nigerian states.

LAND AND ECONOMY

The varied landscape of Nigeria forms ten different regions. In the far northwestern corner of the country lie the Sokoto Plains—an area of flat, low-lying land named for the Sokoto River. Along with several other rivers, the Sokoto floods the area in the rainy season. The floodwater deposits rich soil that allows Nigerians to farm the plains, but it can also destroy crops and homes.

In Nigeria's far northeast lies the Chad Basin, a region of short grasses and thinly scattered trees. Sandy ridges cross parts of the region, while other areas become swampy during the rainy season. Serious droughts can also occur in the Chad Basin.

The Northern High Plains cover almost 20 percent of the country and lie about 2,500 feet (762 meters) above sea level. These vast, flat grasslands have only a few hills and granite ridges. Several rivers flow across the plains and create beautiful waterfalls as they tumble into deep gorges.

Within the Northern High Plains, near the center of Nigeria, lies the Jos Plateau. Cattle graze on the grasslands of the plateau, which rises more than 5,000 feet (1,500 meters) above sea level.

The Niger-Benue River Valley forms an arc through the center of Nigeria. The Niger River flows southeastward through the west-central section of the country to meet the Benue flowing from the east. The valley formed by the rivers has grasslands, forests of palms, and swamps, as well as rugged, rocky hills.

The Western Uplands are high grasslands dotted by granite hills. The Eastern Highlands consist of even higher plateaus and rocky hills and mountains.

The heavily forested Southwestern Plains slope down to the swamps and lagoons that line the coast of Nigeria. The Southeastern Lowlands are also covered with swamps and forested plains.

The Niger Delta, the southernmost region of the country, lies along the Gulf of Guinea. Where the Niger River flows into the sea, it deposits clay, mud, and sand. Lagoons, swamps, and mangrove trees cover the region, but the delta is also the site of an important natural resource that has helped change the country—petroleum.

The buildings of Lagos reflect many architectural styles. The largest city, chief port, and commercial center of Nigeria, Lagos lies partly in the Southwestern Plains region and partly on four islands in the Gulf of Guinea.

A cattle herder tends his animals on the Jos Plateau in central Nigeria. In addition to the grasslands that provide pasture for dairy cattle, the plateau has important tin mines.

A giant oil refinery stands at Port Harcourt, near the Gulf of Guinea. Petroleum ranks as Nigeria's most valuable natural resource. The country is one of the world's leading petroleum exporters.

Nigerian workers stack sacks of peanuts ready for market. Nigeria is one of the world's major producers of peanuts.

Nigeria is still a developing nation with an economy based largely on the land. Today, agriculture employs about two-thirds of all Nigerian workers. In the 1960's, however, the oil industry began to be developed, and mining is now the fastest-growing part of the nation's economy.

Today, oil exports are the government's main source of income. Although foreign oil companies operate most of Nigeria's petroleum wells, they pay the government more than half their profits. The government has also established a national oil company to explore for and produce oil.

In addition to petroleum, Nigeria mines coal, gold, iron ore, lead, limestone, natural gas, and zinc. The country also ranks as an important exporter of tin.

The government has used its new wealth to improve the nation's educational system, develop new industry, and modernize agriculture. For example, farms in Nigeria are generally small, and traditionally most farmers have used old-fashioned equipment and methods. Today, the government sponsors programs to distribute new varieties of seeds, fertilizers, and insecticides.

Nigeria ranks among the world's leading producers of cacao, palm oil and palm kernels, peanuts, and rubber. Cotton is also grown. Important food crops include beans, cassava, corn, millet, rice, and yams. Nigerians raise goats, poultry, and sheep throughout the country, and cattle in the north. Coastal waters provide a bountiful catch of shrimp and other seafood.

Most businesses and industries in Nigeria are privately owned, but the government shares ownership of some enterprises. The country's factories produce a wide variety of goods, ranging from clothing and textiles to food products. Other Nigerian industries refine petroleum, process rubber, and produce steel.

PEOPLE

With a population of more than 155 million, Nigeria has more people than any other country in Africa and ranks as one of the most populous nations in the world. Nigeria's population is increasing at a very high growth rate. In 1989, the government launched an educational program designed to limit family size.

Rural villages and crowded cities

About half of Nigeria's people live in rural areas in homes made of grass, dried mud, or wood, with roofs of asbestos, metal, or thatch. Related families live in *compounds*, or clusters of these houses. A typical rural village consists of a group of such compounds.

Nigeria also has several large, crowded cities, including Lagos, Ibadan, and Ogbomosho. Well-to-do city dwellers live in modern houses or apartments, but many Nigerians live in squalid slums where mud huts line unpaved streets. Since the mid-1900's, an increasing number of rural Nigerians have moved to urban areas to look for jobs, and overcrowding is now a serious problem in many cities.

Partly because Lagos is overcrowded and lacks room for expansion, the Nigerian government decided to move the country's capital to Abuja.

At an outdoor market in Maiduguri in northeastern Nigeria, sleeping mats are offered for sale. This region is the homeland of the Kanuri, who trace their ancestry back to the ancient Muslim empire of Kanem.

Nigerian Muslims celebrate the end of Ramadan, the holy month of fasting in the Muslim year. About 50 percent of Nigeria's people are Muslims, and they make up the majority of the population in the north.

More than 250 ethnic groups

The people of Nigeria are as varied as its landscape. Nigerians belong to more than 250 different ethnic groups. The various groups speak different languages, and some follow different traditions.

The three largest groups are the Hausa, the Yoruba, and the Igbo. Together, these three groups account for about 60 percent of the country's total population.

The Hausa people, who have inhabited the area for more than 1,000 years, live primarily in northern Nigeria. Most Hausa are farmers, but many also work as craft workers or traders. The Hausa have become so intermixed with another group, the Fulani, that they are sometimes called the Hausa-Fulani.

The Yoruba live mainly in southwestern Nigeria. Many Yoruba people who live in cities go out to the surrounding countryside to farm the land.

The Igbo are the major ethnic group in southeastern Nigeria, but large numbers of Igbo have lived in other areas of the country since the time Nigeria was a British colony. The Igbo adopted Western ways more quickly than other Nigerian groups, and they were also more willing to travel away from their homes. For those reasons, the Igbo held important business and government positions under British rule.

Other ethnic groups include the Nupe and Tiv in central Nigeria; the Edo, Urhobo, and Itsekiri in the south-central section; the Ijo of the Niger Delta area; the Efik and Ibibio in the southeastern section; and the Kanuri of northeastern Nigeria.

The three most widely used languages in Nigeria are those of the largest ethnic groups—Hausa, Yoruba, and Igbo. Each ethnic group has its own distinct language, and people use their ethnic language most of the time. However, many Nigerians also speak English, the nation's official language, which is taught in schools throughout the country. Nigerian Muslims use Arabic when taking part in religious activities.

Although most Nigerians are either Muslims or Christians, many Nigerians practice traditional African religions based on the worship of gods and spirits. Muslims make up the majority of the population in the north, and Christians live mainly in the south. People throughout the country may combine Muslim or Christian religious practices with their traditional beliefs.

Most people in Nigeria wear traditional clothing, though some city dwellers wear Western-style dress. Traditional garments for men and women include long, loose robes made of white or brightly colored fabrics. Small, round caps are popular head coverings for men, while women often wear scarves or turbans.

ART AND CULTURE

Nigeria is famous for the quality and variety of its art. Few people outside Africa knew anything about Nigerian art—or African art in general—until the 1900's, but it has since influenced artists throughout the world, including such masters as Spanish painter Pablo Picasso and British sculptor Henry Moore.

The Nok

The oldest known African sculptures are figures created about 500 B.C. by the Nok civilization of central Nigeria. The Nok people lived on the Jos Plateau, near the junction of the Niger and Benue rivers, until about A.D. 200.

Nok sculptured figures are admired for their high standards of production, as well as for their artistic quality. The Nok sculptures are *terra-cotta* (clay) figures of animals and humans that range in size from 1 inch (2.5 centimeters) high to life-size. The pieces that represent human heads have pierced ears and hollowed-out eyes.

The Nok art treasures were identified by British archaeologist Bernard Fagg, but scholars do not know what function the sculptures had in Nok society. Some experts believe that the sculpture of other west African peoples shows a definite Nok influence.

Ife

Little is known about life and culture in Nigeria during the 1,000-year period that followed Nok civilization. But around A.D. 1000, villages in southern Nigeria began to merge and form city-states. One such community became the first of several great Yoruba kingdoms—Ife.

Historians believe Ife was the cradle of civilization of the Yoruba people. Superb terra-cotta and bronze sculptured heads were created in Ife in the 1200's. Although Ife never gained great military or political power, it was an important cultural center, and the kingdom had about 400 religious cults. The Yoruba

Magnificent sculpted heads show artistic styles typical of ancient Nigeria. A terra-cotta sculpture from the Nok civilization, far left, has stylized facial features. The Ife people created more realistic carvings, left.

A bronze plaque from the palace of the Benin oba, or king, depicts an acrobatic dance in honor of the god Ogun. Thousands of bronze plaques show scenes from life at the Benin court.

worshiped many gods, including Oduduwa, believed to be the creator of the world and ancestor of the Yoruba kings.

The Yoruba king of Ife, called the *oni*, was elected from a royal family. He supported his court by trading slaves and placing tolls on traded goods. Such goods included the bronze used by Yoruba artists and other materials that were imported in large quantities from North Africa.

The Yoruba used the *lost-wax* process to make their splendid bronze statues. First, the sculptor made a wax model of the figure. The wax figure was then dipped in a kind of clay mixture and *fired* (baked until hard). As the figure hardened, the wax melted and drained out, leaving a hollow mold in the shape of the original figure. The Yoruba sculptor then poured liquid bronze into the mold to complete the process.

A Benin carving from the 1500's shows a struggle between two armed men, possibly Portuguese. By the time Benin became a flourishing kingdom, Europeans had arrived in Nigeria.

Benin

Over several hundred years, the Yoruba people spread out from Ife and founded or took over other territories. One such city-state, Benin, was already inhabited by Edo-speaking people when Ife took control of it. Benin eventually developed into the largest and most powerful state in the forest region of what is now Nigeria.

From the 1400's to the 1600's, the people of Benin produced sculptures that are now famous throughout the world. In addition to bronze, Benin sculptors worked with brass and ivory, fashioning exquisite ornaments and fine jewelry, as well as figures, heads, and plaques.

Many of their works honored the king of Benin. This king, or *oba*, presided over a large court in his wooden palace, where he displayed his treasures of brass, bronze, and ivory works of art.

War with other states and revolts in states that Benin had conquered eventually led to decline. The ancient kingdom of Benin fell to the British in 1897.

Norway, sometimes called the *Land of the Midnight Sun,* is a long, narrow kingdom on the northwestern edge of the European continent. The country forms the western edge of the Scandinavian Peninsula and is bordered on the east by Sweden and in the far northeast by Finland and Russia. Norway's western shores lie along the North Atlantic Ocean.

Norway is noted for the hundreds of *fiords* that line its western coast. These narrow, steep-sided inlets, formed by ice and glaciers millions of years ago, make excellent harbors. Winds warmed by the sea keep these harbors free of ice all year long, even north of the Arctic Circle.

Most Norwegians live on or near the coast, partly because the inland regions are so much colder and partly because the country has relied on the sea for centuries. Since the time of the Vikings, the Norwegians have been a seafaring people. Norway began developing its shipping fleet during the 1600's, and today the nation boasts one of the world's largest fishing and shipping industries.

The people of Norway have much in common with their Scandinavian neighbors, the Swedes and the Danes. Many are tall, with fair hair and blue eyes. Above the Arctic Circle, the Sami live in Lapland. Norway has a population of nearly 5 million.

Early settlements

People lived on the northern and western coasts of what is now Norway even before the Ice Age ended about 10,000 years ago, when most of the region was covered by thick sheets of ice. By 2000 B.C., the ice had melted, and Germanic tribes began to migrate to the region. They continued to arrive for hundreds of years after the time of Christ.

The tribes formed small communities led by local chiefs and kings. In about 800 A.D., Viking sea raiders from these communities began a 300-year reign of terror on the northern seas. The Vikings attacked neighboring coastal regions, such as the British Isles, the Baltic states, northern France, and Ireland, sailing away with slaves and treasure.

About 900, much of present-day Norway was united under the country's first king, Harold I (Fairhair). However, full unification did not come until

KONGSTIND
SVOLVÆR

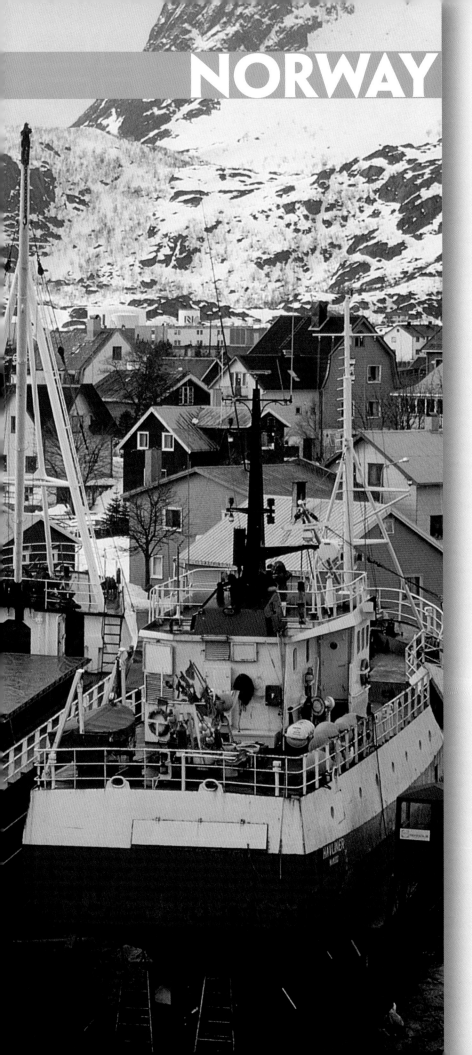

NORWAY

the early 1000's under King Olav II, who firmly established Christianity, which had been introduced to the Norwegian people by Olav I. Olav II was recognized as Norway's patron saint soon after his death in 1030.

In 1397, Queen Margaret, a Danish ruler, united Norway, Denmark, and Sweden in the Union of Kalmar. Norway remained under Danish rule until Sweden defeated Denmark in 1813 during the Napoleonic Wars. In the Treaty of Kiel, signed in 1814, Denmark gave Norway to Sweden.

The Norwegians did not recognize the Treaty of Kiel, and they elected an assembly to draw up a constitution for an independent Norway. However, Sweden refused to grant independence to Norway and attacked the country, quickly defeating it. The Norwegian parliament was then forced to accept Charles XIII of Sweden as ruler.

Independence from Sweden

Norway's merchant fleet was one of the largest in the world during the 1890's, but the Swedish foreign service handled Norway's shipping affairs in overseas trading centers. In May 1905, the Norwegian parliament passed a law creating its own foreign service, but the Swedish king vetoed it. On June 7, the Norwegian parliament ended the country's union with Sweden. In November, a Danish prince became King Haakon VII.

Norway remained neutral during World War I (1914-1918). Its economy expanded, but a postwar economic depression kept 25 to 30 percent of all Norwegian workers unemployed. When World War II (1939-1945) broke out, Norway attempted to remain neutral once again, but German troops invaded the country in 1940 by attacking all its seaports at once. During this time, King Haakon VII fled to London and set up a government-in-exile.

After the Germans surrendered and the war ended, Norway rebuilt its fleets and industries with aid from the United States. By the 1950's, the Norwegian economy was thriving. Today, Norway has one of the highest standards of living in the world.

NORWAY TODAY

Norway is a constitutional monarchy, and the king or queen is held in great respect and affection by the people. However, Norway's monarch has limited political power, with the main duties of office including presiding over state occasions and appointing government officials on the advice of the Cabinet.

The government

The monarch appoints the prime minister, who is usually the leader of the strongest party in parliament, as the head of the government. The prime minister officially appoints the members of the Cabinet—the Council of State—but they are actually selected by the party or coalition in power in the parliament. Unlike the Cabinet system of Canada or the United Kingdom, a Cabinet member in Norway cannot also be a member of parliament. The *Storting* (parliament), Norway's lawmaking body, consists of 169 members elected to four-year terms.

A prosperous country with a relatively low unemployment rate, Norway has a well-developed economy, and its people enjoy a high standard of living. Almost all Norwegians can read and write, and the government provides the people with many welfare services. Because the population is considered small, large families are encouraged by a yearly government allowance to each family for every youngster under the age of 18.

The National Insurance Act guarantees old-age pensions, job retraining, and aid for mothers, orphans, widows, widowers, and handicapped persons. All Norwegians are required to take part in this plan, which is paid for by the insured people, their employers, and the government.

Nearly one-fourth of Norway's people live in rural areas. Norwegian is the official language, with two forms—Bokmål and Nynorsk. Both forms are very similar to each other, and a person who speaks one form can easily understand the other. The two forms are gradually being combined into a single language called *Samnorsk*.

FACTS

Official name:	Kongeriket Norge (Kingdom of Norway)
Capital:	Oslo
Terrain:	Glaciated; mostly high plateaus and rugged mountains broken by fertile valleys; small, scattered plains; coastline deeply indented by fiords; arctic tundra in north
Area:	148,726 mi² (385,199 km²)
Climate:	Temperate along coast, modified by North Atlantic Current; colder interior; rainy the year around on west coast
Main rivers:	Glåma, Lågen, Otra
Highest elevation:	Galdhøpiggen, 8,100 ft (2,469 m)
Lowest elevation:	Norwegian Sea, sea level
Form of government:	Constitutional monarchy
Head of state:	Monarch
Head of government:	Prime minister
Administrative areas:	19 fylker (counties)
Legislature:	Storting (Parliament) with 169 members serving four-year terms
Court system:	Hoyesterett (Supreme Court)
Armed forces:	19,100 troops
National holiday:	Constitution Day - May 17 (1814)
Estimated 2010 population:	4,786,000
Population density:	32 persons per mi² (12 per km²)
Population distribution:	78% urban, 22% rural
Life expectancy in years:	Male, 78; female, 83
Doctors per 1,000 people:	3.8
Birth rate per 1,000:	12
Death rate per 1,000:	9
Infant mortality:	3 deaths per 1,000 live births
Age structure:	0-14: 19%; 15-64: 66%; 65 and over: 15%
Internet users per 100 people:	85
Internet code:	.no
Languages spoken:	Norwegian (official), Sami, Finnish
Religions:	Evangelical Lutheran (state church) 85.7%, Muslim 1.8%, Roman Catholic 1%, other 11.5%
Currency:	Norwegian krone
Gross domestic product (GDP) in 2008:	$456.23 billion U.S.
Real annual growth rate (2008):	1.8%
GDP per capita (2008):	$97,672 U.S.
Goods exported:	Aluminum, chemicals, fish, food, machinery, natural gas, petroleum
Goods imported:	Chemicals, machinery, metals, motor vehicles, petroleum products
Trading partners:	Denmark, France, Germany, Sweden, United Kingdom, United States

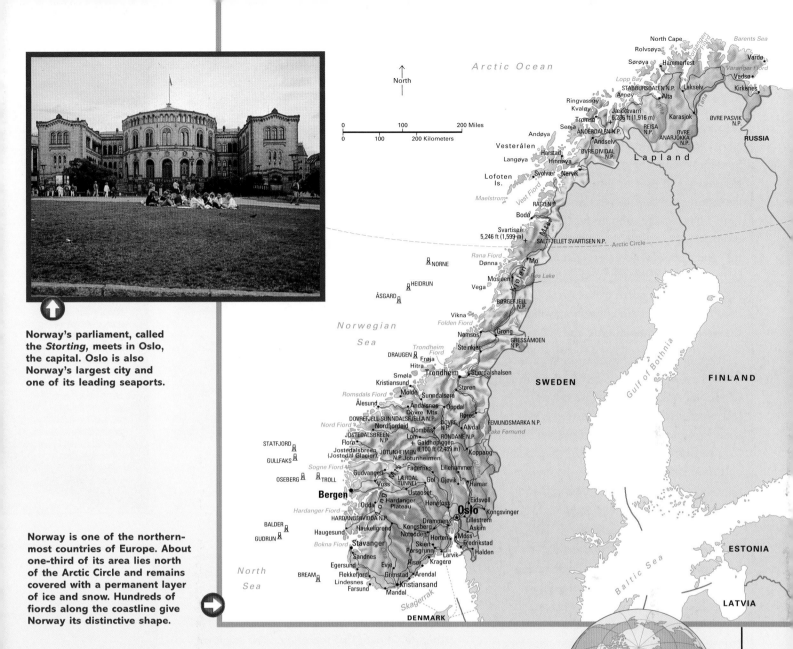

Norway's parliament, called the *Storting*, meets in Oslo, the capital. Oslo is also Norway's largest city and one of its leading seaports.

Norway is one of the northernmost countries of Europe. About one-third of its area lies north of the Arctic Circle and remains covered with a permanent layer of ice and snow. Hundreds of fiords along the coastline give Norway its distinctive shape.

In 1994, Norwegians voted against joining the European Union (EU). Many voters felt Norway was strong enough economically to remain independent, and many opposed giving decision-making power to the EU's central organizations.

Way of life

Norwegians are outdoor sports enthusiasts, and recreation areas lie within short distances of residential areas. Winter sports, such as skiing, ski-jumping, ice hockey, and ice skating, are very popular. Skiing, which may have started in Norway thousands of years ago as a way of traveling across snow-covered land, is the national sport. Summer sports include soccer, sailing, fishing, hiking, and swimming.

Norwegian law requires children from the ages of 6 to 16 to attend school. In addition, all Norwegian cities are required by law to have free public libraries.

A hardy, active people, the Norwegians usually eat four meals a day, and farm families eat five times a day. A typical breakfast includes cereal and open-faced sandwiches with cheese, jam, or marmalade, with goat cheese sandwiches being a particular favorite. Sandwiches are also served at lunch and at late-evening supper. Dinner is generally the only hot meal of the day and may include soup, meat or fish, potatoes, vegetables, and a dessert.

ENVIRONMENT

Norway owes much of its natural beauty to the North Atlantic Current, which is part of the Gulf Stream. Without the current's warming effect, Norway would have as little plant and animal life as Greenland, which lies at the same latitude. Sheep graze even in the country's northernmost regions, and the plentiful rainfall turns the landscape a vivid green in summer. Even as far north as the Lofoten Islands, 150 miles (240 kilometers) north of the Arctic Circle, January temperatures are considerably higher than the average for that latitude elsewhere.

The country does have barren and desolate areas, however—mostly in the inland regions within the Arctic Circle, where the warming effect of the North Atlantic Current is blocked by coastal mountains. The country's northern island territories—Svalbard, Jan Mayen Island, and Bear Island—are also barren, their mountainous landscapes carved by the glacier movements of the last Ice Age.

Mountains and lowlands

Norway has three main land regions: the Mountainous Plateau, the Southeastern Lowlands, and the Trondheim Lowlands. Most of the country is a high, mountainous plateau covered largely by bare rock that has been smoothed and rounded by glaciers. The glaciers also formed many lakes and deep valleys throughout the countryside.

The jagged peaks of the Kjølen Mountains rise in the narrow northern part of Norway along the country's border with Sweden. In the southern part of the country, the Dovre Mountains extend in an east-west direction, and the Long Mountains rise to the south.

Norway's tallest mountain—Galdhøpiggen—lies in the Long Mountains, within the Jotunheimen range, also known as the *home of the giants*. The Hardanger Plateau, which slopes westward down the Long Mountains, is the largest highland plain in Europe. West of the

A peaceful scene in the Southeastern Lowlands is typical of the landscape around Oslo, Norway's capital and largest city. This gently rolling landscape supports Norway's agricultural and forest industries.

Sunset bathes a fiord—one of the most distinctive features of the Norwegian landscape—in warm colors of pink and gold. The almost vertical sides of the fiord were carved by a mighty valley glacier during the last Ice Age.

Hardanger Plateau lies the 188-square-mile (487-square-kilometer) Jostedal Glacier—Europe's largest ice field outside Iceland.

Only about 20 percent of Norway lies less than 500 feet (150 meters) above sea level. This area includes the Southeastern Lowlands and Trondheim Lowlands. The Southeastern Lowlands consist mostly of the middle and lower valleys of several rivers, including the Glåma. The Trondheim Lowlands—the lower ends of several wide, flat valleys—lie farther north, where the country grows narrower. These valleys make up one of the few areas of the country flat enough that railroad track may be laid there.

The warmest part of Norway during the summer, the lowlands are Norway's most densely populated area and have most of the country's few farming areas. Barley and potatoes are grown in the Trondheim Lowlands, and many dairy farms can be found in the region.

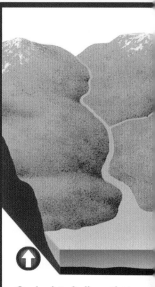

Geologists believe that the long, narrow, and winding inlets called *fiords* were formed by rivers flowing between the rugged slopes of Norway's mountainous plateau.

A church built during the 1100's nestles among the forested slopes of central Norway. Birch, pine and spruce trees from this region provide timber for the country's lumber industry.

The white waters of the Sigfoss waterfall crash down the steep sides of a valley. With its soaring mountains, icy glaciers, and spectacular waterfalls, Norway offers a wealth of dramatic scenery.

The movement of the glaciers flowing in the rivers carved the fiords during the Ice Age.

After the Ice Age ended and the snow melted, the glaciers melted and the sea flowed into the ice-carved depressions. Most fiords have steep, rocky walls with thick woods and foaming, roaring waterfalls.

Coasts and islands

Norway has one of the world's most jagged coastlines. It is broken up by hundreds of fiords and peninsulas and fringed by about 150,000 islands and *skerries* (rocky reefs). Including all the fiords and peninsulas, the full length of the coast is about 13,267 miles (21,351 kilometers), which is about half the distance around the equator. Sogne Fiord, Norway's longest fiord, penetrates inland for 127 miles (204 kilometers).

The Lofoten and Vesterålen islands, situated off the northwestern coast, are Norway's largest offshore island groups, and the waters around them are filled with codfish. A swift and dangerous current known as the Maelstrom flows between two of the outer Lofoten Islands. A menace to sailors for hundreds of years, this current forms an immense whirlpool when the wind blows against it between high and low tide.

ECONOMY

During the mid-1700's, industrialization began to spread throughout western Europe and the United States. However, unlike Great Britain, Belgium, France, and other countries, Norway lacked coal to drive steam engines and make iron. Because Norway had to import its coal, manufacturing was very costly and growth was slow.

By 1900, however, the Norwegians had found a way to develop their own sources of inexpensive hydroelectricity to meet their power needs. In 1906, hydroelectric power enabled Norsk Hydro to become the first national company in the world to make nitrate fertilizers from atmospheric nitrogen. Soon, Norway's range of products greatly expanded, and the country began importing *bauxite* (aluminum ore) for the smelting of its aluminum.

Today, Norway is one of the wealthiest nations in the world in proportion to the number of people who live there. The country is one of the leading producers of aluminum and continues to import bauxite in order to refine it. In addition, petroleum and natural gas account for a large part of the national income. Government programs that promote investment and industry, as well as an increased demand for Norwegian goods and services, have helped fuel the rapid growth of Norway's economy.

The availability of cheap electricity has greatly benefited Norway's manufacturing industries. The nation's most important products include clothing, electrical machinery, furniture, petroleum products, processed foods, small ships, and such metals as aluminum and magnesium.

Mineral resources

Norway's oil and gas fields, which began to be worked in the 1970's, lie offshore in its territorial waters in the North Sea. Here, communities of workers live and work on immense rigs—often for months at a time.

During the mid-1980's, a drop in oil prices caused a temporary financial crisis for the oil industry and, to a lesser extent, for the country as a whole. To solve the crisis, the oil companies reinvested oil revenues in other industries rather than oil. World oil prices rose again in the late 1980's.

Iron ore and *pyrite* (a compound of iron and sulfur) are also mined in Norway. Other minerals include aluminum, limestone, nickel, titanium, and zinc. Norway's only coal deposits lie in the northern island territory of Svalbard.

Factory ships process huge quantities of fish caught off the Norwegian coast. Since the late 1900's, however, some kinds of fish, such as the cod found in the waters around the Lofoten Islands, have shown a reduction in numbers.

Fishing and forestry

The abundant stocks of fish in the waters of the North Sea and the Norwegian Sea have provided a livelihood for Norwegians for many centuries. Norway's fishing fleet—which ranks among the largest and most efficient in the world—catches millions of tons of fish each year. Norwegian fishing crews bring in capelin, cod, haddock, herring, and mackerel.

Norway once had a thriving whaling industry, but it declined sharply during the 1960's, when large catches by Norway and other major whaling nations endangered many kinds of whales. In 1987, Norway joined an international *moratorium* (temporary halt) on commercial whaling. However, in 1993, Norway resumed limited commercial whaling of minke whales, claiming they were no longer in danger.

Like its coastal waters, Norway's forests have also been a traditional source of income for its people. Timber has been an important export since the 1500's, and today much of it is used to produce wood pulp and paper. Government restrictions aim to ensure that the cutting of timber never outstrips forest regrowth.

Although Norway has little suitable farmland, sizable crops of grains, potatoes, and vegetables, as well as hay and roots for livestock feed, are grown in the lowlands. Norwegian farmers also raise beef and dairy cattle, chickens, hogs, and sheep. Livestock products account for over two-thirds of the country's food production.

An oil rig operates in the North Sea off the coast of Norway. The country possesses rich petroleum and natural gas deposits in the North Sea. Exports of petroleum and natural gas have greatly stimulated Norway's economy.

The lumber industry has been an important part of Norway's economy for hundreds of years. The wood is used for building houses and making furniture throughout the country. Some timber is exported in the form of wood pulp and paper.

NORWEGIAN CITIES

Because Norway's mostly rugged, mountainous terrain has discouraged settlement in the more remote areas, most of the population is concentrated on or near the coasts. Many towns have grown up around fishing harbors. Oslo, Norway's capital and largest city, has about half a million people. Other large cities include Bergen, Drammen, Kristiansand, Stavanger, Tromsø, and Trondheim. Each town has a special charm all its own. Norway's cities provide a glimpse of a picturesque land where old traditions mix with the sophisticated ways of modern life.

Oslo—old and new

In addition to being Norway's capital and largest city, Oslo is the nation's chief economic, industrial, and cultural center and one of its leading seaports. Situated on the southeast coast at the head of the great Oslo Fiord, the city has magnificent surroundings of hills, forests, and fiords.

Founded by King Harold Hårdråde about 1050, Oslo is a historic city. Fire destroyed the city in 1624, but the people rebuilt it northeast of Akershus Castle, which had been built on a rocky peninsula overlooking the fiord in 1299. Between 1624 and 1925, Oslo was called Christiana, in honor of King Christian IV of Denmark, which ruled Norway at the time.

By the mid-1800's, the city had grown into a major administrative, economic, and military center. Since then, the city has spread westward and eastward both inland and along the shores of the fiord. Today, with its shipping facilities, industry, and forest and agricultural resources, Oslo plays a major role in the nation's economy.

In spite of its growth and importance, Oslo is a clean and spacious city with an air of old-fashioned serenity. More than two-thirds of Oslo's metropolitan area consists of forests and lakes, and its peo-

Bergen is Norway's second largest city and the country's chief seaport. A produce market lies near the harbor, along with many fine old stone warehouses.

ple live in comfortable, modern apartment buildings. Attractive office buildings and modern stores stand next to carefully renovated historic buildings. Many parks and gardens add to the scenic beauty of the city.

Oslo's museums have carefully preserved many of Norway's most historic treasures, including many objects from the Viking period. Just outside the city, a museum at Bygdøy displays the ship used by Roald Amundsen as he sailed through the Northwest Passage between 1903 and 1906.

Reminders of the past also abound in Stavanger, in the extreme southwest region of Norway, where colorful wooden houses bring the past to vivid life. Today, however, Stavanger is more famous as the center of Norway's bustling oil industry. Many international corporations own large office blocks in the city, and much of Stavanger Fiord's landscape is dominated by drilling rigs.

The Oslo City Hall is one of the city's most famous buildings. It houses the city government and art studios and galleries. The structure opened in 1950. The Nobel Peace Prize ceremony is held in the City Hall every year.

Wooden warehouses perch on stilts above the water along the Nidelv River in Trondheim, Norway's third largest city. The city is surrounded by low hills, and the city center is almost entirely encircled by the Nidelv River.

Former capitals

Bergen, the second largest city in Norway, lies at the head of By Fiord and ranks as the chief seaport of western Norway. Seven mountains tower behind this busy port, which carries on a large trade in dried fish, herring, and machinery. The city was founded in 1070, and it served as the capital until 1300.

From the 1300's to the 1500's, Bergen became a trading center of the Hanseatic League—a confederation of northern German cities. The old port area of Bryggen as well as churches, the Bergenhus fortress, the old city hall and the colorful flower and fish markets have been preserved from medieval times.

Farther north, but still only halfway up Norway's coastline, lies Trondheim, which also served as the capital during the Middle Ages. Its cathedral—built over the tomb of King Olav II during the mid-1100's to early 1300's—is the traditional site of Norway's coronations. The fortress of Kristiansten, dating from the 1600's, overlooks a medieval monastery on the island of Munkholm, which lies in Trondheim Fiord.

A magnificent bridge connecting the western part of the city of Tromsø with the mainland was built after World War II, when the previous one was destroyed. Tromsø, the largest town in northern Norway, lies on a small offshore island.

SVALBARD

Lying in the Arctic Ocean about 700 miles (1,100 kilometers) from the North Pole, Svalbard is a group of islands that belongs to Norway. The group consists of five large islands and many smaller ones. The main islands, in order of size, are Spitsbergen, North East Land, Edge Island, Barents Island, and Prince Charles Foreland.

Svalbard covers 23,958 square miles (62,050 square kilometers). It has a population of about 3,500. Mining companies, radio and weather stations, and a scientific research station provide jobs in Svalbard.

Svalbard's islands are the highest point of a submerged landmass that was once connected to Europe. The sharply folded rocks that make up their landscape date from more than 570 million years ago and include some of the oldest rocks in the world. On Spitsbergen, these rocks form rugged mountain chains. The sharp peaks rising from the icy ground led the Dutch explorer Willem Barents to name the island *Spitsbergen* (sharp mountains) when he arrived there in 1596.

Long before Barents landed on Spitsbergen, Svalbard was probably visited by Norse Vikings. Early Norwegian stories mention the island group, and in the Middle Ages, Norwegian kings claimed Svalbard.

Spitsbergen is a Norwegian island, the largest island of the Svalbard archipelago in the Arctic Ocean. Because Spitsbergen lies far within the Arctic Circle, the sun is always above the horizon from late April to late August.

European explorers first discovered Svalbard's coal deposits in 1610. Since then, deposits of phosphates, asbestos, and iron ore have also been found. Today, mining companies provide many jobs for Svalbard's inhabitants.

Natural resources

During the 1600's, when many European nations began hunting whales, Dutch and English explorers reported that the Arctic waters were filled with whales. This news brought whalers to the Arctic from many countries, including Denmark, Great Britain, Germany, and the Netherlands. They found that bowhead whales were especially plentiful around Svalbard.

Svalbard thus became a major center of Arctic whaling, and Dutch and English whalers developed profitable industries there. But by 1720, whalers had killed all the whales around Svalbard and moved on to other areas of the Arctic.

A polar bear guards its cub in the waters off the island of Spitsbergen. The area is also home to walruses, seals, whales, reindeer, the Arctic fox, and immense seabird colonies.

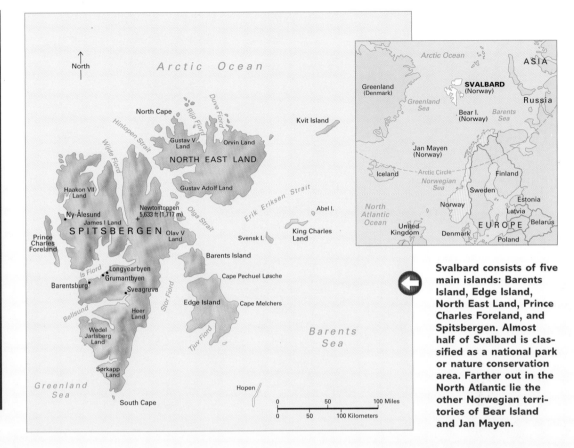

Svalbard consists of five main islands: Barents Island, Edge Island, North East Land, Prince Charles Foreland, and Spitsbergen. Almost half of Svalbard is classified as a national park or nature conservation area. Farther out in the North Atlantic lie the other Norwegian territories of Bear Island and Jan Mayen.

The Norwegians opened the first coal mines in Svalbard in the 1890's. Large-scale mining in Svalbard began in 1906, when John Munro Longyear, an American mining engineer, opened the first commercial mine. The growth of commercial mining led to a dispute over the ownership of the island group.

In 1920, the Svalbard Treaty officially recognized Norway's claim to Svalbard. The 38 other nations who signed the treaty have equal rights of access to Svalbard's natural resources.

Despite the area's harsh weather conditions, low taxes attract many people to Svalbard. Many of the Norwegians who live in Svalbard work for the national mining company, and many other miners from former Soviet republics work in the Barentsburg and Pyramiden areas.

Svalbard's dramatic scenery and fascinating plant and animal life draw many visitors. The glistening, ice-covered land-scape, pierced by deep blue fiords, has a tranquil beauty all its own. In spring, the tundra bursts into bloom, and millions of migratory birds return from the south to breed on the steep cliffs. Polar bears, arctic foxes, reindeer, northern fur seals, whales, and walruses add to the natural wonders of the Arctic landscape.

Bear Island and Jan Mayen

About midway between Svalbard and Norway, Bear Island, a Norwegian territory, occupies an area of about 69 square miles (179 square kilometers) in the Arctic Ocean. The cold, wet climate often cloaks the island in fog, and the staff of a Norwegian weather and radio station are its only inhabitants.

Between Greenland, Iceland, and Norway lies Jan Mayen, another island possession of Norway. Jan Mayen covers an area of 147 square miles (380 square kilometers). Discovered by the British explorer Henry Hudson in 1607, the island took its name from the Dutch captain Jan Jacobzoon May, who set up a whaling station there a few years later. Jan Mayen was formed by volcanic action and consists almost entirely of hard volcanic rock formations.

TABLE OF CONTENTS

A GENTLE, ROSE-SCENTED BREEZE DRIFTS LAZILY THROUGH THE WINDOW, STIRRING A STACK OF PAPERS ON THE WRITING DESK.

Pausing with pen poised above the paper, Jane Austen gazes absently at the well-groomed, lavish gardens of the country estate, where her sister strolls, pausing now and again to cut a flower for her basket. Looking farther down the road, she sees her mother returning from a visit to her aunt's house in town. Jane smiles, then glances around her room at the elegant four-poster bed, the perfectly papered walls, the delicate gown she will wear to tonight's ball. Ah, yes, the ball. Jane hurriedly turns back to her papers. She will have plenty of time to dress for her own ball later, but for now, she must see to it that the heroine of her latest novel gets to dance with the man of her dreams.

Romance stories are love stories. Their primary focus is on the developing relationship between the heroine and the hero. Although other things may happen in the story (a crime may need to be solved, for example), such events are of secondary importance. During the course of a romance, the hero and heroine will likely be separated by circumstances or misunderstandings, but nearly every romance ends "happily ever after," with the two characters coming together at last in a committed relationship, usually a marriage or an engagement.

The oldest love stories in the Western world can be found in the Bible and in ancient Greek myths. During the Middle Ages, which lasted from about the 5th to the 15th centuries, romances written in verse became popular in Europe. These tales were not the same as love-story romances today, however. They focused primarily on feats of daring and adventure, and they often included elements of myth and fantasy.

The romance genre as we think of it today began with the publication of the first English novels in the 18th century. Among the earliest novelists was English author Samuel Richardson, whose *Pamela; or, Virtue Rewarded* (1740) is an epistolary novel (written as a series of letters). The heroine, a young servant named Pamela, must refuse the repeated physical advances of her master, a nobleman called Mr. B. Although he is at first violent in his overtures, eventually Mr. B. begins to treat Pamela more gently, and she falls in love with him, to her own surprise, as she indicates in a letter to her parents: "*Love*, did I say? But come, I hope not: At least it is not, I hope, gone so far as to make me *very* uneasy: For I know not *how* it came, nor *when* it began; but crept, crept it has, like a thief, upon me; and before I knew what was the matter, it looked *like* love." *Pamela* met with great success, and soon similar romantic, epistolary novels began appearing in both England and the

The popularity of **Pamela** *inspired English painter Joseph Highmore to capture scenes from it in a series of 12 paintings completed in 1742 and 1744.*

Even after Mr. Rochester declares his love for Jane Eyre, the hero and heroine must undergo many obstacles before they can be together.

United States. When English-born American author Susanna Rowson's novel of seduction, *Charlotte: A Tale of Truth*, was published in the U.S. in 1794, it became the country's first best seller.

Even as readers were eagerly devouring books such as *Pamela* and *Charlotte*, other authors began to turn the novel in new directions with the Gothic story. Although Gothic tales focused on horror—featuring forbidding castles, seemingly supernatural threats, and mysterious occurrences—they also often included a love story, with a hero coming to the heroine's rescue at just the right moment. These stories remained popular into the early decades of the 1800s, and Gothic romances would periodically be revived over the next 200 years, including, most famously, in British author Charlotte Brontë's *Jane Eyre* (1847), which is still regarded as one of the most important works of the genre.

Lighter in tone than the horror-filled Gothic novels were the works of England's Regency period (1811–20). Among the greatest romance writers of that time was Jane Austen, whose witty novels portrayed the life of England's middle-class citizens—a world of gentlemen and ladies, balls and gowns, manors and estates. Known as "comedies of manners," these works featured energetic dialogue and a mild satire of social customs—along, of course, with stories of love.

In America, a group of women writers who later came to be known as the "domestic sentimentalists" had become the dominant force in the romance market by the 1850s. The works of the domestic sentimentalists often evoked strong emotions, focused on domestic concerns (such as home and the family), and chronicled women's hardships and triumphs. In the sentimental novel *The Wide, Wide World* (1851), American author Elizabeth Wetherell (the pseudonym of Susan Warner) creates a tearful scene as the hero embraces his dying sister: "She felt his tears on her cheek, and put up her hands to his face to wipe them away; kissed him

Although a romance novel is often told from the heroine's point of view, her thoughts, actions, and problems usually center on the hero. And who that hero is can make a major difference to the story. Throughout much of the history of romance, the hero has been a strong, decisive, proud man who is unwilling to acknowledge or reveal his feelings. Mr. Darcy in Jane Austen's **Pride and Prejudice** *(1813) is such a hero, as seen in his less-than-romantic proposal to the protagonist, Elizabeth Bennet: "'In vain have I struggled. It will not do. My feelings will not be repressed. You must allow me to tell you how ardently I admire and love you.'... He spoke well, but there were feelings besides those of the heart to be detailed.... His sense of her inferiority—of its being a degradation—of the family obstacles." More recent romances often feature more understanding, sensitive heroes who are willing to listen to their heroines but who do not like to take risks.*

Heroes of either type (and every type in between) are generally handsome, although some of today's romance authors choose to give their heroes physical flaws. These flaws (or others, such as emotional scars from a difficult past) may cause the hero to be bitter for a time, but in the end, they may make him more sensitive. Ultimately, the hero in any romance novel has to be someone for whom readers will root; if they don't want the heroine to end up with him, there's really no point in reading the novel.

British actor Colin Firth played the role of Mr. Darcy in the 1994 television miniseries of Pride and Prejudice, *setting the modern standard for the character.*

then, and then once again laid her head on his breast.... He felt the arms unclasp their hold; and, as he laid her gently back on the pillow, they fell languidly down.... Her brother looked for a moment, closed the eyes, kissed, once and again, the sweet lips, and left the room." Such emotion-packed scenes led the book to become the first American novel to reputedly sell more than one million copies.

While romances continued to be published in the novel format, by the late 19th century, story papers were also being widely circulated. These weekly papers, which were usually 8 to 16 pages long, featured a number of serialized romance novels, short stories, and poems in each issue, selling for the inexpensive price of 5 or 10 cents an issue. Romances could also be purchased cheaply in short paperback books known as dime novels (which actually cost anywhere from 5 to 25 cents). Dime romances often portrayed sensational scenes, such as abductions or the threat of physical violence.

Although the dime novel had fallen in popularity by about the 1920s, people continued to read romances. By then, many of the most popular romances featured historical settings. Historical romances were particularly popular in the 1930s and '40s, as the concerns of the Great Depression and World War II (1939–45) led people to seek refuge in a simpler, more romantic past. By the 1950s, however, contemporary settings had become the focus of most romances. The 1960s marked the beginning of a Gothic revival in the romance genre, which, in turn, sparked an increase in overall romance readership.

During the 1970s, American authors such as Kathleen E. Woodiwiss and Rosemary Rogers introduced a new type of romance that departed drastically from the Gothic novels then in vogue. Their works featured a stronger, more independent heroine, along with explicit bedroom scenes. This change in the nature of romance led to a boom in the market that lasted into the 1980s. At that time, romances

< 14 >

*In many romance stories, the tension between the main characters is
either resolved or heightened when the hero and heroine finally share that first kiss.*

also began to reflect women's changing role in society, with heroines in positions of power and authority and possessing goals beyond marriage and motherhood. It was also during this period that romances—long regarded as simple, mindless love stories—began to receive critical notice, with new attention placed on both emerging and classic romance novels and the reasons for their appeal to readers.

The romance genre continued to change and expand into the last decades of the 20th century and the first years of the 21st. A number of authors featured multicultural heroines or heroes in their works, while others crossed genres, bringing elements of science fiction, fantasy, or mystery into their romantic stories. In diverging trends, some authors created romantic comedies, while others dealt with serious social issues, depicting characters dealing with problems such as alcoholism or abuse.

Today, the vast majority of romance readers—about 90 percent—are women. Although romance is popular with women of all ages, most romance readers are between the ages of 31 and 49. Romance readers continue to pick up enduring classics in the genre, such as works by Jane Austen, but they also read enough new romance fiction that the genre accounts for 38 percent of all fiction (and about 50 percent of mass-market paperback books) sold in the U.S. today.

< 16 >

Aⁿll romances tell a love story, but not all romances do so in the same way. Works in the genre can be divided into a number of subgenres, or sub-categories. Each subgenre has its own characteristic setting, theme, or character types.

More than half of all romance novels published today fall into the contemporary subgenre, whose stories are set in the present. Apart from the time period, however, the setting can vary widely, from a small town to a big city, a seaside resort to a run-down diner, a high-stakes business office to a laid-back ranch. American author Barbara Freethy's *Golden Lies* (2004), for example, is set in the present-day California city of San Francisco. The author uses contemporary details to establish the time period:

> *[Riley McAllister] cast a frustrated look at the people around them.... When he'd agreed to help his grandmother clear out her attic, he'd never imagined he'd be standing in the parking lot at the Cow Palace Arena in San Francisco early Monday morning with a bunch of people who wanted to have their trash appraised by a traveling antiques show....*
>
> *"Why don't you let me sell this stuff on the Internet?" he suggested for the twentieth time.*
>
> *"And let someone take advantage of me? I don't think so."*
>
> *"What makes you think these people won't take advantage of you?"*
>
> *"Because* Antiques on the Road *is on television," she said with simple logic.*

Although the author has changed the name of the popular, real-life television program *Antiques Roadshow* to *Antiques on the Road*, references to this show, as well as to the Internet, help readers in the 21st century imagine the action occurring within their own time.

< 17 >

Henry VIII, infamous for the number of wives he divorced or had executed,
was first married to the Spanish-born Catherine of Aragon for 24 years.

The heroine in most of today's contemporary romances is looking not only for love but also for professional success—and she usually finds both. This is a change from the past: in contemporary romances written before the 1970s, women either did not work or left their jobs after marrying. In contrast, many of today's heroines continue to work after marriage and childbirth, embodying women who "have it all."

While many contemporary novels are single titles, a number are published in the category form, or as series linked by a specific formula or pattern. Although the various books in each category do not necessarily follow the same characters, they all have the same feel, so readers know exactly what to expect of a book in any given category. Books in the Harlequin American Romance series, for example, are heartwarming, family-centered stories set in present-day America.

In contrast to contemporary romances, historical romances are set in the past, usually before about 1945. Some historical romances feature real-life historical characters and events, as in British author Norah Lofts's *The King's Pleasure* (1969), which follows the relationship between the English queen Catherine of Aragon and her husband, King Henry VIII. The plot of historical romance novels is largely shaped by the events of the time, including wars or political intrigue, and authors are generally careful not to change or contradict recorded historical facts (although they give free rein to their imaginations in depicting undocumented areas of a historical figure's life).

Period romances also take place in a historical setting, but their stories do not hinge on that setting. With the change of a few details, they could just as easily have taken place in another time period. Among the most popular period romances are those known as Regency novels. These works, set in England in the early years of the 19th century, focus especially on the manners and social customs of the time. Like all period romances, Regencies often include detailed descriptions

< 19 >

A ROMANCE ACTIVITY

An important aspect of a romance novel is the chemistry between the hero and the heroine. Often, the two characters begin by disagreeing with, disliking, or even downright despising one another, but over time they fall in love. Even then, they may be reluctant to admit their feelings—to themselves or to anyone else.

Try your hand at creating your own disputing hero and heroine. First, think about two characters who might be at odds with one another. Maybe their personalities clash (one proud and distant, the other warm and bubbly, for example) or perhaps they are put into a situation in which they must take opposite sides (as in the case of a defense lawyer and a prosecuting attorney). Write a brief description of each character, along with a short summary of why they don't get along. With this background information in mind, write a scene in which the two characters confront one another. Focus especially on dialogue. What do they say? How do they say it? Are they calm, or do they shout? Are they in a crowded place or alone? How do they react? Does one character storm out of the room? Are there tears? Now, think farther ahead in your story. What could make these two characters reconcile and fall in love? Does one or the other realize they were mistaken? Do both? Write a short scene describing the moment when they make up. Make us feel that this moment will lead to a "happily ever after" ending for your hero and heroine.

< 20 >

The mythological god of romantic love, Cupid (or Eros), has been portrayed as a chubby boy with a bow and arrow in art and images for the past 2,300 years.

In 1923 alone, the year she was 21, Georgette Heyer published three novels in three different subgenres: Regency, historical, and contemporary.

of the era's food, clothing, architecture, manners, and language. British author Georgette Heyer's Regency novel *Cousin Kate* (1968), for example, provides a lavish description of the protagonist Kate Malvern's first dining experience at the grand home of her aunt and uncle: "The dining-room, which was reached by way of the picture-gallery, the Grand Stairway, a broad corridor, and an anteroom, was an immense apartment on the entrance-floor of the mansion, panelled in black oak, and hung with crimson damask. Several rather dark portraits did little to lighten it." As for the food served, Heyer names dozens of dishes, including "pigeons à la Crapaudine, petits pâtés, a matelot of eels, and a fricassée of chicken ... a green goose, two rabbits, a dressed crab, some broccoli, some spinach, and an apple pie." Such details help readers feel as if they have stepped back into the Regency time period.

Stories in the saga subgenre can take place in contemporary or historical settings—or both, since these works generally span multiple generations of a single family's history. Many sagas are centered on the American Civil War or English Victorian periods. Like sagas, Christian or inspirational romances can take place either in the past or the present. In addition to focusing on the relationship between the hero and the heroine, these stories also involve the spiritual growth of one or both characters.

Young adult romance addresses the particular concerns of younger audiences. In Canadian author L. M. Montgomery's *Anne of Green Gables* (1908), for example, Anne Shirley (who is 11 years old at the outset and 16 by the end), has to deal with being teased for her red hair by schoolmate—and future love interest—Gilbert Blythe:

> *Gilbert reached across the aisle, picked up the end of Anne's long red braid, held it out at arm's length, and said in a piercing whisper:*
>
> *"Carrots! Carrots!"*
>
> *Then Anne looked at him with a vengeance!*

< 23 >

She did more than look. She sprang to her feet....

"You mean, hateful boy!" she exclaimed passionately. "How dare you!"

And then—Thwack! Anne had brought her slate down on Gilbert's head and
cracked it—slate, not head—clear across.

Many young readers can relate to Anne's experience, and her very real emotions help draw them into the story.

Some romance subgenres blend romance with another genre. Romantic stories that also include elements of science fiction or fantasy are often called alternative reality romances. As the name suggests, these works depart from reality in some way, often by featuring fantastic creatures such as vampires or a science-fiction setting such as the future. Romantic suspense, on the other hand, offers action-packed stories of suspense and danger, in addition to love.

In general, romances in all subgenres tend to be written in the novel form, although romantic short stories have been published in magazines and story papers since the mid-18th century. While some of these stories were written to stand alone, many were serialized installments of longer works, often appearing in several issues over a period of weeks or months. Often, such short fiction was intended not only to entertain but also to send a message, presenting a heroine of good character to serve as an example for readers. Among the most prolific of the story-paper writers was American Laura Jean Libbey, whose tales of poor girls finding their way in the big city were popular from the 1880s through the 1920s. Today, a number of romance authors produce novellas (short novels), which are often published in anthologies, or collections, based on a specific theme, such as a holiday.

< 24 >

The setting of a dark and magical forest could make for a romantic—albeit eerie or mysterious—meeting place in an alternative reality romance.

Samuel Richardson, the author widely credited with writing the first romance novel, began his career as a printer. While writing a book of "sample letters" to help readers with their own correspondence, Richardson was inspired with the idea of a novel written as a series of letters on a single topic. The result was *Pamela; or, Virtue Rewarded*, with a plot based in part on a true story he had heard of a young maid who resisted seduction. The novel marked a turning point in literature with its psychological emphasis on the anguished heroine's inner thoughts. Richardson's 1747 novel *Clarissa; or, the History of a Young Lady* likewise features a young woman who must attempt to retain her virtue in the face of repeated advances. Ultimately, the heroine is drugged and raped, and she eventually dies of the physical and emotional strain she has endured. Although English audiences and critics initially considered the story indecent, it later achieved strong influence, and a number of authors took up the theme of seduction in their works.

While Richardson's stories were set in contemporary society, another British author, Sir Walter Scott, founded the historical romance novel with his tales of adventure, chivalry, and romance set in Britain's past. After writing a number of romantic poems, Scott anonymously published his first novel, *Waverley*, in 1814. Set during a historic rebellion that occurred in Britain in 1745, the story revolves around Edward Waverley, who starts out as a soldier of the English army but later sides with the rebels. During the course of his adventures, the hero meets two women with whom he falls in love, later rejecting one in favor of the other. After *Waverley* met with critical and popular acclaim, Scott published 26 additional historical novels, now known as the Waverley novels since they were signed simply, "by the author of *Waverley*." The best-known Waverley tale, *Ivanhoe* (1819), depicts the knights and ladies of 12th-century England, offering rich descriptions of the

< 26 >

After oil painter Charles Landseer created the work Clarissa Harlowe
in the Prison Room of the Sheriff's Office, *it was made into the engraving shown.*

The "romantic" aspects of The Scarlet Letter *are more tortured and
tragic than in many romance stories, for the lovers are punished for their love.*

era, as in this scene of a knightly tournament: "The clang of the blows and the shouts of the combatants mixed fearfully with the sound of the trumpets, and drowned the groans of those who fell, and lay rolling defenceless beneath the feet of horses. The splendid armour of the combatants was now defaced with dust and blood.... The ladies around encouraged the combatants, not only by clapping their hands and waving their veils and kerchiefs, but even by exclaiming, 'Brave lance! Good sword!'" In addition to inspiring a number of writers, such works helped to fuel public fascination with the past and especially with medieval times.

Although American author Nathaniel Hawthorne was so disappointed with the results of his first novel, *Fanshawe* (1828), that he destroyed as many copies as he could find, he honed his craft and in 1850 published his masterpiece, *The Scarlet Letter*. A dark tale of romance set in the Puritan society of 17th-century Boston, the novel presents the story of Hester Prynne, a young married woman convicted of adultery after bearing another man's child. Although forced to wear a scarlet letter "A" to represent her sin, Hester refuses to reveal the identity of the child's father—the man she loves. In the end, the man proves to be the town's minister, who dies from the torment of his guilt. In addition to its compelling storyline, *The Scarlet Letter* has been praised for its flowing prose, complex symbolism, and insight into human guilt and morality.

Despite the fact that her books are out of print today, English novelist Charlotte Yonge was a popular and influential romance writer in her time, publishing nearly 160 novels. Yonge's most influential work was perhaps *The Heir of Redclyffe* (1853), which combines a religious message with a new level of emotional involvement, as the reader is brought so close to the characters that he or she feels their pains and pleasures. Because of this emotional intensity, as well as its conclusion that all problems can be solved with love, *The Heir of Redclyffe*

< 29 >

Born in 1775 in the English village of Steventon, Jane Austen grew up in a family that encouraged learning. Austen began writing around 1787, although her first novel, **Sense and Sensibility**, was not published until 1811. **Pride and Prejudice** appeared two years later, followed by **Mansfield Park** (1814) and **Emma** (1815). All these works remained anonymous until after Austen's 1817 death, when **Persuasion** (1817), **Northanger Abbey** (1817), and **Lady Susan** (1871) were also published.

Austen's heroines are strong and independent-minded, unwilling to marry for anything but love (at a time when marriage for money was often necessary). **Pride and Prejudice** demonstrates the author's skill at creating playful, witty dialogue as the heroine, Elizabeth Bennet, talks with her father about the prospect of marrying a man she does not love:

> "Come here, child," cried her father as she appeared…. "I understand that Mr. Collins has made you an offer of marriage…. And this offer of marriage you have refused?"
>
> "I have, Sir."…
>
> "Your mother insists upon your accepting it…. An unhappy alternative is before you, Elizabeth. From this day you must be a stranger to one of your parents.—Your mother will never see you again if you do not marry Mr. Collins, and I will never see you again if you *do*."

Austen is today ranked among the most important authors of all time, and her novels are widely read and studied.

< 30 >

Jane Austen was already composing stories as a teenager, completing her first mature work (though last to be published), Lady Susan, at 19.

is often considered to mark the beginning of popular romance.

Another prolific romance writer was Italian-English author Rafael Sabatini, who, having spent parts of his childhood in various European countries, set his historical novels in locales ranging from England, France, and Italy to the Caribbean and America. Sabatini achieved international success with the publication of *Scaramouche* in 1921. Like many of Sabatini's historical novels, *Scaramouche* is set against a realistic historical backdrop (in this case, the French Revolution), but its main character comes solely from the author's imagination. Sabatini, who believed that thorough research was essential in the creation of historical fiction, loosely based the characters in some of his other works, such as *Captain Blood, His Odyssey* (1922), on actual people. Noted for their high adventure and lively dialogue, Sabatini's novels were among the most popular of the early 20th century.

While Sabatini set his historical works in various time periods and countries around the world, British author Georgette Heyer is best known for her romances set in a single time and place: Regency England. Inspired by the works of Jane Austen, Heyer created novels depicting the lives and manners of the aristocracy of the period. In order to accurately describe that society, Heyer conducted thorough research, keeping notes on everything from costumes to the price of candles. Heyer's light-hearted stories, which rarely feature tragedy, set the standard for all Regency novels that followed. Heyer also wrote novels set in the medieval period, the 16th century, and the Civil War era. Among the most successful of the novels Heyer produced in her 50-year career (which spanned the 1920s to the 1970s) was *Frederica* (1965), a Regency in which the heroine attempts to marry off her younger sister, never expecting to fall in love herself.

In contrast to Heyer's bright, humorous works, British author Daphne du

*Opposite Janet Leigh as love interest Aline, Stewart Granger starred
as the swashbuckling hero in 1952's film version of* Scaramouche.

The first name of the narrator of Rebecca—*the second Mrs. de Winter—is never given in either the book or the 1940 movie, which stars Joan Fontaine.*

Maurier created suspenseful, heart-stopping Gothic romances, many set in the remote English county of Cornwall on the Atlantic coast, where du Maurier spent part of her life. Her best-known work is *Rebecca* (1938), in which the heroine (who serves as the story's first-person narrator) marries a wealthy man much older than herself. When she arrives at his mysterious mansion, Manderley, she finds that she must compete with the memory of her husband's dead first wife, Rebecca, along with Rebecca's evil servant, Mrs. Danvers, to win his love. Throughout the novel, a feeling of foreboding and suspense prevails, as illustrated in the following scene inside the mansion: "A board creaked in the gallery. I swung round, looking at the gallery behind me. There was nobody there.... A current of air blew in my face though, somebody must have left a window open in one of the passages.... I went beneath the arch again, and when I came out on to the long corridor I saw that the door to the west wing had blown open and swung back against the wall. It was dark in the west passage, none of the lights had been turned on.... The grey evening light cast queer shadows on the floor." Such intense scenes set the standard for future authors of the Gothic romance.

< 35 >

Until the mid-20th century, nearly all popular romance novels followed the loves and lives of the elite or middle class. In 1950, however, British author Catherine Cookson published *Kate Hannigan*, the first of many novels she would produce featuring working-class heroines and situations. Having been raised in poverty, Cookson was intimately acquainted with the difficult conditions faced by the heroines of her works, including poor working conditions and constant conflicts with characters of higher social classes. In *The Black Velvet Gown* (1984), for example, the young heroine Biddy Millican is sent to work in the laundry room of a large mansion. When she attempts to teach the other servants to write, she is reprimanded by the master: "You are here to work. You have been assigned to a certain position. That is all that is required of you. If I wished my staff to be educated, I would give the order for it." In the end, most of Cookson's heroines shy away from the elegant heroes of traditional romance, choosing instead the safety and security of solid, dependable men, some of whom have physical disabilities.

In the 1960s, the Gothic foundation that had earlier been laid by Daphne du Maurier's *Rebecca* was built upon by British author Eleanor Hibbert, who wrote under such pseudonyms as Victoria Holt, Jean Plaidy, and Philippa Carr. Hibbert's first Gothic novel, *Mistress of Mellyn* (written as Victoria Holt) was published in 1960 and helped to spark a Gothic revival. As Jean Plaidy, Hibbert also created historical romances, most often depicting the lives of prominent women from history. *The Captive Queen of Scots* (1963), for example, details the 19-year political captivity of Mary, Queen of Scots, which ended with her execution in 1587:

> *Dismounting, Mary could scarcely stand.... Lord Lindsay who was at her side, said in a tone which had an edge of roughness in it and was devoid of the respect due to a Queen: "The boat is waiting."*

< 36 >

Mary, Queen of Scots inherited the Scottish throne from her father when she was only 6 days old, but the country was ruled by others until she was 18.

*Cheryl Ladd and Christopher Plummer were cast as Liane and Armand De Villiers
in the 1986 television miniseries based on Danielle Steel's* Crossings.

"Boat! Then where are you taking me?"

"You will know in time."

How dared they! She turned to Lindsay, and goaded out of her exhaustion, cried:
"I'll have your head for this, my lord."

In addition to queens, Plaidy's works often featured the wives, daughters, or sisters of European royalty, presenting history from their point of view.

In 1972, American author Kathleen Woodiwiss published *The Flame and the Flower*, a novel that was much longer and more sensual than the romances popular at the time. Set at the beginning of the 19th century, Woodiwiss's novel included many intimate scenes between the hero and the heroine and sparked a movement toward sensual historical romances. Reflecting the changing attitudes and roles of women during the 1970s, Woodiwiss also presented intelligent, capable, independent heroines who sought equality as well as romance in their relationships. Woodiwiss's revolutionary changes to the genre were recognized when she was presented with the Romance Writers of America's lifetime achievement award in 1988.

Like Woodiwiss, American author Danielle Steel was first published in the 1970s. Rather than focusing on the sensual, Steel's novels rely on drama. Having grown up in a wealthy home, Steel often creates strong, wealthy, and glamorous heroines who must face difficult situations and make heart-rending decisions. Unlike the traditional romance, Steel's novels do not always end "happily ever after." In addition, Steel explores not only romantic love but also love between parents and children, siblings, and friends. Steel remains among the most popular romance authors today, having more than 590 million copies of her books in print.

< 39 >

In 1847, British author Charlotte Brontë published Jane Eyre under the pseudonym Currer Bell. The novel met with immediate success, and it continues to be well read—and well loved—today. Part of the enduring appeal of the story lies in its strong Gothic flavor—its atmosphere of suspense, its secrets, and its setting (which includes a large mansion in which mysterious events occur). But the novel has also moved generations of readers by drawing them into the world of the title character, Jane Eyre, a strong figure who grows from an abused orphan into a mature, independent woman.

Just as it appears that Jane will get her happily ever after, she learns that the man she is about to marry—the dark, moody, hot-tempered Edward Rochester—is already secretly married. His insane wife (whom he was tricked into marrying) is kept locked in the attic of his mansion. Jane leaves Rochester, and soon afterward, she inherits a large sum of money. Although she is almost persuaded to marry a young clergyman, she mysteriously hears Rochester's voice calling to her. Jane returns to him, finding that his home has been burned to the ground by his wife, who died in the fire. Although Rochester was blinded and lost a hand in the fire, Jane pledges her love to him: "I love you better now, when I can really be useful to you, than I did in your state of proud independence." Then she tells us simply of her happy ending: "Reader, I married him."

< 40 >

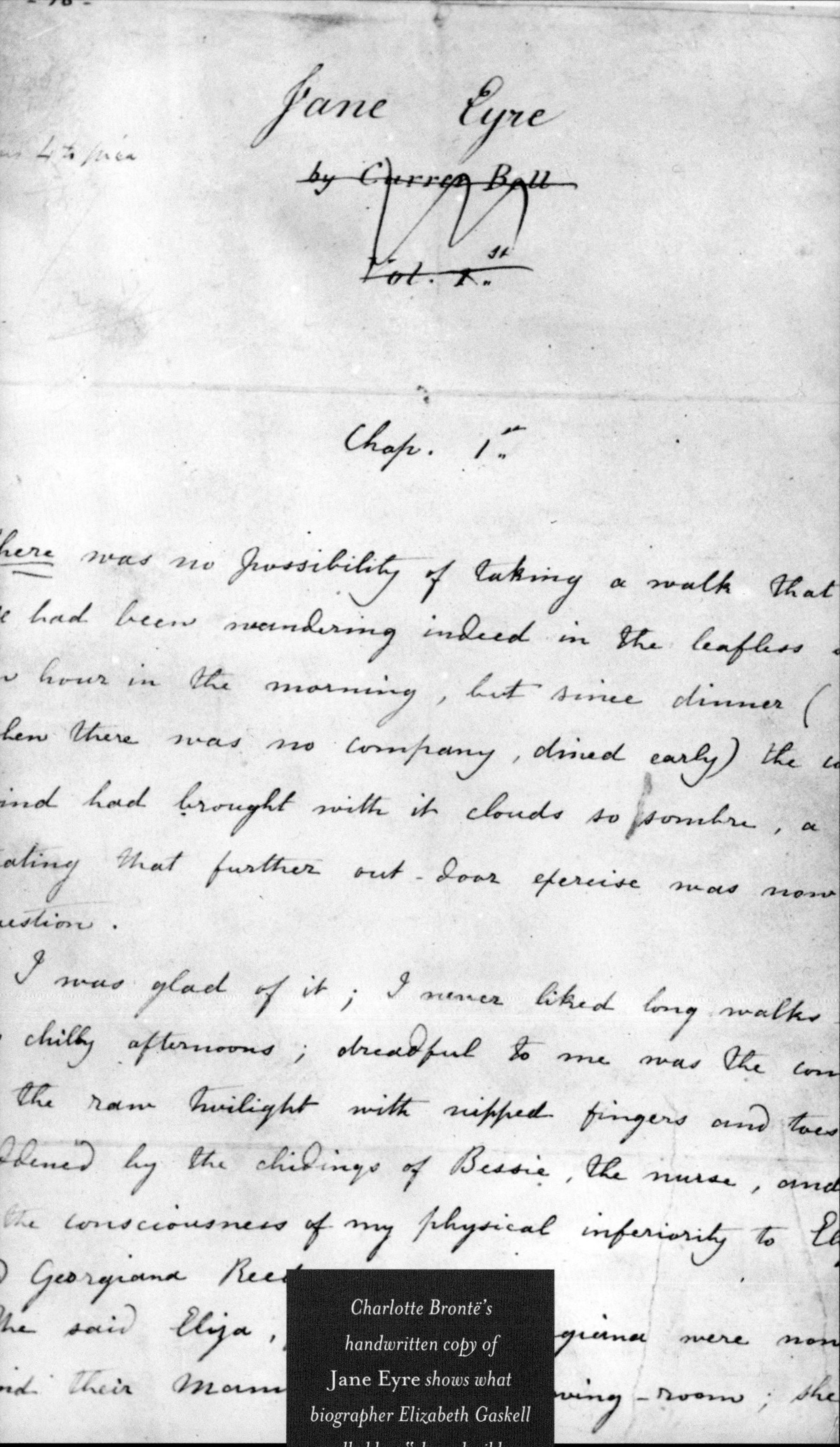

Jane Eyre

~~by Currer Bell~~

~~Vol. I.~~ Ist

Chap. 1st

here was no possibility of taking a walk that
 had been wandering indeed in the leafless
 hour in the morning, but since dinner (
hen there was no company, dined early) the
ind had brought with it clouds so sombre, a
ating that further out-door exercise was now
uestion.

I was glad of it; I never liked long walks
 chilly afternoons; dreadful to me was the com
 the raw twilight with nipped fingers and toes
ddened by the chidings of Bessie, the nurse, and
 the consciousness of my physical inferiority to El
 Georgiana Reed
 he said Eliza, … giana were now
nd their Mam… wing-room; the

Charlotte Brontë's handwritten copy of **Jane Eyre** shows what biographer Elizabeth Gaskell called her "clear, legible, delicate traced writing."

American author Jayne Ann Krentz, who published her first novel in 1979, also continues to produce best sellers today, writing in three distinct subgenres of romantic suspense (contemporary, historical, and alternative reality) under three different names (Jayne Ann Krentz, Amanda Quick, and Jayne Castle). Her 1986 novel *Sweet Starfire*, which depicts the hero and heroine's journey through the galaxy, was among the first futuristic romances published. A firm advocate of the genre, Krentz also edited *Dangerous Men and Adventurous Women: Romance Writers on the Appeal of the Romance* (1992), a series of scholarly essays on romance writing that won an award for feminist studies.

By the time British author Erin Pizzey began writing romantic fiction in the 1980s, she was already well known as a women's activist, having opened England's first shelter for abused women in 1971. Her romance novels often delve into topics rarely covered in the genre, including child abuse (based on her own experiences), homosexuality, and drugs. In her 1984 novel *In the Shadow of the Castle*, the heroine, Bonnie Fraser, repeatedly returns to her abusive husband before being saved from his continued torments by his suicide. Despite such dark topics, Pizzey's works often conclude with the heroine achieving both a sense of freedom and a truly loving relationship with a worthy man.

Since beginning her writing career in 1981, American author Nora Roberts (pseudonym of Eleanor Marie Robertson) has written 200 books, among them traditional romance and romantic suspense (as well as futuristic detective novels written under the pen name J. D. Robb). In all her works, Roberts is noted for her fast-paced action, believable characters, and intense emotion. Many of her novels are permeated by a tense atmosphere as the hero and heroine find themselves in scenes of real danger. In *Sacred Sins* (1987), for example, psychiatrist Tess Court learns that a serial killer has been watching her. Then there's a knock

< 42 >

Nora Roberts has lived in western Maryland for the past 30 years and in 2008 rebuilt the Inn BoonsBoro to create a romantic boutique hotel.

Twilight author Stephenie Meyer posed with actor Taylor Lautner, who plays the character Jacob Black in the movies, in November 2011.

at the door: "She'd put a hand to the curtain to draw it closed when the knock on her door made her slam back against the wall in an animal panic she'd never before experienced. Terror swam into her as she looked around for a means of defense, a place to hide, a way to escape. She fought it back as she reached for the phone—911. She had only to dial it, give her name and address. But when the knock came again, she looked at the door and saw she'd forgotten to put on the chain." Such scenes bring the suspense of Roberts's novels to a peak, although the heroine is usually safe—and with the hero—by the end of the story. Once remarking that "there's enough misery in the world," Roberts is thoroughly dedicated to the happy ending.

While Roberts remains one of the most popular romance writers today, she has been joined by a number of up-and-coming romantics. Among them is Jessica Bird, an American author who writes contemporary romances under her own name as well as dark alternative reality romances featuring vampires under the name of J. R. Ward. American author Stephenie Meyer also writes vampire romance novels in her wildly successful Twilight series (2005–2008), which has gained international readership and spawned highly popular movie versions of all the books.

From the early days of the seduction story to today's vampire romances, the romance genre has seen a number of changes and developments. Yet, through all those changes, one thing has continued to draw readers to the genre again and again: romance readers know that, no matter how many twists and turns or misunderstandings and mishaps get in the way, in the end, everything will (almost always) turn out right.

< 45 >

adultery: sexual relations between a married person and someone other than his or her spouse

aristocracy: the highest social class in a society and those who belong to it

contemporary: living or existing at the same time as someone or something else

explicit: portraying nudity or sex in graphic detail

first-person: a point of view in which a character tells his or her own story, using the pronouns "I" or "we"

genre: a category in which a literary work can be classified on the basis of style, technique, or subject matter

Great Depression: a period from 1929 to 1939 marked by a decline in the economy and industry, widespread job loss, and poverty in the U.S. and several other countries

mass-market: produced in large quantities, often for lower cost and to be sold at supermarkets or drugstores

point of view: the perspective from or attitude with which the narrator of a literary work sees events

protagonist: the main character in a work of fiction

pseudonym: a made-up name, often used by an author in place of his or her real name

psychological: having to do with the mind and effects on the mind

Puritan: characteristic of religious views widely held in 16th- and 17th-century England and America that supported strict moral discipline

Regency: a period in British history (1811–20) when George, Prince of Wales, ruled as regent (or substitute) for his insane father, George III

satire: the use of ridicule or sarcasm to criticize or expose human folly or vice

serialized: published in parts

supernatural: relating to objects or powers that have no natural explanation and seem to exist outside natural laws

symbolism: the use of one thing, such as a character or color, to represent something else, often an idea, such as love or evil

Victorian: occurring during or relating to the reign of Queen Victoria of England (1837–1901), especially regarding the attitudes and values of this period

Western: coming from or having to do with the part of the world that includes Europe and North and South America, where culture has been influenced by ancient Greek and Roman civilizations as well as Christianity

WEBSITES

Forever Anne
http://foreveranne.com/make-anne-green-gables-costume-0
Learn more about Anne of Green Gables and her world through fun projects and games.

History: Women's Rights Quiz
http://www.bbc.co.uk/history/british/victorians/launch_gms_womens_rights.shtml
Discover what life was like for women such as Charlotte Brontë during the Victorian era.

The Jane Austen Society of North America: About Jane
http://www.jasna.org/info/about_austen.html
Read a brief biography of Jane Austen and see maps of where her stories took place.

Prince Edward Island: Green Gables
http://www.gov.pe.ca/greengables/
Find out more about Prince Edward Island and Green Gables, and take a virtual tour of the house.

Every effort has been made to ensure that these sites are suitable for children, that they have educational value, and that they contain no inappropriate material. However, because of the nature of the Internet, it is impossible to guarantee that these sites will remain active indefinitely or that their contents will not be altered.

SELECTED BIBLIOGRAPHY

Bouricius, Ann. *The Romance Readers' Advisory. The Librarian's Guide to Love in the Stacks.* Chicago: American Library Association, 2000.

Cecil, Mirabel. *Heroines in Love: 1750–1974.* London: Michael Joseph, 1974.

Fallon, Eileen. *Words of Love: A Complete Guide to Romance Fiction.* New York: Garland Publishing, 1984.

Ramsdell, Kristin. *Romance Fiction: A Guide to the Genre.* Englewood, Colo.: Libraries Unlimited, 1999.

Rogers, Jane, ed. *Good Fiction Guide.* New York: Oxford University Press, 2005.

Rosenberg, Betty. *Genreflecting: A Guide to Reading Interests in Genre Fiction.* Littleton, Colo.: Libraries Unlimited, 1982.

Saricks, Joyce. *The Readers' Advisory Guide to Genre Fiction.* Chicago: American Library Association, 2001.

Vasudevan, Aruna. *Twentieth-Century Romance and Historical Writers.* Detroit: St. James Press, 1994.

< 47 >

< 48 >